Crisis

CRISIS

Readings in Environmental Issues and Strategies

Edited by
ROBERT M. IRVING
and GEORGE B. PRIDDLE

Macmillan & Co. Ltd. London

First published 1971 by
THE MACMILLAN PRESS LTD.
London and Basingstoke
Associated companies in Toronto Dublin
Melbourne Johannesburg and Madras

SBN 333 13240 6

Printed in Canada by
T. H. Best Printing Company Limited
Don Mills, Ontario

Contents

Jane, Ruth, Stephen, Jennifer, and Lisa

. . . this is for you.

Introduction

At some time during the decades of the fifties and the sixties, a few people from widely disparate walks of life began to discover that all was not quite right with the glittering world humanity had created for itself on this planet.

The signs were isolated at first, and often of mere local concern. Green scum began to form on the surface of a few blue-water lakes; game fish in a favourite trout stream were washed, belly-up and dying, onto the shore. In some of the great cities, people began to complain of a host of minor ailments. Their eyes smarted, they suffered from headaches, and a haze obscured the sun. Whole populations of animals and birds disappeared from their accustomed breeding places and flyways. Soil erosion accelerated as farmers struggled to maintain yields, and new mining techniques turned vast areas into dying wastelands whose precious soils ran down to the sea.

As these events steadily multiplied, most of us felt a vague unease. Something was definitely wrong—but what? By this time, a few of our scientists began making alarming statements to the effect that our environment—so long the uncomplaining servant of Man—was becoming unstable and was in imminent danger of coming apart at the seams.

For the most part, during the earlier years of the two decades, university courses reflected an almost total lack of concern for the havoc man was creating in his wild drive for more products, better houses, bigger cars, indestructible plastics, faster aircraft, more power. Courses in ecology, for instance, were developed around the usual theories of succession, of biological niche and habitat, without reference to the multitude of degenerative changes that were taking place in the biosphere due to the activities of man.

By 1960, a few people were beginning to be concerned about the environment, but throughout most of the decade the general public was apathetic. If there is any justification for this failure to recognize a gradual intensification of the danger signals indicating a serious increase in man-made environmental stress, it may best be found in the temper of the times in which we were then living. The decade of the sixties was one of feverish activity. The race was on to put a man on the moon; signs of increasing material prosperity—in North America, at least—were to be seen everywhere; public figures were being assassinated and martyred; Watts was put to the torch; riots swept the campuses of many universities, leaving devastation, frustration and fury in their wake. Social traditions, judicial procedures—almost anything representative of the *status quo*—was vigorously attacked, analysed and questioned.

Against such a background, it is easy to understand how the more subtle warnings from our environment were overshadowed by the immediacy and the magnitude of our human affairs. Thus it was that the scum on our lakes grew thicker, pesticide residues began their steady build-up in the bodies of animals thousands of miles from where the material was sprayed, and the air over our cities became a chemical menace to the coughing, red-eyed populace below.

Almost overnight, the scientists who had quietly been issuing their periodic warnings of the multitude of dangers we were facing were no longer regarded as cranks. People and their governments began to listen. As the spotlight of publicity focussed upon environmental problems, the polemics began. The polar ice caps were going to melt, swamping our coastal cities under sixty feet of water; or, the quality of our air was deteriorating to the point where so little sunlight could penetrate that a new ice age was in the offing.

Statistics were trotted out to prove that the Great Lakes were dying, only to be countered by a barrage of data to show that they were not. Pesticides were labelled by some as a curse and by others as the salvation of huge segments of the population. Any intelligent person listening from the sidelines to this barrage of conflicting opinions could be excused if he threw up his hands in disgust and forgot the whole thing.

The purpose of this collection of readings is, in the main, threefold: It attempts, first, to impose some rational perspectives upon the multifaceted problem of environmental deterioration. We cannot, after all, begin to solve a problem until its boundaries have been defined with some precision. Until this is done, the confusion will continue and the professional in the field will be able to do little more than extinguish localized pollution "brush fires" as best he can.

Second, the emphasis shifts from the broader theoretical and philosophical considerations to specific, urgent issues that now confront us. Selected papers illustrate the physical, economic and social hurdles that must be crossed in any concerted attack upon air and water pollution, the indiscriminate use of pesticides, urban deterioration, and—of increasing importance—the pressures exerted by a growing and affluent population on our shrinking wilderness areas.

The third purpose is to attempt to examine some of the more promising courses of action that have been proposed to retard and eventually reverse environmental deterioration. It will be noted that certain of the papers thus classified return us to the fundamental theme which underlies the entire work. It is agreed that restoring health to an ailing environment, and creating a reasonable balance between what we as a species want and what we can have, is an incredibly complex problem. Piecemeal solutions are often necessary, but much of their effectiveness is lost if we do not work from within the compass of some analytical framework that embraces the total problem.

The study of environmental science can be a very frustrating business indeed, and one of the purposes of this collection is to reflect some of the frustrations involved when one comes to grips with the study. As the underlying ideas are traced back to first principles, we find ourselves confronted with nothing less than the very roots of our most cherished traditions. These fundamentals, so basic that they are in the main philosophical, are examined by Lynn White, Jr., in "The Historical Roots of Our Ecological Crisis."

In his essay, White claims that the roots of our crisis extend into the very heart of the Judeo-Christian tradition. This is strong stuff, but it can nevertheless be supported with great cogency.

What better licence to chop down, tear up and otherwise modify his environment could Western man have than the text of his own holy book? Does the Bible not specify that all the earth and everything that lives upon it has been put here for the sole use and enjoyment of man? As White puts it: "No item in the physical creation had any purpose save to serve man."

This divine mandate did more than justify the beginnings of what has come to be known as the growth ethic; it created a dualism between man and nature that had not existed before. Since a spirit no longer lived in the tree, there was no longer any need to apologize to it before chopping the tree down. Thus was man given absolute stewardship over nature, and he has been chopping with a vengeance ever since.

Closely associated with this dualism is Western man's longstanding conviction that nature is to be conquered and bent to the will of man. Pioneers in North America regarded the wilderness as their enemy, to be beaten back at all costs, with the spoils going to the victor.

If the victory now seems more than a little hollow, what can be done to make peace with nature? Certainly, neither science nor technology can be relied upon to pull some marvellous rabbit from the hat and save us from disaster. In White's view, technology played a decisive role in getting us into trouble in the first place. White proposes another kind of solution as fundamental and provocative as his thesis.

So much for philosophy. The second part of this collection deals, as has already been indicated, with some of the countless insults that have been inflicted upon our environment in the name of progress and the "good life." For the most part, these are thoughtful essays rather than mere diatribes, and the reader might enjoy the mental exercise of attempting to fit the specific facts and forecasts of each into the frames of reference developed in section one.

Perhaps our most precious resource is pure, fresh water. Our bodies demand it, our major industries could not operate without it, the global energy cycle depends upon it, and our toilets, washing machines and bathtubs would be useless if deprived of it. It is thus somewhat ironic that the earth's finite reserves of this most important resource have been treated more harshly than those of any other resource. It required no genius to discover that the stream running past his door could be used for many things besides drinking. One could chuck animal entrails, dung, dead cats, brewing dregs and all manner of muck into a watercourse and watch it sail conveniently out of sight around the first bend or else sink quietly into the depths.

Small populations of a basically rural nature could get away with this sort of thing without causing undue harm to the environment. The complex life systems of our waters have a remarkable capacity for breaking down all manner of wastes and eventually restoring the purity of a stream, a lake or a river. Unfortunately, this capacity is limited. Dump in more wastes than the system can handle and pollution is the inevitable result.

Because the greatest store of available fresh water in North America is to be found in the Great Lakes basin, Peter Schrag's article on Lake Erie, "Life on a Dying Lake," is an appropriate beginning for the second part of the work. In some ways, Schrag's title is misleading. For analytical purposes, Erie must be studied as three lakes in one: the shallow western basin, the slightly deeper central basin, and the deepest, eastern basin, with each region responding in a characteristic way to the load of pollutants being dumped into the water.

From the data available, we can conclude that, even if the entire lake is not dying, there is no doubt that certain parts of it are very sick indeed. The western basin, with its shallow waters, is the region in the lake most sensitive to pollution, and unfortunately it takes a heavier waste influx than either of the other two regions.

If decisive, co-ordinated action is taken to reduce the influx of pollutants from sources on both sides of the international boundary, we should see a dramatic improvement within a relatively short time. Lake Erie has a flushing period of only six years, as opposed to about a hundred years for longer, deeper lakes such as Lake Michigan.

In any pollution situation, our first inclination is to seek simplistic answers. So it is that phosphates have been branded the villains primarily responsible for the rapid deterioration of our fresh-water supplies. Science writer David Spurgeon points out in a brief article in this collection of readings that we would do well not to expect any miraculous results from a ban on the manufacture of phosphate detergents. Undoubtedly, these compounds are responsible for a certain amount of pollution, but their removal is far from a cure-all. We do not yet know what the long-term effects of substitute materials such as nitrilotriacetic acid (NTA) will be.

The deteriorating quality of our global atmosphere may well be an even more difficult problem to deal with. Pollutants emitted in one place circulate over the entire planet, with the result that enforceable international constraints will be required to bring the problem under control. Whether or not mankind has attained sufficient political maturity to take such a step is a question well worth pondering.

A survey of this collection is likely to leave the reader with two essential ideas: He will appreciate the hazards to living organisms—man included—if we continue to increase the production of air pollutants at our present rate, and he will realize that combating the problem is not purely a job for engineers and scientists. Technology is equal to the task of providing us with air that is fit to breathe, but the cost in dollars will be very high indeed. This opens up a regular Pandora's box. Who shall pay the bill? The citizens of a smog-blanketed city who clog the highways with their automobiles? State or provincial governments? Federal agencies? The industries that actually do much of the polluting?

No matter who signs the cheque, it will ultimately be redeemed in the form of higher taxes, higher prices, lowered profits or a combination of all three.

One dangerous human activity as it relates to environmental stress is the wholesale release of new chemicals to our air, water and soil. These molecules are often toxic and virtually immune to the natural processes of degradation, and some of the by-products of those that do eventually come apart are just as lethal as the originals.

The most highly publicized of these are the chlorinated hydrocarbons. It is from this group that the insecticide DDT comes. Though virtually insoluble in water, it dissolves easily in fat—and stays there. It is this property that gives DDT both its affinity for living organisms with fatty tissue and its increase in concentration as it moves through our ecological food chains from the grazing animals that first pick it up from the environment to the top predators such as man.

As a study of this section reveals, there are two sides to the argument about DDT. Wildlife biologists and ecologists damn DDT for causing serious damage to some species and for wiping out others. Agricultural scientists argue that the use of DDT and other chemicals has not only increased yields from land already under cultivation, but has wiped out disease-carrying insects over great areas of the earth. Prosperous farms are now springing up in places where once men knew only sickness and death.

Given two such polarized opinions, what course of action is open to our decision-makers?

There was a time, not so many years ago, when the environmentalist, seeking some succinct, shocking statement that would make people listen to him, would cry out: "We are choking in our own garbage!" As the years went by, and the decade of the sixties drew to a close, what was once mere rhetoric became more like a simple statement of fact. Ours became the throw-away generation. "Use it once and pitch it out" became the slogan of many consumer-products manufacturers.

But where shall we pitch it all? Readers enamoured of large numbers will be interested to know that, in 1969, North Americans threw away 54 billion tin cans, 32 billion glass containers, 4 million tons of plastics and—believe it or not—more than 1 million television sets. Almost 10 million automobiles are junked each year, many simply abandoned on city streets. Each day, about 150 of these rusting hulks are abandoned by their owners on the streets of New York alone. Some of this witches' brew of refuse can be reclaimed, broken down and used again. The rest is burned—to the detriment of our atmosphere—or buried in what is called sanitary land fill. This latter, of course, is a less pungent name for an immense garbage dump. The tin cans will eventually oxidize, but what about those billions of glass bottles? They will not decompose, so the piles must inevitably grow.

It was remarked, in earlier paragraphs, that an essential concern facing the scientist who undertakes the analysis of an environmental problem is the setting of boundary conditions within which he can objectively work. Perhaps the most elusive problem of all is that of the gradual deterioration of our cities.

Depending upon whose point of view is being put forth at the time, any given city can be described as a Mecca of culture, or as a jungle where women and children are afraid to walk the streets at night; it is a centre of learning, or a seething cauldron of crime; it may be the seat of responsible government, or the nerve centre of political extremism. It is a thing of beauty to some and a blight upon the landscape to others.

One thing may be said with some degree of certainty: the quality of city life leaves much to be desired for the majority of its inhabitants. Houses are lined up side by side like so many books on a shelf, streets are designed for machines rather than people, and the sheer, overpowering size of the city creates a sense of isolation and alienation in the people who dwell there. Here, indeed, is an instance where the structure has grown too big for those who built it.

In the future, the designers will be forced to take cognizance of people in their calculations. Their task is not to be envied, because even given cleaner air, purer water, and some reduction in the endless racket, there are exceedingly frustrating questions to cope with: When does a city become too big? How much green space is enough? Can overcrowding cause illness in humans to the extent that it does in some other species, and if so, what are the limits at which overcrowding becomes unendurable? There is a pressing need for solutions to all of these problems, but the reader will note that most of them relate to the needs, values and goals of the individual human being, and, as David Lowenthal points out, beauty is in the eye of the beholder.

You will find most of the multitude of woes and dangers that plague humanity and this planet touched upon here and in the papers that follow. In the third section you will find recounted some of the most recent and important attempts to bring the problems within manageable bounds.

Systems analysis may prove to be a promising tool. Computers are now being programmed in such a way that any particular long-range planning solution may be modified as the natural, physical and social scientists identify new problems and feed in appropriate data. In the first paper of the third section, Douglas Brooks provides a framework for environmental quality analysis.

We find, too, that one of the most effective forces in the struggle for change is an informed and determined citizenry. The University of Toronto's Pollution Probe, together with similar organizations, has proven more than once that a battle lost in the courts may, in the end, be won with a printing press.

It is hoped that this book will spark an awareness of environmental problems in the minds of its readers. If it does, the editors will consider themselves well rewarded, for the title was aptly chosen. We are, indeed, face to face with a global crisis.

In the preparation of this book we consulted many colleagues at Waterloo and elsewhere and wish to acknowledge their cooperation. We likewise extend our appreciation to the authors, journals and publishers whose cooperation has made this book possible.

On a more personal note, we recognize the keen interest of Mr. Ted Pulford, Science Editor of the Macmillan Company of Canada Limited, whose contribution is manifest in the Introduction. To Paul Kendall and Joan Gilmore, we record our thanks for commentary at particularly critical times.

Crisis

P 178

Seven Days

GARY DUNFORD

in the beginning,
man created the mudhole and the marsh
    damming streams for viaducts
    and routing waters for his own benefit
        waters, white as crystal, moving through trenches
        trickling through makeshift reed piping
        splashing clean into clay bowls
        bubbling to do man's bidding
    and it was the morning and the evening of the first day
    and the seagulls were dying

on the second day,
man created the slaughterhouse and the zoo
    and the wild animals of the earth
    which had wandered at will across the planet
        watched man from behind wire mesh
        scruffy lions with sad faces
        and elephants, their bottoms calloused
                                        from sitting on cement
    and it was the morning and the evening of the second day
    and the seagulls were dying

on the third day
the buffalo disappeared. simply disappeared.

---

and across the pampas
safaris, $495 per person, sought out exotic creatures
to mount in rec rooms or multiply in cages

and the ice floes ran red
and jungle monkeys reeled in terror

and it was the morning and the evening of the third day
and the seagulls were dying

on the fourth day,
man created the sewer and the sump

and pumps to pipe sewer to sump and sump to sewer
at incredible cost
to nose and pocket
and the pumps pumped
and the sumps drained
and the sewers flowed
into creeks and lakes
and every drop of sewage makes
an ocean spreading across the world
the universal garbage apocalypse

and it was the morning and the evening of the fourth day
and the seagulls were dying

on the fifth day,
man crated and canned atomic wastes
and made up the word megaton

packing the wastes in rusty old drums and concrete
caissons
cramming biological uglies into old trains
that run on undetermined schedules
across the landscape

and somewhere, sunken tanks of arsenic
are cloaked in barnacles
and rust slowly in salt water

and now and then, on october afternoons
underground explosions occur
and smiling spokesmen describe them as
necessary and safe

while desert floors collapse
and islands tremble
and the smiling spokesman says
the san andreas fault
remains faultless
and it is the morning and the evening of the fifth day
and the seagulls are dying

on the sixth day
man created the additive

which differed in name, but never in purpose
and was gleefully installed in cereals and fertilizers
soft drinks and cookies
field and bug sprays
creams and cosmetics
it was added to everything man ate or drank
was added to smokestacks
and sewage
and lakes
and eventually,
even the additives had additivies
and counter-antidotes to combat the counter-pollutants
and even the experts gave up explaining
exactly what the additives were to accomplish

and it was the morning and the evening of the sixth day
and the seagulls were dying

on the seventh day
there was quiet over all the earth
except for the lapping of waves
and the bubbling of storm drains

and the seagulls were dying
and the plankton
and the oceans
and the atmosphere
and the trees were dying

and man
rested

Part One
Background and Perspective

The Historical Roots of Our Ecologic Crisis

LYNN WHITE, JR.

A conversation with Aldous Huxley not infrequently put one at the receiving end of an unforgettable monologue. About a year before his lamented death he was discoursing on a favorite topic: Man's unnatural treatment of nature and its sad results. To illustrate his point he told how, during the previous summer, he had returned to a little valley in England where he had spent many happy months as a child. Once it had been composed of delightful grassy glades; now it was becoming overgrown with unsightly brush because the rabbits that formerly kept such growth under control had largely succumbed to a disease, myxomatosis, that was deliberately introduced by the local farmers to reduce the rabbits' destruction of crops. Being something of a Philistine, I could be silent no longer, even in the interests of great rhetoric. I interrupted to point out that the rabbit itself had been brought as a domestic animal to England in 1176, presumably to improve the protein diet of the peasantry.

All forms of life modify their contexts. The most spectacular and benign instance is doubtless the coral polyp. By serving its own ends, it has created a vast undersea world favorable to thousands of other kinds of animals and plants. Ever since man

Source: Lynn White, Jr., "The Historical Roots of Our Ecologic Crisis", reprinted from *Science*, Vol. 155, 10 March 1967, pp. 1203-1207. This article also appeared in *Machina Ex Deo: Essays in the Dynamism of Western Culture* and is reprinted here by permission of the author, *Science*, and the Massachusetts Institute of Technology Press.

became a numerous species he has affected his environment notably. The hypothesis that his fire-drive method of hunting created the world's great grasslands and helped to exterminate the monster mammals of the Pleistocene from much of the globe is plausible, if not proved. For six millennia at least, the banks of the lower Nile have been a human artifact rather than the swampy African jungle which nature, apart from man, would have made it. The Aswan Dam, flooding 5000 square miles, is only the latest stage in a long process. In many regions terracing or irrigation, overgrazing, the cutting of forests by Romans to build ships to fight Carthaginians or by Crusaders to solve the logistics problems of their expeditions, have profoundy changed some ecologies. Observation that the French landscape falls into two basic types, the open fields of the north and the *bocage* of the south and west, inspired Marc Bloch to undertake his classic study of medieval agricultural methods. Quite unintentionally, changes in human ways often affect nonhuman nature. It has been noted, for example, that the advent of the automobile eliminated huge flocks of sparrows that once fed on the horse manure littering every street.

The history of ecologic change is still so rudimentary that we know little about what really happened, or what the results were. The extinction of the European aurochs as late as 1627 would seem to have been a simple case of overenthusiastic hunting. On more intricate matters it often is impossible to find solid information. For a thousand years or more the Frisians and Hollanders have been pushing back the North Sea, and the process is culminating in our own time in the reclamation of the Zuider Zee. What, if any, species of animals, birds, fish, shore life, or plants have died out in the process? In their epic combat with Neptune have the Netherlanders overlooked ecological values in such a way that the quality of human life in the Netherlands has suffered? I cannot discover that the questions have ever been asked, much less answered.

People, then, have often been a dynamic element in their own environment, but in the present state of historical scholarship we usually do not know exactly when, where, or with what effects man-induced changes came. As we enter the last third of the twentieth century, however, concern for the problem of ecologic backlash is mounting feverishly. Natural science, conceived as the effort to understand the nature of things, had flourished in several eras and among several peoples. Similarly there had been an age-old accumulation of technological skills, sometimes growing rapidly, sometimes slowly. But it was not until about four generations ago that Western Europe and North America arranged a marriage between science and technology, a union of the theoretical and the empirical approaches to our natural environment. The emergence in widespread practice of the Baconian creed that scientific knowledge means technological power over nature can scarcely be dated before about 1850, save in the chemical industries, where it is anticipated in the eighteenth century. Its acceptance as a normal pattern of action may mark the greatest event in human history since the invention of agriculture, and perhaps in nonhuman terrestrial history as well.

Almost at once the new situation forced the crystallization of the novel concept of ecology; indeed, the word *ecology* first appeared in the English language in 1873. Today, less than a century later, the impact of our race upon the environment has so increased in force that it has changed in essence. When the first cannons were fired, in the early fourteenth century, they affected ecology by sending workers scrambling to the forests and mountains for more potash, sulfur, iron ore, and charcoal, with some resulting erosion and deforestation. Hydrogen bombs are of a different order: a war fought with them might alter the genetics of all life on this planet. By 1285 London had a smog problem arising from the burning of soft coal, but our present combustion of fossil fuels threatens to change the chemistry of the globe's atmosphere as a whole, with consequences which we are only beginning to guess. With the population explosion, the carcinoma of planless urbanism, the new geological deposits of sewage and garbage, surely no creature other than man has ever managed to foul its nest in such short order.

There are many calls to action, but specific proposals, however worthy as individual items, seem too partial, palliative, negative: ban the bomb, tear down the billboards, give the Hindus contraceptives and tell them to eat their sacred cows. The simplest solution to any suspect change is, of course, to stop it, or, better yet, to revert to a romanticized past: make those ugly gasoline stations look like Anne Hathaway's cottage or (in the Far West) like ghost-town saloons. The "wilderness-area" mentality invariably advocates deep-freezing an ecology, whether San Gimignano or the High Sierra, as it was before the first Kleenex was dropped. But neither atavism nor prettification will cope with the ecologic crisis of our time.

What shall we do? No one yet knows. Unless we think about fundamentals, our specific measures may produce new backlashes more serious than those they are designed to remedy.

As a beginning we should try to clarify our thinking by looking, in some historical depth, at the presuppositions that underlie modern technology and science. Science was traditionally aristocratic, speculative, intellectual in intent; technology was lower-class, emperical, action-oriented. The quite sudden fusion of these two, towards the middle of the nineteenth century, is surely related to the slightly prior and contemporary democratic revolutions which, by reducing social barriers, tended to assert a functional unity of brain and hand. Our ecologic crisis is the product of an emerging, entirely novel, democratic culture. The issue is whether a democratized world can survive its own implications. Presumably we cannot unless we rethink our axioms.

The Western Traditions of Technology and Science

One thing is so certain that it seems stupid to verbalize it: both modern technology and modern science are distinctively *occidental.* Our technology has absorbed elements from all over the world, notably from China; yet everywhere today, whether in Japan or in Nigeria, succesful technology is Western. Our science is the heir to all the sciences of the past, especially perhaps to the work of the great Islamic scientists of the Middle Ages, who so often outdid the ancient Greeks in skill and perspicacity: al-Rāzī in medicine, for example; or ibn-al-Haytham in optics; or Omar Khāyyám in mathematics. Indeed, not a few works of such geniuses seem to have vanished in the original Arabic and to survive only in medieval Latin translations that helped to lay the foundations for later Western developments. Today, around the globe, all significant science is Western in style and method, whatever the pigmentation or language of the scientists.

A second pair of facts is less well recognized because they result from quite recent historical scholarship. The leadership of the West, both in technology and in science, is far older than the so-called scientific revolution of the seventeenth century or the so-called industrial revolution of the eighteenth century. These terms are in fact outmoded and obscure the true nature of what they try to describe—significant stages in two long and separate developments. By A.D. 1000 at the latest—and perhaps, feebly, as much as 200 years earlier—the West began to apply water power to industrial processes other than milling grain. This was followed in the late twelfth century by the harnessing of wind power. From simple beginnings, but with remarkable consistency of style, the West rapidly expanded its skills in the development of power machinery, labor saving devices, and automation. Those who doubt should contemplate that most monumental achievement in the history of automation: the weight-driven mechanical clock, which appeared in two forms in the early fourteenth century. Not in craftsmanship but in basic technological capacity, the Latin West of the later Middle Ages far outstripped its elaborate, sophisticated, and esthetically magnificent sister cultures, Byzantium and Islam. In 1444 a great Greek ecclesiastic, Bessarion, who had gone to Italy, wrote a letter to a prince in Greece. He is amazed by the superiority of Western ships, arms, textiles, glass. But above all he is astonished by the spectacle of waterwheels sawing timbers and pumping the bellows of blast furnaces. Clearly, he had seen nothing of the sort in the Near East.

By the end of the fifteenth century the technological superiority of Europe was such that its small, mutually hostile nations could spill out over all the rest of the world, conquering, looting, and colonizing. The symbol of this technological superiority is the fact that Portugal, one of the weakest states of the Occident, was able to become, and to remain for a century, mistress of the East Indies. And we must remember that the technology of Vasco da Gama and Albuquerque was built by pure empiricism, drawing remarkably little support or inspiration from science.

In the present-day vernacular understanding, modern science is supposed to have begun in 1543, when both Copernicus and Vesalius published their great works. It is no derogation of their accomplishments, however, to point out that such structures as the *Fabrica* and the *de revolutionibus* do not appear overnight. The distinctive Western tradition of science, in fact, began in the late eleventh century with a massive movement of translation of Arabic and Greek scientific works into Latin. A few notable books—Theophrastus, for example—escaped the West's avid new appetite for science, but within less than 200 years effectively the entire corpus of Greek and Muslim science was available in Latin, and was being eagerly read and criticized in the new European universities. Out of criticism arose new observation, speculation, and increasing distrust of ancient authorities. By the late thirteenth century Europe had seized global scientific leadership from the faltering hands of Islam. It would be as absurd to deny the profound originality of Newton, Galileo, or Copernicus as to deny that of the fourteenth century scholastic scientists like Buridan or Oresme on whose work they built. Before the eleventh century, science scarcely existed in the Latin West, even in Roman times. From the eleventh century onward, the scientific sector of occidental culture has increased in a steady crescendo.

Since both our technological and our scientific movements got their start, acquired their character, and achieved world dominance in the Middle Ages, it would seem that we cannot understand their nature or their present impact upon ecology without examining fundamental medieval assumptions and developments.

MEDIEVAL VIEW OF MAN AND NATURE

Until recently, agriculture has been the chief occupation even in "advanced" societies; hence, any change in methods of tillage has much importance. Early plows, drawn by two oxen, did not normally turn the sod but merely scratched it. Thus, cross-plowing was needed and fields tended to be squarish. In the fairly light soils and semi-arid climates of the Near East and Mediterranean, this worked well. But such a plow was inappropriate to the wet climate and often sticky soils of northern Europe. By the latter part of the seventh century after Christ, however, following obscure beginnings, certain northern peasants were using an entirely new kind of plow, equipped with a vertical knife to cut the line of the furrow, a horizontal share to slice under the sod, and a moldboard to turn it over. The friction of this plow with the soil was so great that it normally required not two but eight oxen. It attacked the land with such violence that cross-plowing was not needed, and fields tended to be shaped in long strips.

In the days of the scratch-plow, fields were distributed generally in units capable of supporting a single family. Subsistence farming was the presupposition. But no peasant owned eight oxen: to use the new and more efficient plow, peasants pooled their oxen to form large plow-teams, originally receiving (it would appear) plowed strips in proportion to their contribution. Thus, distribution of land was based no longer on the needs of a family but, rather, on the capacity of a power machine to till the earth. Man's relation to the soil was profoundly changed. Formerly man had been part of nature; now he was the exploiter of nature. Nowhere else in the world did farmers develop any analogous agricultural implement. Is it coincidence that modern technology, with its ruthlessness toward nature, has so largely been produced by descendants of these peasants of northern Europe?

This same exploitative attitude appears slightly before A.D. 830 in Western illustrated calendars. In older calendars the months were shown as passive personifications. The new Frankish calendars, which set the style for the Middle Ages, are very different: they show men coercing the world around them—plowing, harvesting, chopping trees, butchering pigs. Man and nature are two things, and man is master.

These novelties seem to be in harmony with larger intellectual patterns. What people do about their ecology depends on what they think about themselves in relation to things around them. Human ecology is deeply conditioned by beliefs about our nature and destiny—that is, by religion. To Western eyes this is very evident in, say, India or Ceylon. It is equally true of ourselves and of our medieval ancestors.

The victory of Christianity over paganism was the greatest psychic revolution in the history of our culture. It has become fashionable today to say that, for better or worse, we live in "the post-Christian age." Certainly the forms of our thinking and language have largely ceased to be Christian, but to my eye the substance often remains amazingly akin to that of the past. Our daily habits of action, for example, are dominated by an implicit faith in perpetual progress which was unknown either to Greco-Roman antiquity or to the Orient. It is rooted in, and is indefensible apart from Judeo-Christian teleology. The fact that Communists share it merely helps to show what can be demonstrated on many other grounds: that Marxism, like Islam, is a Judeo-Christian heresy. We continue today to live, as we have lived for about 1700 years, very largely in a context of Christian axioms.

What did Christianity tell people about their relations with the environment?

While many of the world's mythologies provide stories of creation, Greco-Roman mythology was singularly incoherent in this respect. Like Aristotle, the intellectuals of the ancient West denied that the visible world had had a beginning. Indeed, the idea of a beginning was impossible in the framework of their cyclical notion of time. In sharp contrast, Christianity inherited from Judaism not only a concept of time as nonrepetitive and linear but also a striking story of creation. By gradual stages a loving and all-powerful God had created light and darkness, the heavenly bodies, the earth and all its plants, animals, birds and fishes. Finally, God had created Adam and, as an afterthought, Eve, to keep man from being lonely. Man named all the animals, thus establishing his dominance over them. God planned all of this explicity for man's benefit and rule: no item in the physical creation had any purpose save to serve man's purposes. And, although man's body is made of clay, he is not simply part of nature: he is made in God's image.

Especially in its Western form, Christianity is the most anthropocentric religion the world has seen. As early as the second century both Tertullian and Saint Irenaeus of Lyons were insisting that when God shaped Adam he was foreshadowing the image of the Incarnate Christ, the Second Adam. Man shares, in great measure, God's transcendence of nature. Christianity, in absolute contrast to ancient paganism and Asia's religions (except, perhaps, Zoroastrianism), not only established a dualism of man and nature but also insisted that it is God's will that man exploit nature for his proper ends.

At the level of the common people this worked out in an interesting way. In antiquity every tree, every spring, every stream, every hill had its own *genius loci*, its guardian spirit. These spirits were accessible to men, but were very unlike men; centaurs, fauns, and mermaids show their ambivalence. Before one cut a tree, mined a mountain, or dammed a brook, it was important to placate the spirit in charge of that particular situation, and to keep it placated. By destroying pagan animism, Christianity made it possible to exploit nature in a mood of indifference to the feelings of natural objects.

It is often said that for animism the Church substituted the cult of saints. True; but the cult of saints is functionally quite different from animism. The saint is not *in* natural objects; he may have special shrines, but his citizenship is in heaven. Moreover, a saint is entirely a man; he can be approached in human terms. In addition to saints, Christianity of course also had angels and demons inherited from Judaism and perhaps, at one remove, from Zoroastrianism. But these were all as mobile as the saints themselves. The spirits *in* natural objects, which formerly had protected nature from man, evaporated. Man's effective monopoly on spirit in this world was confirmed, and the old inhibitions to the exploitation of nature crumbled.

When one speaks in such sweeping terms, a note of caution is in order. Christianity is a complex faith, and its consequences differ in differing contexts. What I have said may well apply to the medieval West, where in fact technology made spectacular advances. But the Greek East, a highly civilized realm of equal Christian devotion, seems to have produced no marked technological innovation after the late seventh century, when Greek fire was invented. The key to the contrast may perhaps be found in a difference in the tonality of piety and thought which students of comparative theology find between the Greek and the Latin churches. The Greeks believed that sin was intellectual blindness, and that salvation was found in illumination, orthodoxy—that is, clear thinking. The Latins, on the other hand, felt that sin was moral evil, and that salvation was to be found in right conduct. Eastern theology has been intellectualist. Western theology has been voluntarist. The Greek saint contemplates; the Western saint acts. The implications of Christianity for the conquest of nature would emerge more easily in the Western atmosphere.

The Christian dogma of creation, which is found in the first clause of all the Creeds, has another meaning for our comprehension of today's ecologic crisis. By revelation, God had given man the Bible, the Book of Scripture. But since God had made nature, nature also must reveal the divine mentality. The religious study of nature for the better understanding of God was known as natural theology. In the early Church, and always in the Greek East, nature was conceived primarily as a symbolic system through which God speaks to men: the ant is a sermon to sluggards; rising flames are the symbol of the soul's aspiration. This view of nature was essentially artistic rather than scientific. While Byzantium preserved and copied great numbers of ancient Greek scientific texts, science as we conceive it could scarcely flourish in such an ambience.

However, in the Latin West by the early thirteenth century natural theology was following a very different bent. It was ceasing to be the decoding of the physical symbols of God's communication with man and was becoming the effort to understand God's mind by discovering how his creation operates. The rainbow was no longer simply a symbol of hope first sent to Noah after the Deluge: Robert Grosseteste, Friar Roger Bacon and Theodoric of Freiberg produced startingly sophisticated work on the optics of the rainbow, but they did it as a venture in religious understanding. From the thirteenth century onward, up to and including Leibnitz and Newton, every major scientist, in effect, explained his motivations in religious terms. Indeed, if Galileo had not been so expert an amateur theologian he would have got into far less trouble: the professionals resented his intrusion. And Newton seems to have regarded himself more as a theologian than as a scientist. It was not until the late eighteenth century that the hypothesis of God became unnecessary to many scientists.

It is often hard for the historian to judge, when men explain why they are doing what they want to do, whether they are offering real reasons or merely culturally acceptable reasons. The consistency with which scientists during the long formative centuries of Western science said that the task and the reward of the scientist was "to think God's thoughts after him" leads one to believe that this was their real motivation. If so, then modern Western science was cast in a matrix of Christian theology. The dynamism of religious devotion, shaped by the Judeo-Christian dogma of creation, gave it impetus.

AN ALTERNATIVE CHRISTIAN VIEW

We would seem to be headed toward conclusions unpalatable to many Christians. Since both *science* and *technology* are blessed words in our contemporary vocabulary, some may be happy at the notions, first, that, viewed historically, modern science is an extrapolation of natural theology and, second, that modern technology is at least partly to be explained as an occidental, voluntarist realization of the Christian dogma of man's transcendence of, and rightful mastery over, nature. But, as we now recognize, somewhat over a century ago science and technology—hitherto quite separate activities—joined to give mankind powers which, to judge by many of the ecologic effects, are out of control. If so, Christianity bears a huge burden of guilt.

I personally doubt that disastrous ecologic backlash can be avoided simply by applying to our problems more science and more technology. Our science and technology have grown out of Christian attitudes toward man's relation to nature which are almost universally held not only by Christians and neo-Christians but also by those who fondly regard themselves as pose-Christians. Despite Copernicus, all the cosmos rotates around our little globe. Despite Darwin, we are *not*, in our hearts, part of the natural process. We are superior to nature, contemptuous of it, willing to use it for our slightest whim. The newly elected governor of California, like myself a churchman, but less troubled than I, spoke for the Christian tradition when he said (as is alleged), "when you've seen one redwood tree, you've seen them all." To a Christian a tree can be no more than a physical fact. The whole concept of the sacred grove is alien to Christianity and to the ethos of the West. For nearly two millennia Christian missionaries have been chopping down sacred groves, which are idolatrous because they assume spirit in nature.

What we do do about ecology depends on our ideas of the man-nature relationship. More science and more technology are not going to get us out of the present ecologic crisis until we find a new religion, or rethink our old one. The beatniks, who are the basic revolutionaries of our time, show a sound instinct in their affinity for Zen Buddhism, which conceives of the man-nature relationship as very nearly the mirror image of the Christian view. Zen, however, is as deeply conditioned by Asian history as Christianity is by the experience of the West, and I am dubious of its viability among us.

Possibly we should ponder the greatest radical in Christian history since Christ: Saint Francis of Assisi. The prime miracle of Saint Francis is the fact that he did not end at the stake, as many of his left-wing followers did. He was so clearly heretical that a general of the Franciscan Order, Saint Bonaventura, a great and perceptive Christian, tried to suppress the early accounts of Franciscanism. The key to an understanding of Francis is his belief in the virtue of humility—not merely for the individual but for man as a species. Francis tried to depose man from his monarchy over creation and set up a democracy of all God's creatures. With him the ant is no longer simply a homily for the lazy, flames a sign of the thrust of the soul toward union with God; now they are Brother Ant and Sister Fire, praising the Creator in their own ways as Brother Man does in his.

Later commentators have said that Francis preached to the birds as a rebuke to men who would not listen. The records do not read so: he urged the little birds to praise God, and in spiritual ectasy they flapped their wings and chirped rejoicing. Legends of saints, especially the Irish saints, had long told of their dealings with animals but always, I believe, to show their human dominance over creatures. With Francis it is different. The land around Gubbio in the Apennines was being ravaged by a fierce wolf. Saint Francis, says the legend, talked to the wolf and persuaded him of the error of his ways. The wolf repented, died in the odor of sanctity, and was buried in consecrated ground.

What Sir Steven Ruciman calls "the Franciscan doctrine of the animal soul" was quickly stamped out. Quite possibly it was in part inspired, consciously or unconsciously, by the belief in reincarnation held by the Cathar heretics who at that time teemed in Italy and southern France, and who presumably had got it originally from India. It is significant that at just the same moment, about 1200, traces of metempsychosis are found also in western Judaism, in the Provençal *Cabbala*. But Francis held neither to transmigration of souls nor to pantheism. His view of nature and of man rested on a unique sort of pan-psychism of all things animate and inanimate, designed for the glorification of their transcendent Creator, who, in the ultimate gesture of cosmic humility, assumed flesh, lay helpless in a manger, and hung dying on a scaffold.

I am not suggesting that many contemporary Americans who are concerned about our ecologic crisis will be either able or willing to counsel with wolves or exhort birds. However, the present increasing disruption of the global environment is the product of a dynamic technology and science which were originating in the Western medieval world against which Saint Francis was rebelling in so original a way. Their growth cannot be understood historically apart from distinctive attitudes toward nature which are deeply grounded in Christian dogma. The fact that most people do not think of these attitudes as Christian is irrelevant. No new set of basic values has been accepted in our society to displace those of Christianity. Hence we shall continue to have a worsening ecologic crisis until we reject the Christian axiom that nature has no reason for existence save to serve man.

The greatest spiritual revolutionary in Western history, Saint Francis, proposed what he thought was an alternative Christian view of nature and man's relation to it: he tried to substitute the idea of equality of all creatures, including man, for the idea of man's limitless rule of creation. He failed. Both our present science and our present technology are so tinctured with orthodox Christian arrogance toward nature that no solution for our ecologic crisis can be expected from them alone. Since the roots of our trouble are so largely religious, the remedy must also be essentially religious, whether we call it that or not. We must rethink and refeel our nature and destiny. The profoundly religious, but heretical, sense of the primitive Franciscans for the spiritual autonomy of all parts of nature may point a direction. I propose Francis as a patron saint for ecologists.

The Economics of the Coming Spaceship Earth

KENNETH E. BOULDING

We are now in the middle of a long process of transition in the nature of the image which man has of himself and his environment. Primitive men, and to a large extent also men of the early civilizations, imagined themselves to be living on a virtually illimitable plane. There was almost always somewhere beyond the known limits of human habitation, and, over a very large part of the time that man has been on earth, there has been something like a frontier. That is, there was always some place else to go when things got too difficult, either by reason of the deterioration of the natural environment or a deterioration of the social structure in places where people happened to live. The image of the frontier is probably one of the oldest images of mankind, and it is not surprising that we find it hard to get rid of.

Gradually, however, man has been accustoming himself to the notion of the spherical earth and a closed sphere of human activity. A few unusual spirits among the ancient Greeks perceived that the earth was a sphere. It was only with the circumnavigations and the geographical explorations of the fifteenth and sixteenth centuries, however, that the fact that the earth was a sphere became at all widely known and accepted. Even in the nineteenth century, the commonest map was Mercator's pro-

Source: Kenneth E. Boulding, "The Economics of the Coming Spaceship Earth", in H. Jarrett (ed.), *Environmental Quality in a Growing Economy*, published for Resources For The Future, Inc., by The Johns Hopkins Press, 1966, pp. 3-14. Reprinted by permission of the publisher and author.

jection, which visualizes the earth as an illimitable cylinder, essentially a plane wrapped around the globe, and it was not until the Second World War and the development of the air age that the global nature of the planet really entered the popular imagination. Even now we are very far from having made the moral, political, and psychological adjustments which are implied in this transition from the illimitable plane to the closed sphere.

Economists in particular, for the most part, have failed to come to grips with the ultimate consequences of the transition from the open to the closed earth. One hesitates to use the terms "open" and "closed" in this connection, as they have been used with so many different shades of meaning. Nevertheless, it is hard to find equivalents. The open system, indeed, has some similarities to the open system of von Bertalanffy,[1] in that it implies that some kind of a structure is maintained in the midst of a throughput from inputs to outputs. In a closed system, the outputs of all parts of the system are linked to the inputs of other parts. There are no inputs from outside and no outputs to the outside; indeed, there is no outside at all. Closed systems, in fact, are very rare in human experience, in fact almost by definition unknowable, for if there are genuinely closed systems around us, we have no way of getting information into them or out of them; and hence if they are really closed, we would be quite unaware of their existence. We can only find out about a closed system if we participate in it. Some isolated primitive societies may have approximated to this, but even these had to take inputs from the environment and give outputs to it. All living organisms, including man himself, are open systems. They have to receive inputs in the shape of air, food, water, and give off outputs in the form of effluvia and excrement. Deprivation of input of air, even for a few minutes, is fatal. Deprivation of the ability to obtain any input or to dispose of any output is fatal in a relatively short time. All human societies have likewise been open systems. They receive inputs from the earth, the atmosphere, and the waters, and they give outputs into these reservoirs; they also produce inputs internally in the shape of babies and outputs in the shape of corpses. Given a capacity to draw upon inputs and to get rid of outputs, an open system of this kind can persist indefinitely.

There are some systems—such as the biological phenotype, for instance the human body—which cannot maintain themselves indefinitely by inputs and outputs because of the phenomenon of aging. This process is very little understood. It occurs, evidently, because there are some outputs which cannot be replaced by any known input. There is not the same necessity for aging in organizations and in societies, although an analogous phenomenon may take place. The structure and composition of an organization or society, however, can be maintained by inputs of fresh personnel from birth and education as the existing personnel ages and eventually dies. Here we have an interesting example of a system which seems to maintain itself by the self-generation of inputs, and in this sense is moving towards closure. The input of people (that is, babies) is also an output of people (that is, parents).

Systems may be open or closed in respect to a number of classes of inputs and outputs. Three important classes are matter, energy, and information. The present world economy is open in regard to all three. We can think of the world economy or "econosphere" as a subset of the "world set," which is the set of all objects of possible discourse in the world. We then think of the state of the econosphere at any one moment as being the total capital stock, that is, the set of all objects, people, organizations, and so on, which are interesting from the point of view of the system of exchange. This total stock of capital is clearly an open system in the sense that it has inputs and outputs, inputs being production which adds to the capital stock, outputs being consumption which subtracts from it. From a material point of view, we see objects passing from the noneconomic into the economic set in the process of production, and we similarly see products passing out of the economic set as their value becomes zero. Thus we see the econosphere as a material process involving the discovery and mining of fossil fuels, ores, etc., and at the other end a process by which the effluents of the system are passed out into noneconomic reservoirs—for instance, the atmosphere and the oceans—which are not appropriated and do not enter into the exchange system.

From the point of view of the energy system, the econosphere involves inputs of available energy in the form, say, of water power, fossil fuels, or sunlight, which are necessary in order to create the material throughput and to move matter from the noneconomic set into the economic set or even out of it again; and energy itself is given off by the system in a less available form, mostly in the form of heat. These inputs of available energy must come either from the sun (the energy supplied by other stars being assumed to be negligible) or from the earth itself, either through its internal heat or through its energy of rotation or other motions, which generate, for instance, the energy of the tides. Agriculture, a few solar machines, and water power use the current available energy income. In advanced societies this is supplemented very extensively by the use of fossil fuels, which represent as it were a capital stock of stored-up sunshine. Because of this capital stock of energy, we have been able to maintain an energy input into the system, particularly over the last two centuries, much larger than we would have been able to do with existing techniques if we had had to rely on the current input of available energy from the sun or the earth itself. This supplementary input, however, is by its very nature exhaustible.

The inputs and outputs of information are more subtle and harder to trace, but also represent an open system, related to, but not wholly dependent on, the transformations of matter and energy. By far the larger amount of information and knowledge is self-generated by the human society, though a certain amount of information comes into the sociosphere in the form of light from the universe outside. The information that comes from the universe has certainly affected man's image of himself and of his environment, as we can easily visualize if we suppose that we lived on a planet with a total cloud-cover that kept out all information from the exterior universe. It is only in very recent times, of course, that the information coming in from the universe has been captured and coded into the form of a complex image of what the universe is like outside the earth; but even in primitive times, man's perception of the heavenly bodies has always profoundly affected his image of earth and of himself. It is the information generated within the planet, however, and particularly that generated by man himself, which forms by far the larger part of the information system. We can think of the stock of knowledge, or as Teilhard de Chardin called it, the "noosphere," and consider this as an open system, losing knowledge through aging and death and gaining it through birth and education and the ordinary experience of life.

From the human point of view, knowledge or information is by far the most important of the three systems. Matter only acquires significance and only enters the sociosphere or the econosphere insofar as it becomes an object of human knowledge. We can think of capital, indeed, as frozen knowledge or knowledge imposed on the material world in the form of improbable arrangements. A machine, for instance, originated in the mind of man, and both its construction and its use involve information processes imposed on the material world by man himself. The cumulation of knowledge, that is, the excess of its production over its consumption, is the key to human development of all kinds, especially to economic development. We can see this preeminence of knowledge very clearly in the experiences of countries where the material capital has been destroyed by a war, as in Japan and Germany. The knowledge of the people was not destroyed, and it did not take long, therefore, certainly not more than ten years, for most of the material capital to be reestablished again. In a country such as Indonesia, however, where the knowledge did not exist, the material capital did not come into being either. By "knowledge" here I mean, of course, the whole cognitive structure, which includes valuations and motivations as well as images of the factual world.

The concept of entropy, used in a somewhat loose sense, can be applied to all three of these open systems. In the case of material systems, we can distinguish between entropic processes, which take concentrated materials and diffuse them through the oceans or over the earth's surface or into the atmosphere, and anti-entropic processes, which take diffuse materials and concentrate them. Material entropy can be taken as a measure of the uniformity of the distribution of elements and, more uncertainly, compounds and other structures on the earth's surface. There is, fortunately, no law of increasing material entropy, as there is in the corresponding case of energy, as it is quite possible to concentrate diffused materials if energy inputs are allowed. Thus the processes for fixation of nitrogen from the air, processes for the extraction of magnesium or other elements from the sea, and processes for the desalinization of sea water are anti-entropic in the material sense, though the reduction of material entropy has to be paid for by inputs of energy and also inputs of information, or at least a stock of information in the system. In regard to matter, therefore, a closed system is conceivable, that is, a system in which there is neither increase nor decrease in material entropy. In such a system all outputs from consumption would constantly be recycled to become inputs for production, as for instance, nitrogen in the nitrogen cycle of the natural ecosystem.

In regard to the energy system there is, unfortunately, no escape from the grim Second Law of Thermodynamics; and if there were no energy inputs into the earth, any evolutionary or developmental process would be impossible. The large energy inputs which we have obtained from fossil fuels are strictly temporary. Even the most optimistic predictions would expect the easily available supply of fossil fuels to be exhausted in a mere matter of centuries at present rates of use. If the rest of the world were to rise to American standards of power consumption, and still more if world population continues to increase, the exhaustion of fossil fuels would be even more rapid. The development of nuclear energy has improved this picture, but has not fundamentally altered it, at least in present technologies, for fissionable material is still relatively scarce. If we should achieve the economic use of energy through fusion, of course, a much larger source of energy materials would be available, which would expand the time horizons of supplementary energy input into an open social system by perhaps tens to hundreds of thousands of years. Failing this, however, the time is not very far distant, historically speaking, when man will once more have to retreat to his current energy input from the sun, even though this could be used much more effectively than in the past with increased knowledge. Up to now, certainly, we have not got very far with the technology of using current solar energy, but the possibility of substantial improvements in the future is certainly high. It may be, indeed, that the biological revolution which is just beginning will produce a solution to this problem, as we develop artificial organisms which are capable of much more efficient transformation of solar energy into easily available forms than any that we now have. As Richard Meier has suggested, we may run our machines in the future with methane-producing algae.[2]

The question of whether there is anything corresponding to entropy in the information system is a puzzling one, though of great interest. There are certainly many examples of social systems and cultures which have lost knowledge, especially in transition from one generation to the next, and in which the culture has therefore degenerated. One only has to look at the folk culture of Appalachian migrants to American cities to see a culture which started out as a fairly rich European folk culture in Elizabethan times and which seems to have lost both skills, adaptability, folk tales, songs, and almost everything that goes to make up richness and complexity in a culture, in the course of about ten generations. The American Indians on reservations provide another example of such degradation of the information and knowledge system. On the other hand, over a great part of human history, the growth of knowledge in the earth as a whole seems to have been almost continuous, even though there have been times of relatively slow growth and times of rapid growth. As it is knowledge of certain kinds that produces the growth of knowledge in general, we have here a very subtle and complicated system, and it is hard to put one's finger on the particular elements in a culture which make knowledge grow more or less rapidly, or even which make it decline. One of the great puzzles in this connection, for instance, is why the take-off into science, which represents an "acceleration," or an increase in the rate of growth of knowledge in European society in the sixteenth century, did not take place in China, which at that time (about 1600) was unquestionably ahead of Europe, and one would think even more ready for the breakthrough. This is perhaps the most crucial question in the theory of social development, yet we must confess that it is very little understood. Perhaps the most significant factor in this connection is the existence of "slack" in the culture, which permits a divergence from established patterns and activity which is not merely devoted to reproducing the existing society but is devoted to changing it. China was perhaps too well-organized and had too little slack in its society to produce the kind of acceleration which we find in the somewhat poorer and less well-organized but more diverse societies of Europe.

The closed earth of the future requires economic principles which are somewhat different from those of the open earth of the past. For the sake of picturesqueness, I am tempted to call the open economy the "cowboy economy," the cowboy being symbolic of the illimitable plains and also associated with reckless, exploitative, romantic, and violent behavior, which is characteristic of open societies. The closed economy of the future might similarly be called the "spaceman" economy, in which the earth has become a single spaceship, without unlimited reservoirs of anything, either for extraction or for pollution, and in which, therefore, man must find his place in a cyclical ecological system which is capable of continuous reproduction of material form even though it cannot escape having inputs of energy. The difference between the two types of economy becomes most apparent in the attitude towards consumption. In the cowboy economy, consumption is regarded as a good thing and production likewise; and the success of the economy is measured by the amount of the throughput from the "factors of production," a part of which, at any rate, is extracted from the reservoirs of raw materials and noneconomic objects, and another part of which is output into the reservoirs of pollution. If there are infinite reservoirs from which material can be obtained and into which effluvia can be deposited, then the throughput is at least a plausible measure of the success of the economy. The gross national product is a rough measure of this total throughput. It should be possible, however, to distinguish that part of the GNP which is derived from exhaustible and that which is derived from reproducible resources, as well as that part of consumption which represents effluvia and that which represents input into the productive system again. Nobody, as far as I know, has ever attempted to break down the GNP in this way, although it would be an interesting and extremely important exercise, which is unfortunately beyond the scope of this paper.

By contrast, in the spaceman economy, throughput is by no means a desideratum, and is indeed to be regarded as something to be minimized rather than maximized. The essential measure of the success of the economy is not production and consumption at all, but the nature, extent, quality, and complexity of the total capital stock, including in this the state of the human bodies and minds included in the system. In the spaceman economy, what we are primarily concerned with is stock maintenance, and any technological change which results in the maintenance of a given total stock with a lessened throughput (that is, less production and consumption) is clearly a gain. This idea that both production and consumption are bad things rather than good things is very strange to economists, who have been obsessed with the income-flow concepts to the exclusion, almost, of capital-stock concepts.

There are actually some very tricky and unsolved problems involved in the questions as to whether human welfare or well-being is to be regarded as a stock or a flow. Something of both these elements seems actually to be involved in it, and as far as I know there have been practically no studies directed towards identifying these two dimensions of human satisfaction. Is it, for instance, eating that is a good thing, or is it being well fed? Does economic welfare involve having nice clothes, fine houses, good equipment, and so on, or is it to be measured by the depreciation and the wearing out of these things? I am inclined myself to regard the stock concept as most fundamental, that is, to think of being well fed as more important than eating, and to think even of so-called services as essentially involving the restoration of a depleting psychic capital. Thus I have argued that we go to a concert in order to restore a psychic condition which might be called "just having gone to a concert," which, once established, tends to depreciate. When it depreciates beyond a certain point, we go to another concert in order to restore it. If it depreciates rapidly, we go to a lot of concerts; if it depreciates slowly, we go to few. On this view, similarly, we eat primarily to restore bodily homeostasis, that is, to maintain a condition of being well fed, and so on. On this view, there is nothing desirable in consumption at all. The less consumption we can maintain a given state with, the better off we are. If we had clothes that did not wear out, houses that did not depreciate, and even if we could maintain our bodily condition without eating, we would clearly be much better off.

It is this last consideration, perhaps, which makes one pause. Would we, for instance, really want an operation that would enable us to restore all our bodily tissues by intravenous feeding while we slept? Is there not, that is to say, a certain virtue in throughput itself, in activity itself, in production and consumption itself, in raising food and in eating it? It would certainly be rash to exclude this possibility. Further interesting problems are raised by the demand for variety. We certainly do not want a constant state to be maintained; we want fluctuations in the state. Otherwise there would be no demand for variety in food, for variety in scene, as in travel, for variety in social contact, and so on. The demand for variety can, of course, be costly, and sometimes it seems to be too costly to be tolerated or at least legitimated, as in the case of marital partners, where the maintenance of a homeostatic state in the family is usually regarded as much more desirable than the variety and excessive throughput of the libertine. There are problems here which the economics profession has neglected with astonishing singlemindedness. My own attempts to call attention to some of them, for instance, in two articles,[3] as far as I can judge, produced no response whatever; and economists continue to think and act as if production, consumption, throughput, and the GNP were the sufficient and adequate measure of economic success.

It may be said, of course, why worry about all this when the spaceman economy is still a good way off (at least beyond the lifetimes of any now living), so let us eat, drink, spend, extract and pollute, and be as merry as we can, and let posterity worry about the spaceship earth. It is always a little hard to find a convincing answer to the man who says, "What has posterity ever done for me?" and the conservationist has always had to fall back on rather vague ethical principles postulating identity of the individual with some human community or society which extends not only back into the past but forward into the future. Unless the individual identifies with some community of this kind, conservation is obviously "irrational." Why should we not maximize the welfare of this generation at the cost of posterity? "*Après nous, le déluge*" has been the motto of not insignificant numbers of human societies. The only answer to this, as far as I can see, is to point out that the welfare of the individual depends on the extent to which he can identify himself with others, and that the most satisfactory individual identity is that which identifies not only with a community in space but also with a community extending over time from the past into the future. If this kind of identity is recognized as desirable, then posterity has a voice, even if it does not have a vote; and in a sense, if its voice can influence votes, it has votes too. This whole problem is linked up with the much larger one of the determinants of the morale, legitimacy, and "nerve" of a society, and there is a great deal of historical evidence to suggest that a society which loses its identity with posterity and which loses its positive image of the future loses also its capacity to deal with present problems, and soon falls apart.[4]

Even if we concede that posterity is relevant to our present problems, we still face the question of time-discounting and the closely related question of uncertainty-discounting. It is a well-known phenomenon that individuals discount the future, even in their own lives. The very existence of a positive rate of interest may be taken as at least strong supporting evidence of this hypothesis. If we discount our own future, it is certainly not unreasonable to discount posterity's future even more, even if we do give posterity a vote. If we discount this at 5 per cent per annum, posterity's vote or dollar halves every fourteen years as we look into the future, and after even a mere hundred years it is pretty small—only about 1½ cents on the dollar. If we add another 5 per cent for uncertainty, even the vote of our grandchildren reduces almost to insignificance. We can argue, of course, that the ethical thing to do is not to discount the future at all, that time-discounting is mainly the result of myopia and perspective, and hence is an illusion which the moral man should not tolerate. It is a very popular illusion, however, and one that must certainly be taken into consideration in the formulation of policies. It explains, perhaps, why conservationist policies almost have to be sold under some other excuse which seems more urgent, and why, indeed, necessities which are visualized as urgent, such as defense, always seem to hold priority over those which involve the future.

All these considerations add some credence to the point of view which says that we should not worry about the spaceman economy at all, and that we should just go on increasing the GNP and indeed the gross world product, or GWP, in the expectation that the problems of the future can be left to the future, that when scarcities arise, whether this is of raw materials or of pollutable reservoirs, the needs of the then present will determine the solutions of the then present, and there is no use giving ourselves ulcers by worrying about problems that we really do not have to solve. There is even high ethical authority for this point of view in the New Testament, which advocates that we should take no thought for tomorrow and let the dead bury their dead. There has always been something rather refreshing in the view that we should live like the birds, and perhaps posterity is for the birds in more senses than one; so perhaps we should all call it a day and go out and pollute something cheerfully. As an old taker of thought for the morrow, however, I cannot quite accept this solution; and I would argue, furthermore, that tomorrow is not only very close, but in many respects it is already here. The shadow of the future spaceship, indeed, is already falling over our spendthrift merriment. Oddly enough, it seems to be in pollution rather than in exhaustion that the problem is first becoming salient. Los Angeles has run out of air, Lake Erie has become a cesspool, the oceans are getting full of lead and DDT, and the atmosphere may become man's major problem in another generation, at the rate at which we are filling it up with gunk. It is, of course, true that at least on a microscale, things have been worse at times in the past. The cities of today, with all their foul air and polluted waterways, are probably not as bad as the filthy cities of the pretechnical age. Nevertheless, that fouling of the nest which has been typical of man's activity in the past on a local scale now seems to be extending to the whole world society; and one certainly cannot view with equanimity the present rate of pollution of any of the natural reservoirs, whether the atmosphere, the lakes, or even the oceans.

I would argue strongly also that our obsession with production and consumption to the exclusion of the "state" aspects of human welfare distorts the process of technological change in a most undesirable way. We are all familiar, of course, with the wastes involved in planned obsolescence, in competitive advertising, and in poor quality of consumer goods. These problems may not be so important as the "view with alarm" school indicates, and indeed the evidence at many points is conflicting. New materials especially seem to edge towards the side of improved durability, such as, for instance, neolite soles for footwear, nylon socks, wash and wear shirts, and so on. The case of household equipment and automobiles is a little less clear. Housing and building construction generally almost certainly has declined in durability since the Middle Ages, but this decline also reflects a change in tastes towards flexibility and fashion and a need for novelty, so that it is not easy to assess. What is clear is that no serious attempt has been made to assess the impact over the whole of economic life of changes in durability, that is, in the ratio of capital in the widest possible sense to income. I suspect that we have underestimated, even in our spendthrift society, the gains from increased durability, and that this might very well be one of the places where the price system needs correction through government-sponsored research and development. The problems which the spaceship earth is going to present, therefore, are not all in the future by any means, and a strong case can be made for paying much more attention to them in the present than we now do.

It may be complained that the considerations I have been putting forth relate only to the very long run, and they do not much concern our immediate problems. There may be some justice in this criticism, and my main excuse is that other writers have dealt adequately with the more immediate problems of deterioration in the quality of the environment. It is true, for instance, that many of the immediate problems of pollution of the atmosphere or of bodies of water arise because of the failure of the price system, and many of them could be solved by corrective taxation. If people had to pay the losses due to the nuisances which they create, a good deal more resources would go into the prevention of nuisances. These arguments involving external economies and diseconomies are familiar to economists, and there is no need to recapitulate them. The law of torts is quite inadequate to provide for the correction of the price system which is required, simply because where damages are widespread and their incidence on any particular person is small, the ordinary remedies of the civil law are quite inadequate and inappropriate. There needs, therefore, to be special legislation to cover these cases, and though such legislation seems hard to get in practice, mainly because of the widespread and small personal incidence of the injuries, the technical problems involved are not insuperable. If we were to adopt in principle a law for tax penalties for social damages, with an apparatus for making assessments under it, a very large proportion of current pollution and deterioration of the environment would be prevented. There are tricky problems of equity involved, particularly where old established nuisances create a kind of "right by purchase" to perpetuate themselves, but these are problems again which a few rather arbitrary decisions can bring to some kind of solution.

The problems which I have been raising in this paper are of larger scale and perhaps much harder to solve than the more practical and immediate problems of the above paragraph. Our success in dealing with the larger problems, however, is not unrelated to the development of skill in the solution of the more immediate and perhaps less difficult problems. One can hope, therefore, that as a succession of mounting crises, especially in pollution, arouse public opinion and mobilize support for the solution of the immediate problems, a learning process will be set in motion which will eventually lead to an appreciation of and perhaps solutions for the larger ones. My neglect of the immediate problems, therefore, is in no way intended to deny their importance, for unless we at least make a beginning on a process for solving the immediate problems we will not have much chance of solving the larger ones. On the other hand, it may also be true that a long-run vision, as it were, of the deep crisis which faces mankind may predispose people to taking more interest in the immediate problems and to devote more effort for their solution. This may sound like a rather modest optimism, but perhaps a modest optimism is better than no optimism at all.

References

[1]Ludwig von Bertalanffy, *Problems of Life* (New York: John Wiley and Sons, 1952).

[2]Richard L. Meier, *Science and Economic Development* (New York: John Wiley and Sons, 1956).

[3]K. E. Boulding, "The Consumption Concept in Economic Theory," *American Economic Review*, 35:2 (May 1945), pp. 1-14; and "Income or Welfare?," *Review of Economic Studies*, 17 (1949-50), pp. 77-86.

[4]Fred L. Polak, *The Image of the Future*, Vols. I and II, translated by Elise Boulding (New York: Sythoff, Leyden and Oceana, 1961).

Part Two
Environmental Issues

Life on a Dying Lake

PETER SCHRAG

North Central flight 940. We take off to the west from the Detroit Metro Airport, turn left in a large loop around the city, and emerge over the crotch of the Detroit River where the patterned effluent spills into the waiting blue water of Lake Erie. *Two weeks before the final countdown for Apollo 11, the supreme $24-billion apotheosis of American technology; the greatest thing, Richard Nixon will say, since the creation.* The brown waters hug the western shore, and beyond, through the thin haze from the Michigan stacks, the ore carriers cut white wakes to feed the factories. We cross the rectilinear fields of Pelee Island and pass Pelee Point on the Ontario shore to the north. Less than 150 miles to the south is Wapakoneta, Ohio, where the first man to set foot on the moon was born.

> Man is destroying Lake Erie. [Says the report from the Federal Water Pollution Control Administration.] Although the accelerating destruction process has been inadvertent, it is as positive as if he had put all his energies into devising and implementing the means. After two generations the process has gained a momentum which now requires a monumental effort to retard. The effort must not only be basin-wide and highly coordi-

---

Source: Peter Schrag, "Life on a Dying Lake", *Saturday Review*, September 20, 1969, pp. 19-21, 55-56.

> nated; it must be immediate. Every moment lost in allowing the destruction to continue will require a longer, more difficult, and more expensive corrective action.

Prosaic language from Washington: eutrophication, secondary treatment, nutrient removal, algal blooms, biological oxygen demand. There is little romance in a sewage plant, and none in the technicalities of oxygen depletion, thermal stratification, or discharge of organic wastes. But the destruction of a lake is not merely a technical or a political problem. To think of it is to think of all America, of our love-hate relationship with our technology, about our ambivalence about who we are and what we are, about the Hudson and the Missouri, about the Santa Barbara Channel and nuclear bombs, about defoliation in Vietnam and DDT-poisoned fish in Michigan—about all the things we value, often in contradiction—in our past and our future.

As the plane descends over the murky waters along the Cleveland shore, the brown edging the blue, I have to imagine kids I know, kids like Corky Divoky years ago, scanning the skies for hawks and heron, or walking the ice in the winter, and now confronting the public servants of the draft board and the crusade for freedom in Asia. I hear the reminiscences of old men, telling fish stories about walleye and whitefish and blue pike, species that have all but disappeared. How much, you ask, setting down at Hopkins Airport, is this worth; how much is romance and sentimentality about a fading past, how much the price of progress, how much the comfortable guilt of safe men who can attack pollution as an undisputable evil (or war, or technology itself) while languishing in their benefits?

Some thirteen million people live in the basin of this lake, 90 per cent of them on the American side, the rest in Ontario, the polluters and the polluted, perpetrators and victims, all of them dependent on a body of water that, according to the best evidence, is not yet dead but in danger. They drink its water, swim on its beaches, eat its fish, and sail from its harbors. At the same time, they, their cities, and their factories each day dump, leak, pipe, or drop into the lake several hundred million pounds of sewage, chemicals, oil, and detergents fouling beaches, killing wildlife, and imperiling the water itself. Sometimes you can smell and taste it as it comes out of the tap, sometimes you can see it on the beaches and often in the rivers—the Maumee, the Auglaize, the Ottawa—but most significantly, you fear, not what already exists, but what might—and could—happen if the process continues.

In parts of the western end of the lake, the blue-green algae, which thrive on the excess of nutrients from sewage, turn blue water to a murky green and accumulate in heavy mounds on the shore; in Sandusky, once one of the largest freshwater ports in the world, a large fishing industry has been reduced to a couple of operators who truck their low-grade catch to Georgia (where, apparently, people are still hungry enough to buy it); and in Cleveland, the industrial stream called the Cuyahoga River is pronounced a fire hazard, a declaration that sounded hyperbolic until, last June, the oil on the river began to burn, damaging two bridges.

Cleveland's two fireboats travel the river periodically, hosing oil off docks and pilings so that the inflammable ooze will slowly make its way downstream and into the lake. At the same time, a broken city main is dumping twenty-five million gallons of raw sewage into the river each day. Periodically, the main is repaired, and now the city, with a $100-million bond issue voted last fall, is preparing to improve collection and treatment for its entire system and for the neighboring communities that it serves. (Cleveland, incidentally, may also be one of the few municipalities in the world that chlorinates its lakefront beaches so they will be safe for swimming.) But when it comes to pollution of the lake, Cleveland is more a victim that a culprit. Cleveland fouls its own nest with its dirty river and its inadequate sewage system, while Detroit, which dumps the waste of a huge industrial population into the Detroit River, stocks Lake Erie. Approximately 65 per cent of the oxygen-depleting wastes in the lake come from Detroit; 9 per cent from Cleveland. "When it comes to polluting the main part of the lake," said a researcher at the U.S. Bureau of Commercial Fisheries, "Cleveland's hardly on the map."

And yet, in a way, everything is on the map. Everything contributes to, and suffers from, the condition of the lake: people in five states and a Canadian province—hundreds of towns and cities from Toledo to Buffalo: Akron, Erie, Cleveland, Lorain,

Conneaut, Ashtabula. The federal government has identified 360 sources of industrial waste—power plants, steel mills, chemical companies, food processors, rubber companies. During every heavy rain, flooding sewers and silt spill into the lake, and even in normal periods silt and fertilizers and pesticides drain into its tributaries. But the greatest polluters may be the city sewage systems themselves. The federal government has estimated that with existing treatment facilities, the cities along the lake discharge effluent equal, in its composition and effects on the lake, to the raw sewage from a population of 4,700,000 people. Some cities are providing secondary treatment, some primary, some none at all. Lake Erie has been called a huge cesspool, an appellation that has at least marginal accuracy. What is absolutely accurate is the statement that in the past fifty years pollution has substantially altered the ecology of the lake, and that it has made the lake far older than its years.

The word, among the scientists, is eutrophication—the process of aging. All lakes grow old as they collect run-off and materials from the surrounding shores. Over thousands of years they eventually accumulate enough silt from erosion and organic materials to turn them into marshes and, finally, into dry land. In Lake Erie man has accelerated that process with his wastes and sewage. An excess of nutrients, primarily phosphates and nitrates, has produced great growths of algae in the water and impaired the oxygen supply, especially in the deeper water during the summer—and especially at the western end, which is hit hardest by the excrement from Detroit. (Biological degrading of the nutrients requires oxygen; when the nutrients are too heavy the oxygen becomes depleted.)

Mayflies, which once grew in huge numbers in the western, the shallowest, end of the lake, and which provided a food supply for fish—cisco, blue pike, walleye, and other species—have declined; the water has been taken over by sheepshead, carp, and other types that are tolerant of low-oxygen conditions and whose eggs can survive the accumulation of sediments at the bottom. Some species that have surmounted changes in food supply and depleted oxygen now take longer to reach maturity. (The total volume of fish caught in the lake each year is as large as ever, but the catch is worth only half of what it was ten years ago; most of the fishing is now done by Canadians.)

On occasion there have been duck kills, flights of birds which have landed on oily water and never flew again, either (it is assumed) because the oil destroyed the birds' natural protection against the water, or because they were poisoned. (There has been some serious talk in recent years about oil drilling in the lake. So far the derricks of the Canadian Pacific Oil and Gas Company, which have been erected on the Ontario side of the lake, are producing only natural gas.) There is also a possibility that the algae, under certain conditions, can manufacture their own poisons, endangering wild life—and possibly human life.

Because the lake is relatively shallow, there is hope that once the rate of pollution is retarded (hopefully, but not certainly, through improved sewage treatment), the lake, with proper oxygen circulation, can recover, spilling its wastes into Lake Ontario and, ultimately, into the Atlantic. The certainty of that recovery and the effectiveness of the measures now being planned (which, among other things, include the removal of phosphates before effluent is discharged into the lake) are still matters of debate and of time. What is not a matter of debate is that in the past fifty years, Lake Erie has aged 15,000 years.

Barry Commoner, a Washington University (St. Louis) biologist, who has long been concerned with the abuses of technology, writes:

> The lake is threatened with death. . . . Since the area was first settled, Lake Erie has been increasingly burdened with organic wastes and with inorganic nutrients that the lake's algae convert to organic materials. These organic materials would long ago have asphyxiated most of the lake's living things had it not been for the peculiar power of Iron III [an iron compound called ferric iron] to form insoluble complexes with the materials of the bottom mud. The protective skin of Iron III has held the enormous accumulation of potential oxygen-demanding material in the muddy bottom of the lake. But this protective skin can remain intact only so long as there is sufficient oxygen present in the water over the mud. For many years this was so, and the layer of Iron III held the accumulating mud materials out of the lake water. But a serious oxygen

> depletion now occurs in the summer months. As a result, the protective layer of Iron III has begun to break down—exposing the lake to heavy impact of the accumulated algal nutrient long stored in the mud. If the process continues, we may face a sudden biological cataclysm that will exhaust, for a time, most of the oxygen in the greater part of the lake water. Such a catastrophe would make the lake's present difficulties seem slight by comparison.

The fear is that under existing conditions, Erie could, without warning, turn into a huge swamp. Among the officials of the Federal Water Pollution Control Administration (FWPCA), which is charged with enforcing pollution control measures, Commoner is regarded as a prophet of gloom, a false Cassandra who is trying to frighten people. Nonetheless, FWPCA paraphrased Commoner's statement in its own report on the lake. "Some of that," said one FWPCA official, "was a little exaggerated. We know that the Iron III tends to break down and to release nutrients from the bottom, but there hasn't been any cataclysm, and there's not going to be one."

And yet, perhaps, that's not the issue—shouldn't be the issue. The trouble with conservation is that it has always been a matter of calamities and cataclysms. In the confusion of state, local, and federal anti-pollution responsibilities, there is always a large measure of sympathy for the company or the city that has to spend money for better treatment facilities, for the corporate taxpayer who might move somewhere else, for the time it takes, for the problems involved. The questions are thus always questions of resources, of priorities, of urgency and time. How much are fish worth? What's the value of a duck? What is the relationship between defoliants in Vietnam (or the price of automobiles in Detroit) and an acid discharge on the Cuyahoga or the Maumee?

If a major corporation can increase its earnings $60 million a year by raising prices, then is the expenditure of $18 million for new waste-treatment facilities at its plant in Cleveland something to brag about? How much passion and effort are required by the hypothetical impairment of a municipal water supply? ("The time's going to come," said an angry conservationist in Cleveland, "when they won't be able to put any more chlorine into the drinking water. What the hell are they going to do then?") And to what extent is water or air pollution a problem that only the comfortable can afford? The kids from Cleveland's Hough ghetto (and many others) rarely worry about swimming from polluted beaches; for them and their parents, urban pollution has other, more virulent forms. Their problem, among other things, is rats, not fish.

In the meantime, life on the lake goes on. In most places the problem is invisible; in others it becomes part of the background, an element of lore, like a volcanic mountain on a South Sea island. "People come here expecting to see a swamp," said a Cleveland newspaper reporter. "But there isn't any." On the west side of Catawba Island, near Sandusky, the cabin cruisers and the yawls luxuriate in their elegant marinas, and on the northern tip the Chevies back their trailer-borne runabouts onto concrete ramps for a few hours of fishing or a cruise to Put-in-Bay. At Huntington Park, just west of Cleveland, a kid pinches his toe on the beach and asks whether there's a species of crab that lives only in polluted water; and in Sandusky, Tony DeMore, one of the few remaining commercial fish operators on the American side, stands on his wharf and complains that the problem isn't pollution but overfishing and inequitable regulations that permit Canadians to haul what Americans have to throw back. "*Now they're stocking the lake with coho salmon like they did Lake Michigan to bring the sport fishermen back, but they're driving out the small fish. If Lake Erie had been meant for big fish, the big fellow up there would have put 'em in. It wasn't pollution that drove the fish out. It was . . . nature. If somebody doesn't pull the coho out, they'll take over the lake.*"

On the Cuyahoga River, twice each day, the excursion boat *Goodtime II* takes tourists on a run of the industrial sites; a tape-recorded spiel piped over the *Goodtime*'s loud speakers describes the adjacent activities of the Great Lakes Towing Company, U.S. Steel, Republic Steel, Sherwin-Williams Paint, National Sugar Refining, and Standard Oil. (No word about waste discharges, about the phenols and oils and acids that ooze into the river. "If you fall in," they say along the river, "you won't drown, you'll decay.") On summer evenings at the foot of the river, on the flats off Front Street, the customers of Fagan's Beacon House sit at their tables just above the ooze listening to Dixieland, drinking beer and watching the ships go by. It is, they say in Cleveland, one of the places "where everybody goes."

The lake is a presence, a landmark, an opening in the undifferentiated Midwestern landscape, a hole in the world. Every day the ships come through the seaway—the French, the Swedes, the Norwegians—unloading their cargoes on the city piers. In Vermilion, the lagoon, despite its murky surface, its oil slicks, and its junk, becomes a backdoor roadway to space. One ties his boat to the cleats in the back yard and takes the folks on a Sunday cruise; in Sandusky an octogenarian Negro sits on a pier with one of his twenty-one children, casting for sheepshead or carp or whatever cares to bite. The lake is not large, yet large enough to be infinite. It offers its lore of ships and waves and weather, the summer storms that drift across the water, driving the waves into the narrow beaches, perpetuating sailor stories and quarrels about which can be worse, the lakes or the Atlantic. Thus there are legendary events and records of disaster: huge steamboats that went down in flames, taking their immigrant passengers with them, Commodore Perry in 1814, Indians in their silent canoes.

The lake is life: Euclid Beach and Cedar Point, Catawba and Sandusky Bay, amusement parks, boats for hire, elegant summer houses tree-shielded from the curious roadway, beach-club privacy, and breakwaters spiny with the antennae of fishing poles. The beer cans collect between the rocks of the jetties, and behind them ragged rubber tires, twigs and oily cartons undulate against the stones. A CLEAN BEACH IS A FUN BEACH reads a sign posted two hundred yards from Cleveland's own outfall of sewage. "Why can't we have swimming in Lake Erie?" the mayor asks his commissioner of public utilities, and so the water around the beaches is fenced in with heavy sheets of Dacron anchored to the bottom, the chlorine is piped in, and the black workmen rake the accumulated algae into little piles. On July 4 the beach is dedicated to safe swimming. "I have this vision," says a smart mouth. "The mayor arrives in a helicopter and climbs down a rope ladder onto the algae, while the Cleveland Orchestra plays 'Shifting Sands.'"

Who controls this environment? Whose rights are invested in it? The mayor—in this case Carl B. Stokes of Cleveland—is accused of being more interested in creating an image through waterfront chlorination projects than in attacking the fundamental problems. After the Cuyahoga fire, he begins legal action to make the state enforce its own anti-pollution standards against the industries on the river (and perhaps to put a little pressure on the corporate managers); the state, in turn, accuses the mayor and the city of lagging behind in their own anti-pollution efforts: "It is obvious," said an official of the Ohio Health Department, "that Cleveland itself is a major contributor to the problems of the Cuyahoga River and that a major cleanup cannot be accomplished until the city corrects its own faults."

All the states claim that their industries are in compliance with state health and pollution regulations, which simply means that each year they issue a few admonitions, ask the corporations what efforts they propose to make, and let them continue to operate. "All they're doing," someone said in Cleveland, "is licensing the polluters. It seems that it's impossible for anyone to be in violation." (To which the federal people reply that industry is making more progress with waste-treatment than the cities.)

The buck is supposed to stop at the federally conducted enforcement conferences. Under the club of federal authority, all the states in the lake region—Indiana, Ohio, Michigan, New York, and Pennsylvania—have committed themselves to upgrading their municipal waste-treatment facilities to the point where 80 per cent of all phosphates are removed from sewage effluent before it is discharged into the lake. (Some cities are already behind schedule and have received extensions.) Detroit and Cleveland, among others, are building new plants and collection facilities, using local, state and a little federal money. At the same time, their officers are angry at the paltry federal contribution. While Detroit is scheduled to spend $159 million and Cleveland has voted its $100-million bond issue for better treatment and collection, the federal government spends barely more than $200 million a year on pollution research and development for the entire nation. "The federal people are the biggest hypocrites in the bunch," said a Detroit official. "They go around the country making speeches. Maybe if they made as much noise about getting us more money as they do about dirt, we'd be able to move a little faster." The reply from Washington: "The people who are polluting are responsible."

So far, the lake has been unaffected, and there is doubt that even after the scheduled projects are completed they will be sufficient. In New York State, a Health Department advisory committee of scientists was asked the question: Will phosphate removal retard eutrophication in Lake Erie? The answer, in simple words: Don't expect too much. Nonetheless, FWPCA has committed itself to the process as a necessary first step: phosphates, which come largely from detergents, say the FWPCA technicians, are essential to the growth of algae and plankton, so (because it is relatively easy) phosphates will be removed. No one has yet figured out what to do with the phosphates once they are precipitated out. They will be trucked to . . . where? (Nor is it certain that nitrates, which flood into the lake from agricultural fertilizers, and other sources, are not major factors in eutrophication.)

"The scientists can raise all sorts of questions," says Murray Stein, who is charged with FWPCA's enforcement work. "It doesn't mean they aren't good questions, but every day's delay in studying means time lost forever. You can only hope." (In Ontario, the Water Resources Commission, which has its own problems, speaks about a "breakthrough" in sewage treatment—a chemical-physical process that is said to remove nutrients more effectively and cheaply than existing methods. But the process, so far, has only been tried under experimental, not operational, conditions.)

The FWPCA has estimated that it will cost $1.1 billion in pollution-control projects to arrest the process of eutrophication in the next twenty years. Some critics believe the figure is far too low, and a few believe that the job is already impossible, that the lake may already be too far gone.

Who controls this environment? Whose rights are affected, whose life? The issue of pollution creates its own bureaucracies, its own inertia, its own zones of indistinct responsibility. Even though there are federal laws dating back to 1899 that prohibit the dumping of oil and refuse into navigable waters, and even though the various states have established their own regulations, there has never been—in the memory of federal officials—one suit or one criminal proceeding against a polluter. "Pollution law is a little like antitrust law," a federal official tells you. "It's hard to establish a connection between discharges and damage." (In September 1969, the Interior Department began to show signs of impatience with the polluters. For the first time since the 1965 Water Pollution Control Act was passed, the government threatened to take court action against private corporations and municipalities that pollute Lake Erie and other bodies of water. Among those cited in the government's announcement were three steel companies—James & Laughlin, U.S. Steel, and Republic—and the city of Toledo.)

Whose rights are affected, whose environment is it? "Every year there's more talk," says David Blaushild, a Cleveland automobile dealer who heads a group called Citizens for Clean Air and Water. "The governor and the mayor come to the conferences, and make speeches, and go home, and the pollution goes on. You don't have to study anymore. You can smell and see it. It's time to file lawsuits. Why should people take this crap?"

Does the individual have a constitutional right to clean air and water? "It's going to take a disaster to wake people up," Blaushild says. "If this generation doesn't do it, the next generation won't know any better. They'll think that swimming in filth is the normal thing to do. They'll think the moon is supposed to be yellow. They'll think they're breathing clean air and drinking clean water, because they won't know any better." Blaushild writes the Cleveland science museums to ask why they don't take a stronger position against industrial polluters. (Among their trustees are directors of several local corporations.) One of them answers that Blaushild, by selling Detroit's products, has his own share of responsibility.

Who controls this environment? Pollution, pesticides, fallout. The world's experience with nuclear tests has begun to create a wholly new concept of civility and community. In a strange way pollution became a problem by analogy: we learned, for example, that the same ecological processes that concentrate strontium-90 in bones concentrate DDT in fish, that contamination in one place jeopardizes life in others. A bomb test in New Mexico kills infants in Mississippi and Alabama; pesticides on Michigan farms poison fish in distant lakes; sewage from Detroit fouls beaches in Ohio. One can respond cheaply by lamenting the fix that science and technology have gotten us into, but a bumper sticker proclaiming SAVE LAKE ERIE pasted barely a foot above a smoky automobile exhaust is more an illustration of the problem than a solution.

The burden of moral compromise symbolized by Hiroshima and Nagasaki will not be lifted by building a new sewer system in Detroit, however necessary that system may be. Technological amelioration of one facet of environmental destruction can be no more than a surrogate for continued acceptance of its larger and more catastrophic forms. Can one take seriously an organization whose interest in conserving fish is unmatched by a position on the ABM?

The questions are backwards: how much civility can we afford after we have paid for Vietnam? For the car? For our missiles? Can we sustain a decent welfare program despite the war? Can we clean the river without jeopardizing the profits of industry? Because we are trying to satisfy a new, though still unclear, sense of community with old priorities, evasion is inevitable. Which is to say that a professed commitment to protect an environment that ends with a squabble over sewer taxes is no commitment at all. The issue of pollution can produce a paranoid fanaticism just like every other; no one has died from swimming on a contaminated beach on Lake Erie or from drinking its water. Yet somehow, if we cannot distinguish between fanaticism on behalf of a distant generation and that which defends immediate returns and private ends, we have simply lost our claim to live.

As Barry Commoner wrote in *Science and Survival*:

> The environment is a complex, subtly balanced system, and it is this integrated whole which receives the impact of all the separate insults inflicted by pollutants. Never before in the history of this planet has its thin life-supporting surface been subjected to such diverse, novel, and potent agents. I believe that the cumulative effects of these pollutants, their interactions and amplification, can be fatal to the complex fabric of the biosphere. And because man is, after all, dependent on

> part of this system, I believe that continued pollution of the earth, if unchecked, will eventually destroy the fitness of this planet as a place for human life.

If the greatest thing since the creation is worth twenty-four billion clams, how much is the creation worth?

Detergents – Boon or Bane?

P. H. JONES
in conversation with Tom Davey

Lakes must be counted as amongst Canada's greatest assets, rivaling if not exceeding our vast mineral lodes in monetary values alone. They are now in dreadful danger from eutrophication. This and other factors could transform the Great Lakes from valuable assets to net liabilities within the next 20-30 years.

Algae respond very quickly to minute changes in their nutrient supplies. They can multiply very rapidly after changes in nitrogen, phosphorus, and other simple or complex nutrient elements which can be effected by a variety of causes. Soil erosion, chemical fertilizers and animal wastes all play significant roles in promoting algae growth, so it would almost be impossible to precisely allocate degree of blame to particular sources.

Because of this, it might seem unfair to single out the nutrient effects of domestic laundry detergents on the eutrophication problem. But many detergents are not only a major nutrient source but cause a situation which could be remedied almost overnight through the use of substitute chemicals. To get an expert appraisal of the situation, we interviewed Dr. P. H. Jones, Associate Professor of Civil Engineering, University of Toronto.

Source: P.H. Jones, Interview with Editor Tom Davey, *Water and Pollution Control*, September 1968. Reprinted by permission of the publisher and authors.

T.D. You once stated that the nutrients from many household laundry detergents were an unnecessary but significant factor in the deterioration of our waterways. Are substitute chemicals available which could do the same job yet not cause eutrophication?

Dr. J. Oh, they're available all right. I can mix up a substitute formula right now in the lab.

T.D. Why aren't they being used, then?

Dr. J. They are not used for a variety of reasons. I think I'd better explain the existing situation first.

The functions which phosphates fulfil in a detergent are basically two. Detergents usually contain a surface-active agent which produces lather and which actually functions as the cleaning agent. In addition there is what they call a filler. The surface-active agent may comprise approximately 10-15% of the material by weight, the bulk of the balance is filler. The phosphorus content of this filler material comprises approximately 50% of laundry detergents, or it may vary from 40-60% in a heavy-duty detergent. Now the polyphosphate makes all waters equally amenable to cleaning. In other words you don't have any hard water or any soft water.

All waters become somewhat equal in their cleaning potential. The way the phosphate does this is by chelating out the hardness ions—calcium and magnesium. Their concentrations vary in natural waters; surface water is usually quite low, in well waters it's usually quite high. Out in the prairies it might go up as high as 300, 400 or even 500 parts per million. In Toronto it may be 100. So the phosphate chelates the ions. Chelate is to bind together, to pull into some loose matrix, and it holds these ions so that they can't form the precipitate which they normally do in hard water. More of the soap then is allowed to do the cleaning and less precipitates out with the hardness. So this therefore makes all waters equal. Additionally, it performs a useful role in controlling pH.

The pH is a measure of the intensity of the acid or alkaline in water. It is, strictly speaking, the negative logarithm of the concentration of active hydrogen ion. The pH of seven is neutral. As the pH gets lower towards 2 it becomes more acid; as it goes up towards 10 or 11, it becomes more alkaline. The best pH for washing is around pH 9.5 to 10.5. Now this is a fine pH to wash in but very rough on your hands. With the advent of the automatic washing machine, women don't have to put their hands in the water any more so now you can in fact control the proper pH for washing.

T.D. In other words there was a cosmetic consideration which previously kept down the level of phosphates in detergents. Automatic washing machines removed this limitation.

Dr. J. That's right. With no need to worry about people they can hold the pH at that optimum range for washing. Of course the problem is that phosphate is not consumed in the process but is simply there to control pH. It holds the hardness ions without being used up. When the water goes down the drain there is just as much phosphate in it as before.

T.D. Is there an "over-kill" in many detergent phosphates to suit the wide range of waters? Do manufacturers put in enough to suit the highest common denominator?

Dr. J. They certainly do. They put in enough phosphate to deal with any contingency because they are not marketing for any specific region. To tailor a detergent for particular regions would become expensive.

T.D. So they have designed their formulas to accommodate any waters to obviate any logistic problems?

Dr. J. Exactly. Now the phosphate concentrations at sewage plants is between two and three times what it was before detergents were on the market. Detergents came in about 1940; before that time the average concentration of phosphates was between ½ and ⅓ of what it is today. Now this implies right away that detergents—which are the only major change which has taken place—were responsible for doubling or tripling the phosphate concentration reaching the sewage plant. The sewage plant is only capable of removing the stoichiometric amount of nutrients related to the organic carbon available.

The ratio of the Biochemical Oxygen Demand to nitrogen to phosphorus coming into the plant should be in the order of 100 to 20 to 1. That is, the ideal stoichiometric ratio is 100 units of BOD to 1 unit of phosphorus. Now if you've got 100 BOD coming in and 20 phosphorus, you're going to have 19 phosphorus left over.

Even before the advent of detergents, there was an excess of phosphate entering the lakes. Detergents doubled and tripled the phosphates. So now the phosphates still aren't treated—they still go out into the lake. Algae are plants and, as with all plants, they take their nutrients in a soluble form. A plant gets its source of energy from the sunlight. So provided it has all the nutrients it requires it will grow in the sunlight. In any open waters you can't remove sunlight as the source of energy. Now the nutrients which algae basically need are carbon, hydrogen, oxygen, nitrogen and phosphorus. Carbon—it takes as inorganic carbon which is carbon dioxide. You can't eliminate this because it's in the atmosphere and very necessary. So carbon and oxygen is carbon dioxide. So we come to hydrogen—hydrogen and oxygen is water. The plants are living in the water. You can't eliminate that. So you're left with nitrogen and phosphorus. These are the only two missing links. If you could eliminate those, nothing would grow because they can't grow without the complete spectrum. As eighty percent of the atmosphere is nitrogen, you can't eliminate this but fortunately most plants are unable to fix atmospheric nitrogen just as humans are unable to fix it. We have to eat protein as we can't fix the atmospheric nitrogen.

However, there are some algae that can. These are known as the blue green algae. This is a particular class of algae, some of which can fix atmospheric nitrogen and take it as its source of nitrogen.

Nitrogen in our respiratory function plays no role. We breathe in nitrogen—we breathe out nitrogen. Biologically "fix" is the word we're looking for here because you need nitrogen in your makeup because a certain percentage of your body is protein and protein has a considerable amount of nitrogen in it. The nitrogen is in the form of ammonia and nitrate. Actually in protein it is always in the form of amines (NH_2). However, N_2 or N_2O are the gaseous forms which affect some of the blue green algae. But let's leave these species of algae alone for a moment, as there aren't that many of them. We're still left with phosphorus.

There is no natural source of phosphorus so even if we say that some blue greens can fix up atmospheric nitrogen they still couldn't grow without phosphorus, which does not come out of the atmosphere.

Phosphorus can enter waterways from three major sources right now. First there is agricultural runoff from nitrates and phosphates laid down as fertilizers. Then there is human and animal wastes, which are concentrated in phosphorus—finally there are detergents.

In terms of agriculture, phosphorus has been shown to adhere very very closely to the soil. Once it is applied to the soil it doesn't migrate. This is not true of nitrogen. If you put on nitrogen phosphorus in a liquid form in the soil, the phosphorus will stop moving in a matter of a few centimetres. The nitrogen will go on and on until it finds its way into the ground water.

In terms of chemical fertilizers I don't feel that the farmer is a significant contributor—he's just not stupid enough to put his fertilizer on the ground just as it's going to rain to be washed away, or at a non-growing season.

The farmer does contribute in terms of animal wastes. Any farmer that keeps animals usually spreads his manure on the field. Manure spread on a frozen field is going to run off as surface water in spring—a major source of phosphate and nitrate and organic nitrogen.

T.D. But this type of nutrient enrichment has been going on for years. After all it was only 150 years ago that the buffalo "darkened the plains" of this continent.

Dr. J. Eutrophication is a very natural aging process of all lakes. I've got pictures of lakes in Alaska where I'm sure man has never been and they're completely eutrophied. There is also very good evidence that some of the major lakes in the world were eutrophied several million years ago, and subsequently recovered.

T.D. If eutrophication is a natural aging process, are we accelerating it at a rate where there couldn't be any recovery before science finds a solution?

Dr. J. I couldn't say because recovery is a function of the gross activity on the planet earth. Our gross activity appears to be leading towards one of a complete pollution of our environment. Unless we control it this will be the natural outcome. As far as natural aging is concerned, this would happen anyway. It's inevitable. As you say we're accelerating it at a tremendous rate and we may be chopping off thousands of years of the life of our lakes. But every year we are making conditions a little worse and all this means is that each year it costs us more to use the fresh water supplies for the same purpose as we used them last year. Eventually it may become so prohibitive that we will have to import water.

T.D. But much of the damage is unnecessary—surely that is the point?

Dr. J. We have three sources of the problem. The agricultural source could be fairly well controlled if we were to devise an economic way whereby the farmer could treat the animal wastes instead of putting them on the ground in the non-growing season when it's frozen. We could have some proper manure handling practices so that he is able to store the material until the growing season begins. We don't have the technology right now for the farmer economically to handle this problem.

The next source of material results from the activities in the sewage plant. We're going to have to provide better and more complete sewage treatment plants. We can undoubtedly improve on these but the process is pretty expensive right now in terms of capital costs. It seems to be in the order of 70-100% increase in capital costs. Of course improved technology can improve the situation. However, we've got many thousands of sewage plants in North America. How long is it going to take for every one of those to be modified?

T.D. Obviously the cheapest way at the moment would be to get at the source wherever possible.

Dr. J. Well let's say all three treatments should be attended to simultaneously. If we were able to eliminate phosphates in detergents it would have an instantaneous effect...something which would be effective right across North America, maybe the world within a year. This happened with soft detergents. When manufacturers decided to go to a soft detergent within one year they had replaced everything. Now you can't buy hard detergent, unless you look for it as a chemical. Within one or two years, they could replace all the detergents which are in circulation and have no more detergents with phosphate. It's going to be a little more expensive, exactly how much more expensive I can only estimate. But it is certainly the most immediately effective step that could be taken.

T.D. The significant question—would the substitute chemicals be dearer?

Dr. J. It would be dearer. If you speak to the detergent people as I have done many times they will tell you they're working on it. Philosophically I feel they're approaching the problem in the wrong gear. Their principal aim is economics and saleability of the goods whereas our principal aim is to minimize the eutrophication effects caused by this needless addition of phosphates.

T.D. Why isn't remedial action being undertaken?

Dr. J. Because of the corporate conscience I think. The only way this can be remedied is by public awareness or legislation.

T.D. How dramatically did the foaming problem cease when it was visibly brought to people's attention by the news media?

Dr. J. This had been a problem for a long time. And the detergent industry said they couldn't find replacement chemicals. But suddenly when the press showed foaming rivers with foam going over lawns and bridges, they very quickly found a new type of detergent.

T.D. Yet the nutrient problem is much more insidious because it's not apparent...it's an invisible problem therefore hard to publicize.

Dr. J. It's not only invisible, it's even non-toxic. I would be quite prepared to take the filler part of the detergent, dissolve it in a glass of water and drink it. Because it involves a little understanding of biology, biochemistry and chemistry, people haven't got enthusiastic about it.

T.D. They might after this is printed.

Dr. J. I hope so. Many scientists are burying their heads in the sand. Occasionally someone comes up with a statement like "We don't know for sure that nitrogen and phosphorus are the culprits. Maybe it's cobalt." Well I can't say that it isn't cobalt. But on the other hand I can say that if you don't feed aquatic plants phosphorus they are not going to grow, even if they need cobalt—I do know this. So I say whether it's cobalt or whether it's titanium or whether it's cosmic rays from the moon—if you don't feed them phosphate they're not going to grow. And it's as simple as that.

T.D. How much more would your detergents cost using substitute chemicals?

Dr. J. The substitute chemicals are not so special. You can go and buy them right now. We can today buy phosphate-free detergents which we use for washing lab glassware.

T.D. Is it dear?

Dr. J. I have had it quoted to me by some detergent people that it wouldn't cost any more than 10 or 15¢ more per box.

T.D. What if you add the economies of scale? With the gigantic purchasing power of the industry, is it conceivable it would cost any more?

Dr. J. I would be very surprised if it cost more than 15¢ but even suppose it cost 20¢? The average consumption of detergents per person is something like 4 or 5 boxes a year. So you're talking about peanuts really.

T.D. Are we ruining our Canadian fresh water supplies for about $1.25 a head?

Dr. J. Let's not be quite so specific. If that was the only thing we did, and we didn't bother to put nutrient removal in sewage plants and we didn't control the farmer, then we're still only attacking part of the problem. We've got to attack it at all fronts.

T.D. I realize this but surely the substitution chemicals would effect major improvements without capital costs being involved?

Dr. J. Yes. In fact the premiums they're putting in the packets might make the difference between a detergent without nutrients and the present ones. In any event it is a small price to pay to save our waterways.

The attitude of some regulatory authorities, the detergent industry and even some scientists, reminds me of the old T.V. commercial which went: "They said it couldn't be done." A cynical addition we might make to this slogan in the present context is ". . . so we didn't even try."

Replacement for Phosphates

DAVID SPURGEON

Now that phosphate-containing detergents are being gradually eliminated because of their role in water pollution, the question is, what will replace them? It is an important question because it raises another one: will the replacements be any less harmful to the environment, or will they be more so?

The urgency of the matter was underlined by a recent statement of Resources Minister J. J. Greene. He told the Commons that the deadline for total removal of phosphates from detergents may be made sooner than previously announced, in view of the industry's apparent success in its search for phosphate-free formulas. He noted that some manufacturers have taken full-page ads to announce they have achieved total removal of phosphates from detergents, and added: "We are reviewing the matter to see whether or not the Jan. 1, 1972, date can be brought forward."

Likely Replacement

The most likely replacement for phosphates in detergents is nitrilotriacetic acid (NTA). An article in *Chemical and Engineering News* (a publication of the American Chemical Society) said in August: "NTA comes close to being the detergent industry's equivalent of the only game in town."

Source: David Spurgeon, "Replacement for Phosphates", from *The Globe and Mail*, Toronto. Reprinted by permission of the publisher and author.

At the company's annual shareholders' meeting in October, Howard J. Morgens, president of the Procter and Gamble Co., said P&G has already ordered more than $150,000,000 worth of one substitute material.

That substitute material is almost certainly NTA. *Chemical and Engineering News* said P&G "has committed itself to replacing 25 per cent of the phosphates in its detergents with NTA." It also said Lever Brothers has made commitments to purchase substantial quantities of NTA, and that plants producing the substance are vastly increasing their capacities.

NTA is not the only substance being sought as a substitute for phosphates: Colgate-Palmolive is said to be holding back until it is proved safe, and chemicals known as polyelectrolytes are being investigated by some firms. One U.S. firm, DeSoto Inc., has developed a new product said to contain "no phosphates, no NTA, and no other materials believed to be pollutants." Other firms are trying to find substitutes for the constituents of detergents known as surfactants (phosphates are known as builders).

Nevertheless, most of the bets right now are on NTA to replace phosphates, and if NTA is used in this way, large quantities of the material will be dumped into North American water systems, some of it finding its way into the water we drink. What will be the effect of this?

Unsettling Questions

Unfortunately, nobody is sure, and some are concerned by what they know about NTA. Dr. Samuel S. Epstein, chief of the laboratories of environmental toxicology and carcinogenesis at the Children's Cancer Research Foundation, Inc., in Boston, outlined some of these in testimony before a Senate subcommittee on air and water pollution last May.

"There are some unsettling questions concerning NTA that have not yet been answered," he said in a recent article in *Environment* based on his Senate testimony. "...Two-year feeding studies in rats seem to have demonstrated that NTA does not cause cancer. However, increased mortality was noted in male rats, and kidney damage occurred in male and female rats at the higher dosages tested. Additionally, zinc levels in bone and excretion in urine were markedly increased. The significance of these findings has not yet been adequately evaluated. No toxicity or metabolic studies of any kind have been made on heavy metal chelates of NTA."

NTA is what chemists call a chelating agent. That means it can lock up metal ions that are free or on the surface of metal casings, and carry them into solution.

"If high concentrations of NTA were to be used in detergent products, metal chelates might be formed in domestic washing machines, plumbing systems, sewage pumps, in sewage, particularly in septic tanks where biodegradation is limited, and in lake sediments," Dr. Epstein said.

"Additionally, NTA may dissolve and mobilize heavy metals, such as mercury, from lake sediments. This poses a question of the biological safety of the various chelates as environmental factors and as contaminants of drinking water. On the other hand, if the chelates were degraded in receiving waters they might liberate free metals, including lead, mercury, iron, arsenic, zinc, and copper, with obvious toxicological implications both to fish and to man."

Still another problem with NTA is the possibility that it could produce substances called nitrosamines during its breakdown, Dr. Epstein contends. Most nitrosamines are cancer-causing in a wide range of organs of various species at very low doses, and some have been shown capable of causing mutations and damage to developing embryos.

Dr. P. H. Jones, professor of civil engineering, associate professor of microbiology and vice-chairman of the Environmental Sciences and Engineering Program at the University of Toronto, disagrees with some of Dr. Epstein's views. He contends, for example, that experience in Sweden and to a more limited extent in Canada has shown that NTA-based detergents, if properly formulated, will have no more corrosive effect on washing machines than phosphates. He also contends that NTA will carry no more heavy metals than phosphates do, and that it will lose its chelating properties in normal secondary sewage treatment plants.

(Dr. Jones was involved in the development of a detergent that uses NTA among its ingredients, but it is not yet on the market, being under test for environmental effects).

Two Billion Pounds

The fact remains that NTA, which has been tested for some years in Sweden, has not yet shown itself to be sufficiently free from environmental effects for the Swedes to want to replace all other detergent formulations with it. And, as Dr. Epstein says: "There simply is not enough known about NTA to comfortably dump up to two billion pounds of it into the nation's waterways annually." Even Monsanto Co., the biggest U.S. producer of NTA (which also produces phosphates), has said through a spokesman: "Caution is urged in changing the exposure levels in the environment from a few thousand pounds per year to a few billion pounds per year. There is always that unforeseen ecological interaction that could be disrupted, causing another severe stress upon the ecosystem. Close monitoring is advisable as the NTA usage level rises."

What then is to be done? Should we all go back to using soap instead of detergents? Such a solution might be possible from the standpoint of cleanliness, for if the water used is sufficiently soft, soap will clean acceptably well, at least in the laundry.

The trouble is there just would not be enough soap to go around. Says *Chemical and Engineering News*:

"Hard water was only one of the reasons . . . that the soap industry went all-out to develop synthetic detergents. Another, equally compelling reason was the increasing competition with the food and feed industries for a limited supply of natural fats and oils.

"William C. Krumrei of Procter and Gamble points out that current annual tallow production is about five billion pounds per year. To produce soap to satisfy the needs of this country would require more than half this supply, thereby providing a serious interruption in the food supply of humans and animals, he (Mr. Krumrei) asserts.

Soap Production

"One may question the completeness of Mr. Krumrei's statistics—tallow is but one of many natural fats and oils—but as a generalization his point is well taken. With most of the world more concerned about malnutrition that about eutrophication, solving the phosphate problem at the expense of the world's food supply is not going to be acceptable. Whether phosphates disappear or not from detergents, it's unlikely that soap will rise again."

So there we have it. The introduction of synthetic detergents solved one problem but created another. Technology made Johnny's clothes cleaner and the rivers and lakes dirtier.

Yet technology cannot be blamed as the primary cause. In the 1940s, as now, one of the major factors involved was the tremendous growth in world population.

It is easy to rail at mindless technology and industrial greed for the world's current ills, but it is not very helpful, nor entirely accurate. A less simple-minded approach is going to be needed to solve future problems.

[Since this article was written, experiments conducted with laboratory animals in the United States have indicated that NTA may be dangerous to humans consuming water into which the substance has been dumped as a waste. It appears to complex with the ionic forms of certain metals to produce a dangerous series of substances.—*Editors*]

Water Pollution by Outboard Motors

RONALD STEWART and H. H. HOWARD

"The British have demonstrated that 15 tons of oil, dropped into a calm sea, can cover eight square miles in less than a week . . ." Rienow (1967). Based on rough estimates, over 200 times that amount of oil is discharged from outboard motors annually in the United States.

In May of 1967 President Johnson ordered a Cabinet-level study of oil contamination problems on both the catastrophic and routine levels. Incidents such as the "Torrey Canyon" disaster led to this order. Although the catastrophic disasters make the newspaper headlines, the everyday low-level water pollution by fuels is rarely publicized. Yet, this source of pollution may destroy an entire oyster industry because *Nitzchia* (the diatom food of the oyster) will not survive where a surface film of oil exists. When a plankton population is damaged or destroyed, the food chain of the aquatic animal life is disrupted.

English and others have shown that tainting of fish flesh occurs at a fuel-usage level of eight gallons of outboard motor fuel per million gallons of lake water per season. An increase in the threshold odor number of the water was noted when approximately one gallon of fuel was consumed per million gallons of lake water per summer season. A threshold odor number of three is considered as objectionable to most people. Some studies of the effects of oils and refinery wastes on fish and other animals

Source: Ronald Stewart and H. H. Howard, "Water Pollution by Outboard Motors", *The Conservationist*, June-July, 1968. Reprinted by permission of the publisher and authors.

have been reported in the *Journal of the Water Pollution Control Federation*, but few of these involve algae.

In most case studies, it has been shown that oil has an adverse effect on fish growth and longevity. Shelford (1917) has shown that fish tend to be attracted to gas polluted water, only to be harmed by it. Algae, depending upon species, may increase or decrease in oil refinery ponds (Minter, 1964; Galtsoff and others, 1936). Aleksandrova and others (1959) have shown that the flora in streams change when the stream is used for the discharge of petroleum and other wastes. Attached marine algae of the littoral zone may be immune to oil spills which remain on the surface (Clendenning, 1958) but these algae are not representative of the taxa composing the phytoplankton of fresh waters. A later study by Reimann (1962) has shown that oil in water attaches to the surface of unicellular plankton. Galtsoff and others (1936) reported that even the more dilute extracts of crude oil inhibit cultures of diatom algae (*Nitzchia Closterium*) after a few days' exposure. These extracts also cause a considerable stimulation of bacterial growth which is significant in that these organisms are competitors with algae for nutrients found in the water. The severe mortality rates of intertidal organisms from emulsifying oil films in coastal areas was reported by George (1961).

Ordinarily, thin films of oil do not kill diatoms in the underlying water, but it does affect their reproduction. Part of this effect may be due to the increased oxygen demand created by the presence of oil, although films less than .001 cm in thickness do not affect the rate of solution of oxygen. About 3,300,000 milligrams of oxygen are required for the complete oxidation of one liter of mineral oil. Such an amount would deplete the oxygen in 12,600 gallons of sea water. Zobell (1963) quotes from one experimental result in which 100 milligrams of a medium grade commercial oil was dispersed in a liter of oxygenated water as a fine emulsion. Forty-seven per cent of the oil disappeared during the first 13 days. As the ambient temperature was lowered, the rate of oil disappearance decreased markedly until, at 5°C, little or no oil disappeared. Obviously, oils from motor boats are not dispersed in this concentration, but neither are they well mixed (i.e., not a fine emulsion). Thus, the oxygen content of the first few centimeters is probably depleted, at least temporarily.

English (1963) has shown that outboard motor exhaust-water contains an average of 105 grams/gal. of non-volatile oil, 57 grams/gal. of volatile oil, 0.53 grams/gal. of lead and 0.60 grams/gal. of phenols.

It was assumed that the non-volatile oil was lubrication oil and the volatile oil was gasoline. About 80 per cent of the non-volatile oils were removed by coagulation, sedimentation and filtration. None of the volatile oils were removed. By tracing the passage of the lubrication oil through the outboard motor by infrared analysis, English also was able to show that some of the waste material had not undergone decomposition. This is understandable because unburned fuel is discharged directly through the engine.

Case Study of the Amount of Fuel Discharge on Lake George

Lake George is located on the southern edge of the Adirondack Mountains. Although it is 51 km. long, for the purposes of this study, only the area below the Narrows and including Northwest Bay, will be included. This area is approximately 22.4 km. by 2.6 km. with a mean depth of 17.9 and a maximum of 58 m. There are 76 km. of shoreline. The winter population of this area is about 4,500 persons, but it is expected that this number will triple within the next fifty years. The summer population in this very popular tourist area is over 40,000 persons, and this is expected to double within the next fifty years. There is also a large transient population which includes over 4,500 people on an average summer day. It is obvious that the population explosion will not miss Lake George.

Along with the population explosion is an increase in the use of most recreational facilities and especially an increase in boating. At present there are twenty-five marinas selling fuel within this given area. Approximately 400,000 gallons of outboard fuels are sold annually between Northwest Bay and Lake George Village. This represents a fuel-usage level of over one gallon per million gallons of lake water per season. This is sufficient to raise the threshold odor level.

The trend of outboard motor fuel sales has been increasing as the following data from one representative marina indicates:

1959	17,500 gallons
1960	16,000 gallons
1961	22,600 gallons
1962	20,700 gallons
1963	23,000 gallons
1964	23,700 gallons
1965	23,500 gallons
1966	25,000 gallons

The owner of this marina stated that in 1959 he sold about 50 per cent of all outboard motor fuel sales in his area. Since that time, new marina facilities have opened and his sales have dropped to about 25 per cent of the total. Allowing for this change in percentages, the above figures represent a tripling of fuel sales over the last eight years. It is obvious that if this rate continues, the lake waters could have a semi-permanent fuel odor within eight years.

Snell (1965) has shown that between 10 per cent and 33 per cent of outboard fuels are normally discharged into the cooling water exhaust stream as unburned wastes from several leading outboard motors. This represents a minimum of 40,000 gallons of fuel being discharged into lower Lake George each season at these present rates. Because Lake George exchanges about 10 per cent of its volume annually, a considerable portion of the fuel is left to contaminate the aquatic life. Allowing for a gas to oil mixture ratio of 50:1, the decomposition of this oil alone would require the total oxygen content of 30,000,000 gallons of lake water. These calculations do not take into consideration accidental spills, inboard bilge pump wastes, etc. Outboard pollution may explain why some of the bays in Lake George are turbid. Usually the stirring of the bottom sediments by the action of outboard motors is blamed, but the turbulent mixing is relatively shallow and reaches the bottom only in very shallow waters. However, if the oxygen level is reduced, biological degradation is reduced and contaminants may accumulate.

The above estimates of fuel pollution are based on available data for a population in 1967. If the predicted population trend is followed, the pollutant level will continue to rise until the smell and taste of gasoline and oil will be noticeable in fish and water supplies. It is obvious that this cannot be allowed to continue. Economically this means a loss of the pure waters which attract tourists. Direct economic loss to the boat owners in lost fuel is $20,000, to say nothing of the increase in slicks which may mar boats and discourage swimmers.

An accumulation of oil can take years to reach the level of contamination to various aquatic life. If we wait for this level to be reached before studying the problem, it may take just as many years to correct our mistakes.

References

Aleksandrova, L. P., Kanygine, A. V., and Pobegailo, P. I. 1959. *Results of a biological and chemical investigation of the Magnilogorsk Reservoir.* Trudy Soveschania Po Problem. Biol. Untren. Vol. 6:485-489. Zhur. Biol. 1961, No. 8D669 (Translation).

Clendenning, K. M. 1958. *The effects of waste discharges on kelp: Fuel oil.* Univer. Calif. Inst. Mar. Resources, Ref. 59-4:4-12.

English, J. N., Surber, E. W., McDermott, G. N. 1963 a. *Pollutional effects of outboard motor exhaust:* Laboratory studies. J. Water Poll. Con. Fed. 35:923.

English, J. N., Surber, E. W., McDermott, G. N. 1963 b. *Pollutional effects of outboard motor exhaust:* Field studies. J. Water Poll. Cont. Fed. 35:1121.

Farmer, Joe A. 1960. *The effects of industrial and domestic pollution of the Black Warrior River on the net plankton population.* J. Alabama Acad. Sci. 31:447. Bio. Abs. 36:7420, 1961.

Galtsoff, P. S., Prytherech, H. F., Smith, R. O., and Koehring, V. 1936. *Effect of crude oil pollution on oysters in the Louisiana waters.* Bull. U.S. Bureau Fisheries. 48:143.

George, M. 1961. *Oil pollution of marine organisms.* Nature. 192:1209. Minter, K. W. 1964. *Standing crop and community structure of plankton in oil refinery effluent holding ponds.* Water Poll. Abs. (Brit.), 38:1182.

Reimann, K. 1962. *Die Schädlichkeit von Öl- und Teerprodukten für Niedere Wasserorganismen.* Münchener Beitr. Abwasser-, Fischerei- und Flussbiologie. 9:60.

Shelford, V. E. 1917. *An experimental study of the effects of gas waste upon fishes, with especial reference to stream pollution.* Bull. Ill. State Lab. Nat. Hist. 11.

Snell, Foster D. 1965. Consulting report to Goggi Corporation. Zobell, C. E. 1963. *The occurrences, effects, and fate of oil polluting the sea.* Air and Water Poll. 7:173.

Relation of Water Pollution to Health

C. L. WILBAR, JR.

"Gardyloo" was a warning cry uttered on throwing water and other wastes into the streets from the windows in Old Edinburgh. The French pronunciation of the word is "gare l'eau" and literally means beware of the water. This could readily be today's warning cry uttered against water pollution.

Man's use of water for drinking and as the most universal solvent, particularly as a solvent for excreta and other wastes, brought about a realization of the need of water pollution control when people began to live together in communities. As the communities grew, they had to be supplied with water for necessary intake and at the same time the streams had to be used for waste disposal. It became apparent that everybody could not live upstream.

Nevertheless, streams became increasingly used for both waste disposal and water supply purposes; so, in Europe during the 19th Century, cholera and typhoid epidemics were common. In 1798 the poet Samuel Taylor Coleridge recognized some of the future water problems when he wrote, while visiting the city of Cologne, Germany:

The river Rhine, it is well known,
Doth wash your city of Cologne;
But tell me nymphs! What power divine
Shall henceforth wash the river Rhine.

Source: C. L. Wilbar, Jr., "Relation of Water Pollution to Health", *Archives of Environmental Health*, November 1964, Volume 9, pp. 664-667.

It was not until the middle 1800's that John Snow, as a result of his studies of the 1848-1849 and 1853-1854 epidemics of cholera in England, delineated the transmission of cholera as due to drinking water contaminated with human excreta. Shortly thereafter, William Budd of London recognized water as a source of spread of typhoid fever and published his discovery: "Typhoid Fever, Its Nature, Mode of Spreading and Prevention."

Gradually, it was realized that drinking water had to be purified before human consumption and that untreated wastes from humans should not be placed in streams used as sources of public water supply. Dr. Gordon M. Fair[1] pointed out at a symposium on human ecology that within the present century it was not uncommon for a city of 100,000 to experience 120 deaths from typhoid fever and 1,200 cases annually. He pointed out the experience in Zermatt, Switzerland, in the early Spring of 1963, when a large number of cases of typhoid developed and were carried by tourists back to their home countries throughout the world; two of these cases turned up in Pennsylvania. The Zermatt outbreak was caused by a cross connection between the sewer system and the public water supply. In 1959, a total of 14 cases of typhoid occurred in Keene, NH,[2] from a typhoid carrier who worked in a logging operation on a watershed of the municipal water supply which passed through a slow sand filter but was not chlorinated. About New Year, 1960, in Ravena, NY,[3] 1,400 persons became ill with *Shigella* dysentery from drinking the town's water supply. The automatic treatment plant, supposed to add chlorine which kills the *Shigella* organism quite easily, did not include "fail-safe" devices.

Water-borne diseases involving public water supplies are uncommon in the United States today. Sewage treatment and particularly the activities of the waterworks industry in applying modern treatment methods to water before it is served to customers have made epidemics rare and individual cases infrequent. Municipalities and states and to some degree the federal government have taken steps to keep the drinking water in this nation pure. Pennsylvania first passed a "Purity of Waters Act" in 1905 and set up its present Sanitary Water Board in 1923. Although these laws include concern for water used by industry and for recreational purposes, they are still primarily aimed at health protection.

In speaking of water-borne diseases, reference is made to those caused by bacteria and by viruses. The most common bacterial diseases transmitted by water are typhoid fever, bacillary dysentery and salmonellosis. Much less is known about the virus-caused diseases transmitted by water. About 100 types of human enteric viruses are known, but there are probably many more. Virologists and epidemiologists tell us that enteric virus diseases are more apt to be transmitted by direct contact than by water. However, a few years ago, clams from Raritan Bay between New York and New Jersey were responsible for an outbreak of infectious hepatitis. In 1956, Curwensville, Pa, had an outbreak of infectious hepatitis; all evidence indicated it was transmitted through a part of the public water supply system which was not chlorinated.

Other pathogenic viruses found in sewage include poliomyelitis viruses and various ECHO and coxsackie viruses. In an article on "Human Enteric Viruses and Sewage" in the January, 1964, issue of *Health Laboratory Science*, Clarke and Kabler[4] of the Taft Center of the Public Health Service point out that "It is only with the viral agents of infectious hepatitis that documented, proven water-borne outbreaks have occurred." They also state that primary sewage treatment has little or no effect on enteric viruses; secondary treatment by trickling filters removes only about 40% of the viruses; secondary treatment by activated sludge removes 90% to 98% of the viruses, and chlorination of effluent is especially effective although some viruses can be recovered from the chlorinated effluent by elaborate concentration techniques. These studies confirm those of Clarke[5] *et al.* and Kelly and Sanderson[6,7] of the New York State Department of Health.

Viral contamination is highest in the warmest months of the year. Petersen and Hines[8] in a 1957 study on "The Relation of Summertime Gastrointestinal Illness to the Sanitary Quality of the Water Supplies in Six Rocky Mountain Communities" indicated a significant relationship between the sanitary quality of a community's water supply and the incidence of gastrointestinal illness in that community. With consistently contaminated water, the attack rate was 14% during the three summer months whereas in those communities lacking contamination the attack rate was 9%.

In warmer climates the effect of swimming as well as of sewage disposal must be considered. We seem now to be aiming at a swimming pool with every home. The purity of swimming pool water can be adequately maintained by proper chlorination. Dr. Donald M. McLean[9] covered this subject before the 1962 meeting of the American Academy of Pediatrics. He stated: "The virtual absence of enteric bacteria from swimming pools or wading pools with detectable free chlorine residuals contrasts sharply with the relatively frequent occurrence of high bacterial counts in unchlorinated lake waters or wading pools. However, chemical evidence of pollution, on the basis of concentrations of ammonia nitrogen, organic nitrogen, and chloride, was greatest in recirculating swimming pools, less in overflow-refill swimming pools, and least in fresh-water lakes."

In a number of respects, hazards from pesticides, insecticide chemicals, radioactive substances, fertilizers, and other known microorganism types of contamination are fast becoming as potentially dangerous as those caused by microorganisms. Dr. Fair points out that some of these hazards are still not understood. The example he gives is goiter in India which occurs at a higher rate in downstream villages than upstream, although the iodine content is the same throughout. We are aware of the dangers of spills of certain chemicals, of toxic wastes from certain industries and of toxic plant growth. Some of the weed killers used today are extremely potent. Some months ago a farmer broke a container of endrin, a very potent chemical often used to control field rodents, into a small stream which ran into the Delaware River just above one of the water intakes for the City of Philadelphia. There was natural alarm as to what might happen to the water supply intake. The only known method of testing for endrin now is a biological method. We had to scurry around and find the right individual with containers of small fish to rush to the spot to test for the possible endrin concentration of water reaching the city's intake area. Fortunately, the dilution of the Delaware was great enough to prevent an endrin concentration that would kill the small fish and, therefore, endanger humans using the water supply.

Chronic effects of chemicals such as nitrates from fertilized soil must be considered as well as the threat of methemoglobinemia to infants who drink water from contaminated shallow wells and the concentration of detergents which go through sewage treatment plants. Fair also points out the eutrophication of ponds and lakes which could destroy even the Great Lakes if the process was not reversed. In this process, phosphates from fertilizers drain into enclosed water and cause the growth of diatoms whose skeletons eventually choke and fill the basin.

The public health aspects of water pollution are in danger of being overshadowed by the need to keep water pure for recreational, industrial, and agricultural purposes. Conservationists in the nation are particularly outspoken on this subject. Physicians need to be interested in these aspects of water pollution control while remembering the primary importance of keeping water clean for health purposes.

As our population areas rapidly thicken and the amount of leisure time increases, the use of our streams and lakes for swimming, boating, fishing and other recreational purposes can be considered to be of increasing importance as a type of outdoor recreation which helps maintain good mental health.

Senator Phillip Hart of Michigan, speaking to the Interstate Commission on the Potomac River Basin in 1961, told of a study conducted on family camping groups in midwest national forests. These campers were predominantly young couples in their 20's and 30's with children. More than 75% of them were there because there was a family problem which they hoped to wash away through this outdoor experience. The Rockefeller Commission on Outdoor Recreation in its 1960 Report to the President said that "water is a prime factor in most outdoor recreation activities." The Commission's studies indicate that by the year 2000 swimming will be the most popular single outdoor recreation activity and that boating, skin-diving, and water-skiing will rapidly grow in popularity.

Whether it be the family that camps together or the businessman fishing the trout stream or the boater relaxing on one of our large rivers or lakes, the mental health of our nation is directly related to water pollution control. In our tension-ridden society with its increasing leisure time we must protect our valuable water resources to enable people to get away, forget their troubles, and relax.

Ground water offers us a tremendous reserve of water for the future and, therefore, must be protected as well as surface water. It is too easy to install a malfunctioning septic tank or drill a borehole for sewage disposal into an underground water supply rather than install the proper sewer system and treatment plant. This "out of sight out of mind" disposal of human wastes to the underground may, before long, catch up with us just as in the early days of our nation the indiscriminate waste disposal to surface streams caught up with us. The Pennsylvania Department of Health has seen fit to employ a ground water geologist to help us in our underground water pollution control program.

What can the practising physician do to help in water pollution control and water management programs? Does he campaign for the passage of a bond issue for a sewer system or a sewage treatment plant in your town? Does he support the bond issue to build a new water treatment plant or distribution system? Has he shown concern about the possible contamination of swimming areas in his community? His influence in his community and at all levels of government in support of public water supplies and water pollution control projects and programs can be very effective in protecting the public health. Then there is the entire field of needed further research into the effect of certain pollutants on humans. We need to know much more about what some of the newer chemicals do to humans when ingested. Comparatively little of detergents are removed from sewage treatment plants. What concentration of detergents can be drunk by humans? We also need better tests to identify pathogenic organisms and viruses. Even the coliform test, so widely used, has been shown to be but a gross indicator of pathogenic contamination. We need to know more about the transmission of virus diseases. We need sounder public health standards for bathing places, based on better knowledge and increased research.

Water is a fixed major resource for humans. Demand for pure water is increasing rapidly as population and industry expand. In the highly populated areas the water of our streams needs to be used over and over again as it flows downstream. The multiple use and reuse of water produces inherent health problems, some of which need further study and understanding. We need continued diligence to protect the gains already made.

References

[1]Fair, G. M.: *Human Ecology: 20th Century*; Public Health Rep 78:749 (Sept.) 1963.
[2]Healy, W. A., and Grossman, R. P.: *Water-Borne Typhoid Epidemic at Keene, New Hampshire,* J New Eng Water Works Ass 75:37 (March) 1961.
[3]Freitag, J. L.: *Water-Borne Outbreak of Dysentery*, Health News (New York State Department of Health) 37:4 (April) 1960.
[4]Clarke, N. A., and Kabler, P. W.: *Human Enteric Viruses in Sewage*, Health Lab Sci 1: 44 (Jan) 1964.
[5]Clarke, N. A., et al.: *Removal of Enteric Viruses from Sewage by Activated Sludge Treatment*; Amer J Public Health 51:1118 (Aug) 1961.
[6]Kelly, S. M., and Sanderson, W. W.: *Effect of Chlorine in Water on Enteric Viruses: II. The Effect of Combined Chlorine on Poliomyelitis and Coxsackie Viruses*, Amer J Public Health 51:14 (Jan) 1960.
[7]Kelly, S. M., and Sanderson, W. W.: *Effect of Chlorine in Water on Enteric Viruses*, Amer J Public Health 48:1323 (Oct) 1958.
[8]Petersen, N.J., and Hines, V.D.: *Relation of Summertime Gastrointestinal Illness to Sanitary Quality of the Water Supplies in Six Rocky Mountain Communities*, Amer J Hyg 71-314 (May) 1960.
[9]McLean, D. M.: *Infection Hazards in Swimming Pools*, Pediatrics 31:811 No. 5; May 1963.

Air Pollution in Cities

ROBERT U. AYRES

It does not seem so long ago that the earth's atmosphere was assumed to be essentially inexhaustible in relation to the foreseeable demands upon it. Los Angeles' smog and London's dirty fogs were considered exceptional, anomalous local situations but, in general, it seemed obvious that there was no actual scarcity of air.[1] On the contrary, air was one of the classic examples (cited by generations of economists) of a good which is free because there is more of it available than could possibly be sold at any finite price.

The above view has rapidly been supplanted by a different and (hopefully) more realistic picture. Today the air—especially the air above cities—is increasingly seen as a scarce and valuable resource whose price is zero not because it is in oversupply but for the more complicated reason that there exists no social institution of ownership or exchange which would permit an economic balance to be struck between incompatible uses through the operation of a competitive free market. If it were not for this "market failure," a party wishing to use the air as a medium for dispersal and disposal of gaseous wastes, for instance, would have to pay some price for this service. Similarly, an individual wishing to utilize the air for breathing would also pay an appro-

Source: Robert U. Ayres, "Air Pollution in Cities", 9 *Natural Resources Journal* 1 (1969), published by the School of Law, University of New Mexico. Reprinted by permission of the author and publisher.

priate price (just as one pays for food). The first use is incompatible with the second: that is, the utility of the air for breathing is reduced if the atmosphere is used as a sink for residuals of combustion or industrial processes.

A decade or two ago the atmosphere was generally thought of as an immense—virtually limitless—but passive reservoir of air in much the same way that the oceans are reservoirs of water. Currently, however, a more sophisticated ecological notion is coming to the fore. The important element in the air is oxygen, without which life cannot exist. Water is constantly being removed from the ocean as vapor and returned to it again as rain or runoff, but water never changes its basic chemical form. However, oxygen is highly reactive. Oxygen in the air is converted to CO_2 by the metabolic processes of animals (as well as by the combustion of fossil fuels), while CO_2 is essential for plants which fix the carbon but release most of the oxygen. Normally the two processes would be in equilibrium, the oxygen-consuming and oxygen-producing activities being adjusted to one another.

Modern (urban) civilization affects this balance in several ways. In the first place, the combustion of fossil fuels—coal, petroleum products, and natural gas—is producing "extra" carbon dioxide and using up oxygen at a staggering rate.

In the United States in 1965 about 1.3 billion tons of fossil fuels were consumed for all purposes along with 2.74 billion tons of atmospheric oxygen—to yield 3.77 billion tons of CO_2 plus immense tonnages of assorted by-products.[2] In comparison, human respiration requires about 60 million tons of atmospheric oxygen (for the population of the United States) and produces 98 million tons of CO_2. Based on biomass, the sum total of all animals—mainly cattle—would require less than five times as much oxygen as the human population alone, or somewhere in the neighborhood of 0.3 billion tons and produce 0.5 billion tons of CO_2 at most. Thus industrialization has multiplied the natural rate of oxygen consumption and CO_2 production by factors of 10 and 7½ respectively in North America. Similar, albeit smaller, multipliers exist in other parts of the world.

There are other factors which may also be tipping the balance in the direction of less oxygen and more CO_2, viz., erosion, deforestation and defoliation of large stretches of countryside, the plowing of grasslands for crops—which leaves the ground bare for part of the year—and the spread of cities and paved areas over sizable areas of productive land. There is evidence also that water pollution may be causing reduced phytoplankton (algae) production in coastal waters.[3] It is far from certain that all the above effects are in the direction of reduced oxygen supply, however. Fertilization of surface waters by organic waste disposal often results in increased algal harvests, and there is even some evidence that higher levels of atmospheric CO_2 stimulate photosynthesis and therefore the oxygen "cycle" and may tend to be self-regulating.[4] Nevertheless, the atmosphere is clearly a finite and extremely valuable resource which is probably being used up or degraded considerably faster than it is being regenerated. It is hardly the unlimited reservoir it was generally imagined to be as recently as a decade or two ago.

As indicated above, the primary use of this resource—to support animal life—is being compromised by other secondary uses of the atmosphere which are not "rationed," as they would be if all such uses were governed by a free competitive market, but are available at no charge to all. The capability of the atmosphere to satisfy all demands put upon it is being exceeded. This is especially so in urban areas where the density of population, as well as commercial and industrial activity, is the greatest.

In the remainder of this paper I shall discuss successively major sources of pollution of the air over cities, physical effects, economic costs, and alternative pollution control policies and technologies.

Sources of Pollution

As hinted above, the single most important source of air pollution is energy conversion, especially where the combustion of fossil fuels is involved. It is convenient to consider the problem in four segments: (1) utility electric power generation, (2) transportation (especially automotive), (3) industry, and (4) households and commerce in general.

The fuel requirements of each sector are notably different, as shown in Table 1.[5]

Table 1: Sources of energy used by various sectors (in per cent)

	Utility	Trans-portation	Industry	Households and Commercial
Coal	55		29.4	0.4
Petroleum	6	99.85	22.8	38.8
Natural gas	22		39.3	42.8
Utility electricity	a	0.15	8.5	14.4
Other	17			3.6
	100	100	100.0	100.0

[a] Not applicable.

In the case of electric power production, minimum cost per British thermal unit (BTU) is of paramount importance: thus, natural gas is dominant in the west and southwest, water power in the upper northwest, coal in the midwest and east, and residual oil imported from Venezuela on the east and Gulf coasts. Natural gas is comparatively clean and contributes very little in the way of unwanted emissions (other than CO_2) except for minor quantities of oxides of nitrogen. Coal and residual oil, on the other hand, both normally contain a considerable amount of sulfur ($\sim$ 2.5 per cent) which burns to form sulfur dioxide (SO_2) and sulfur trioxide (SO_3).

Electric utilities produced an estimated 13.6 million tons of sulfur oxides in 1965, plus 3.7 million tons of oxides of nitrogen, 2.5 million tons of carbon monoxide, and 2.4 million tons of particulates (soot).[6] Oxides of sulfur are toxic in themselves; they also combine with water to form acids (H_2SO_3 and H_2SO_4) which are highly irritating to lungs and bronchial passages as well as to plants, painted surfaces, bare metal and—not least—stone (especially limestone or marble, which are rapidly eroded in the presence of atmospheric sulfur oxides).

In the transporation sector, the prime consideration is that the fuel be liquid, for ease of storage and handling. Thus, petroleum products account for all but 0.15 per cent of the total (over 300 million tons in 1965) and about 90 per cent of this is gasoline—the fuel used by conventional spark-ignited (Otto-cycle) internal combustion engines for automobiles and all except the largest trucks—the remainder being jet fuel (similar to kerosene) and diesel oil.[7]

All of these products are distillates and therefore relatively free of inherent contaminants such as sulfur. However, in order to prevent pre-ignition and "knocking" in internal combustion engines without sacrificing engine performance (by reducing compression ratios) or utilizing more costly aromatics such as xylene and toluene, it is standard practice to add a small quantity of tetraethyl lead to increase the so-called "octane number." However, on a national basis, this amounts to 200,000 tons of lead per year (one sixth of all annual lead production), practically all of which appears as very fine particles in automotive exhausts and is dispersed into the air. Its subsequent pathway through the ecosphere is, at present, largely unknown in detail, although presumably accumulation must be taking place in soil, in plants and animals, and in surface waters.

In addition to additives such as lead, the internal combustion engine is so inefficient that prior to the 1968 model-year as much as 10 per cent of the fuel used in automobiles, or 20 million tons on a national basis in 1965, was wasted and dissipated in the atmosphere unburned or partially burned. Carbon monoxide is produced by uncontrolled vehicles, i.e., those without smog-control devices, at the rate of about one pound (equivalent to 7.5 cubic feet of gas) for each two pounds of fuel burned.[8] Assuming the lethal concentration of CO is somewhere in the range of 200 parts per million or 0.02 per cent, and assuming each automobile in a city drives 10,000 miles per year and obtains 14.7 miles per gallon—the national average figures[9]—each car will produce roughly 2500 pounds of carbon monoxide in a year, while trucks produce considerably more. This adds up to a national total in the neighborhood of 100 million tons for 1965. This is enough to contaminate nearly one hundred million cubic feet of air to the point of lethality. If we further assume an urban population density of 10,000 per square mile with one car or truck for every two persons, a little arithmetic indicates that such a community produces enough carbon monoxide each year to poison *the entire atmosphere above itself.* Clearly, if the carbon monoxide simply accumulated without being dispersed or oxidized to CO_2, cities could not co-exist with automobiles.

Fortunately, due to natural processes, the half-life of carbon monoxide in the atmosphere is apparently fairly short, but peak concentrations as high as 140 parts per million (ppm) have been observed over city streets during periods of heavy traffic.[10] Levels of 40 ppm are thought to be sufficient to have an adverse effect on physiological and mental functions and may be contributory causes of many accidents.

Oxides of nitrogen (NO and NO_2) are also produced by the high-temperature, high-pressure combustion processes characteristic of internal combustion engines—about 5.7 million tons in 1965.[11] These are toxic in themselves, and, together with unburned hydrocarbons, are the main ingredients in the photochemical mixture which constitutes Los Angeles-type "smog."

In addition to gaseous emissions, automotive vehicles are significant sources of particulates. Minor quantities originate in the engine exhausts; others come from mechanical wear, especially rubber from tires and asbestos particles from brake linings. The latter are not directly by-products of combustion, although they are produced mainly because the kinetic energy of vehicular motion is converted into heat as the vehicle is slowed down or brought to a stop.

Although people living in densely populated cities travel by automobile somewhat less than people living in suburbs or smaller towns, the differences on the average are not great. Only in New York City is a significant fraction of total passenger-miles attributed to railroads or rapid transit. Generally speaking, it can be assumed that local trips (50 miles or less) are distributed geographically roughly in proportion to population—which means most of them occur in urban areas—although longer trips would be more likely to utilize intercity or rural routes. However, automobile trips over 100 miles in length account for only 20 per cent of total automobile passenger-miles and, presumably, a comparable fraction of overall emissions.[12]

Industrial processes, especially metallurgy, cement and glass manufacture, and refractories, plus space-heating in households and other buildings, account for the remaining fossil fuel consumption in the United States. All three types of fuel are significantly represented. Thus 188 million tons of coal were used in industry in 1965, of which 96 million were first carbonized, yielding 77 million tons of coke plus coal gas, coal tar, and coal tar derivatives.[13] Low sulfur coal is necessary to produce metallurgical quality coke and the output of low sulfur Pennsylvania and West Virginia sources by the coking industry is mostly tied up by long-term contracts. Coal is no longer used to an appreciable extent for space heating purposes. Thus industry and households together contribute less than electrical utilities to the overall su' fur problem—8.4 million tons of SO_x from these sectors was estimated for 1965. In addition, these sectors yielded 7 million tons of nitrogen oxides (NO_x) and 7 million tons of particulates (soot) and were the major single source of both.[14] Smoke control is, of course, particularly difficult in small heating plants for homes or apartments.

Residuals contributing to urban air pollution arise from two other principal sources: (1) production and processing wastes, and (2) consumption wastes. In the first category one must include such major items as evaporative losses in natural gas production, petroleum refining and petrochemicals, ore beneficiation, and so forth. In the second category must be included not only "final" goods whose ultimate disposal results in combustion (e.g., trash burning), but also a large number of "intermediate" products which never appear physically in a product for final consumption and which are actually dissipated and dispersed into the environment in normal usage. Among this category of products are many which contribute in a major way to air pollution, such as cleaners, solvents, pesticides, explosives, aerosol propellants, and so forth.

Fortunately, a number of the most obnoxious airborne industrial wastes, such as the fluorides which arise from the processing of phosphate rock into "superphosphate" fertilizer, and the sulfur oxides associated with copper, zinc, or lead ore reduction, are not produced in heavily populated areas. Petroleum refining, too, is sometimes restricted to fairly remote locations, although there are also large refineries to serve the local market in most metropolitan areas. Chemicals plants in general, however, tend to be situated in or near cities and these are among the most prolific producers of evil-smelling,[15] corrosive, and irritating fumes.

Among the dissipative intermediates, solvents are the most noteworthy contributors to urban air pollution. This category includes turpentine, benzene, xylene, naphtha, methyl-, ethyl-, and isopropyl alcohols, glycol ethers, acetone, methyl-ethyl-ketone, carbon disulfide, carbon tetrachloride, vinyl chloride, and various other chlorinated hydrocarbons. Most of these substances have a variety of basic chemical uses, so that one cannot simply add up the total quantities produced and assume that it all contributes to air pollution. Nevertheless, this is the ultimate fate of very large tonnages of dry-cleaning agents, paint-removers, diluents and thinners used in many fast-drying paints, varnishes, and lacquers, among others. The function of a solvent is to selectively separate and remove solid substances from places where they are not wanted and/or to permit solids to be deposited easily and uniformly in places where they are needed. The solvent itself may or may not be deliberately thrown away (i.e., allowed to evaporate) after such use, but even if it is distilled and re-used, there is bound to be some loss. If the cycle is repeated frequently, as in commercial dry-cleaning plants, the cumulative loss will be large.

The disposal of "final" goods, such as garbage, household trash, demolition wastes, and junk, may or may not contribute to air pollution, depending on how it is handled. Garbage and trash—about 4 pounds per capita per day, or 150 million tons per year, nationally—are largely (~80 per cent) combustible,[16] whence refuse collection costs can be significantly reduced by incineration at the point of origin. However, local incineration is extremely inefficient and there is virtually no way to control smoke production, in particular. Many cities haul trash and garbage to central locations for processing. Again, to reduce bulk, open burning has been practiced at many such sites—with concomitant ill-effects on the surrounding area. Incineration in enclosed furnaces under controlled conditions is somewhat more efficient, but even so, a significant fraction of the fly ash (and all of the SO_x and NO_x) tends to escape into the atmosphere. Detailed statistics on emissions from refuse incineration are not currently available, but it is clear from materials-balance considerations that if only 100 million tons are burned annually in an uncontrolled manner, of which 20 per cent is incombustible, then somewhere in the neighborhood of possibly several million tons of soot is being injected into the atmosphere annually.

In New York City about 75 tons of particulates a day are attributed to municipal refuse burning and a further 61 tons a day are attributed to dwellings and apartment houses—of which a significant fraction is also due to incineration.[17] All in all, probably half of all particulates (soot) come from this source.

Effects

This is not the place for a detailed explanation of the physical, physiological, and socio-psychological effects of air pollution. It may be of interest, however, to summarize briefly the multitude of ways in which externally induced changes in the chemical composition of its atmosphere may affect the inhabitants of a city.

To begin with, there are direct effects on people, ranging in severity from the lethal to the merely annoying. Fatalities are not, as a rule, traceable individually to the impact of air pollution, primarily because most of the effects are synergistic. Thus, air pollution is an environmental stress which, in cooperation with a number of other environmental stresses, tends to increase the incidence and seriousness of a variety of pulmonary diseases, including lung cancer, emphysema, tuberculosis, pneumonia, bronchitis, asthma, and even the common cold. Statistical studies suggest that most or all of these are definitely correlated with long-term exposure to polluted air.[18] The most dramatic proof of the lethal capabilities of air pollution is the sharp rise in death rates (mainly from the elderly or those already suffering from one or more of the above complaints) during each major air pollution "episode" in a major city. Oft-cited examples include the Meuse Valley, Belgium 1930 (60 deaths); Donora, Pennsylvania 1948 (20 deaths); London 1952 (3500-4000 deaths); New York City 1965 (400 deaths).[19]

For every actual fatality attributable to the effects of pollution, there are many persons who are affected to the point of physical illness and a larger number who may not require medical treatment but who suffer significant annoyance, such as coughing, wheezing, pains in the chest, smarting eyes, and so forth. Finally, there is a still broader class, which probably includes nearly everybody living in an urban area, who object to the soot, bad smells, and other visible or sensory manifestations of pollution. Unfortunately, there are no good yardsticks to measure the disutility experienced by each group or the number of people who belong in each classification. However, one rather significant point deserves emphasis. The disutility arising from minor discomfort and essentially aesthetic objections to air pollution is probably the most underestimated and certainly the fastest-growing component of the total problem. This arises from two interrelated factors: (1) the rising level of education on the part of the population and even more rapid rate of increase in the means and possibilities of communication, all of which results in an explosive increase in the level of awareness and general perception of the pollution problem as compared with a few decades ago, and (2) the fact that comfort and aesthetic satisfaction are "superior goods," as many economists have pointed out, and the demand for them grows nonlinearly with general prosperity and affluence, which are themselves rapidly increasing. Here lies the explanation of the superficially paradoxical fact that a generation ago belching smokestacks were welcomed, as indicators of full employment, whereas today they are more likely to be taken as symbols of technological obsolescence and management irresponsibility.

Direct effects on humans have parallels in the animal and plant worlds. Animals of economic importance (livestock) are not collocated to any appreciable extent with cities and can safely be overlooked in the present context. Effects on pets (dogs, cats and birds) almost certainly exist, although they have not been much documented. To the extent that the effects are chronic, perhaps resulting in discomfort and life-shortening for the animal, the disutility to humans may not be very great in most cases. In fact, since more kittens and puppies are born than are needed to satisfy the demand for pets, replacements of nonpedigreed animals can be had at virtually zero price.[20]

As far as plants are concerned, much the same situation holds. Crops are mostly some distance away from cities, and hazards are likely to be rather special in nature (e.g., fluorides from superphosphate plants, or sulfur oxides from copper smelters). However, there are some districts where truck crops—mostly fruits and vegetables—are grown in close juxtaposition to major cities. This is particularly true of Connecticut, Long Island, New Jersey, eastern Pennsylvania, and Delaware, and of southern California between San Diego and Santa Barbara where citrus groves still exist in considerable abundance. Agricultural damage in the citrus belt of southern California seems to be due mainly to oxidants, such as ozone and peroxy-acyl-nitrate,[21] which are produced by the interaction of unburned hydrocarbons, oxides of nitrogen, and strong sunlight. In the mixed truck-farming region of the Middle Atlantic states (potatoes, tomatoes, leafy vegetables, green peas, sweet corn, apples, peaches, dairy and poultry farming), the major cause of damage seems to be sulfur which often causes leaf-spotting and discoloration—reducing the market value of the product—and sometimes stunted growth or worse. In suburban gardens and city parks, there are deleterious effects on shrubs, flowers, and shade trees.

As with direct effects on human health, it is difficult to unambiguously trace a given symptom or a case of stunted growth to a particular air pollutant. Again, air pollution must be considered an environmental stress, along with drought, extremes of temperature, or pest outbreaks. Very often—in fact, probably in the majority of instances—a healthy organism can withstand a single moderate stress but not two or three different stresses at the same time. Another way of looking at the matter is to say that exposure to constant stress from air pollution tends to weaken the plants' resistance to other environmental stresses, such as cold winters or dry, hot summers. Thus part of the excess mortality associated with events of the latter type should be attributed to the abnormal stress of air pollution, just as part of the excess mortality which might follow a very severe air pollution "episode" might fairly be attributable to the extra cold winter or an extra wet spring. Again, there are no satisfactory methods of allocating the observed damages among a number of synergistically interacting multiple causes, nor can the damages themselves be adequately measured and reduced to economic terms.

A third category of effects comprises damage to property. Here again, sulfur and oxidants are perhaps equally potent. As noted previously, sulfur oxides combine with water to form sulfurous acid (H_2SO_3) and the much more corrosive sulfuric acid (H_2SO_4). These acids will damage virtually any exposed metal surface and will react especially strongly with limestone or marble (calcium carbonate). Sulfur oxides will also cause discoloration, hardening and embrittlement of rubber, plastic, paper, and other materials. Oxidants such as ozone will also produce the latter type of effect. Of course, the most widespread and noticeable of all forms of property damage is simple dirt (soot), which has some secondary effects of its own. Thus, if shirt collars can be worn twice, the shirt itself will last approximately twice as long as if the shirt requires laundering after only one day—since a shirt's useful life is essentially measured in terms of the number of washings it undergoes, rather than the number of days it is worn.[22] Of course, airborne dirt also affects other clothing, furniture, carpets, drapes, exterior paintwork, and automobiles. It leads to extra washing, vacuum cleaning, dry-cleaning, and painting; and, of course, all of these activities do not entirely eliminate the dirt, so that people also must live in darker and dirtier surroundings.

A final category comprises bio-climatic and ecological effects. On the urban scale, it is known that there are distinct, measurable differences between the climate in a city and in its environs. Thus temperatures and humidity are higher, precipitation and cloud cover are slightly more frequent, fog is much more common (especially in winter), and so forth.[23] These differences are almost certainly due in part to the large amount of waste heat generated in cities and very likely also owe a debt to the concentration of particulates (which can serve as condensation nuclei for fog, for instance) and possibly some of the other residuals which are commonly dispersed in the air over cities.

On the continental scale, of course, one must begin to worry seriously about major perturbations to the climate which might be caused by the (apparently) rising level of atmospheric CO_2, as noted earlier. If, as has been suggested, the "greenhouse effect" leads to higher temperatures and results in melting the massive accumulations of ice in Greenland and Antarctica, one obvious consequence would be a distinct rise in the sea-level and a considerable problem for low-lying coastal cities. The rise would occur gradually, over centuries, permitting either evacuation or the building of dikes and protective walls, but in either event the consequences would be quite important for many urban dwellers. On the other hand, it has also been suggested that higher temperatures might trigger a new ice age which would have precisely the opposite effect. If this were to happen, a number of seaports would be stranded, like gasping fish, away from deep water.

Costs

The notion of pollution "cost" is somewhat more elusive than it might at first appear to be. Although one may be forced by practical considerations to take a very simplistic view of the matter in the end, it seems worthwhile to mention some of the underlying difficulties in the concept. Quantitative national estimates of the cost of air pollution are relatively few and, with rare exceptions, not very illuminating.[24]

The usual approach is to add up dollar expenditures, such as extra cleaning or hospital bills, which would not be necessary if there were no pollution, plus lost future income and call these the "cost" of pollution. There are two immediate and cogent objections to this procedure, however. The first is that many, if not most, of the most important disutilities of pollution are not reflected by any such dollar expenditures. Clearly, hospital or burial costs, or even the present value of lost future income, are a poor measure of the value of a human life.[25] In the very large number of cases where the disutilities are sensory and aesthetic, no dollar value at all is allowed by such a measure.

Clearly, what is wrong here is that the real benefits which air pollution has deprived us of—life, health, and clean fresh air—are provided free. But they are free *not* because they exist in over-supply,[26] but because there exists no market in which they can be exchanged and priced. We have, at present, no satisfactory way of attaching a dollar sign to the loss of a free benefit. However, it is misleading and quite incorrect to assume explicitly or implicitly that the loss should be counted as zero.

The second fundamental objection to equating pollution costs with dollar expenditures which would not otherwise be made is the elementary fact that, in an exchange economy, an expense to one individual results in an income to another. Thus the extra cleaning costs noted previously result in extra income for the laundry. There is no *a priori* way of balancing the utilities and disutilities resulting from such a transaction since they depend upon the alternatives which exist for each party. For the person forced to spend more of his income on cleaning than he otherwise would, the welfare loss to him is the difference between the amount of satisfaction he would have received from spending a few cents per day in other ways *vis-à-vis* the satisfaction received from spending it on laundry.

For the economy as a whole, the question is more complicated: it boils down to the comparison of alternative patterns of expenditure and forms of employment for capital and certain categories of labor. If unskilled labor is in short supply, the use of it in a laundry is wasteful of resources, but if it is in oversupply, the alternative might be unemployment. There is no easy universal formula for measuring the marginal social utility of money spent on a particular good or service. Each case would have to be judged on its merits.

However, in a society such as the United States where neither labor nor capital is fully utilized under normal circumstances, it seems likely that, *ceteris paribus*, extra costs imposed by pollution do have some compensating economic benefits in creating employment for otherwise hard-to-employ workers. This is not to say that other forms of socially useful employment may not be found in the future, but at the present time it is probable that money now spent on extra laundry, cleaning, and maintenance produces more jobs for unskilled and semi-skilled labor than alternative modes of expenditure (e.g., on durable goods) would do. This being so, the sum total of dollar expenditures would have to be reduced by the net (dollar) benefits thereby produced to arrive at an estimate of net dollar costs.[27]

The fact is that any change in the pattern of consumption and expenditure has its effect on production and prices also. The example given above postulated that a change in expenditure patterns might result in a reduced demand for certain types of labor which are currently in oversupply.[28] Similarly, in another sphere, it must be pointed out that the economic distortion resulting from the fact that residuals can be disposed of into the environment without cost—or at too little cost—implies that certain products and services are probably being sold too cheaply, whereas others may be more expensive than they would be if *all* goods and services—including those provided by the environment—were exchanged only in a free competitive market.[29]

Electric power is a good case in point. It is produced as cheaply as it is in certain areas only because the electric utilities are allowed to use the air as a place to dispose of smoke and excess heat, without cost. If an economic price were charged for this service, the cheapest means of producing electric power might involve a different technology, and it might conceivably be more expensive.[30] Since electric power is an input to essentially all other industries, production costs would rise in other sectors of the economy. If aluminum production, for instance, depended to any extent on electric power from coal or oil-burning plants (which it does not), the price of aluminum would, in turn, have to be raised. This would affect the price of kitchenware, aircraft, and other products.

Speaking generally, the effects of air pollution on the economy include the sum total of all distortions[31] and implicit readjustments of the above type. To estimate these quantitatively would involve first knowing what the entire economy would be like if these distortions did not exist. A rather elaborate analysis of each industry would be required to estimate what its production costs would be on the basis of an altered set of input costs, including hypothetical payments for environmental services. From the revised set of prices (based on existing demand and elasticities), a new set of demands would have to be derived. From these, in turn, further revisions in calculated prices would be made. Thus, by iteration, a picture of the hypothetical undistorted economy could be derived—assuming one had a reasonable method of assigning virtual prices to the environmental services which are currently free.[32]

Assuming full employment (or making any other reasonable assumption about labor utilization), the GNP of the hypothetical "undistorted" economy could be computed by a linear programming model and compared with the actual one. However, this does not necessarily bring us closer to a realistic estimate of the cost of air pollution, since what counts is the *welfare* output—i.e., the total satisfaction provided—by the two economies. Once more we are reminded that welfare or satisfaction includes many things which are not bought or sold in a competitive market, and it is entirely possible, although not necessarily true, that the "undistorted" economy would produce fewer material goods or a smaller GNP, but greater welfare than our present one.

In summary, the overall costs of air pollution would be the sum of three terms, as follows:

disutility or losses of non-market ("free") benefits (life, health, aesthetics)	+	disutility or net direct dollar expenditures (e.g., laundry, medical costs, etc.)	+	disutility (or utility) of net indirect dollar costs (or benefits) to society (e.g., employment, distorted prices, etc.)

Of these three terms, the first has implicitly been assumed to be zero, although most analysts realize that this is unrealistic. The second term has been computed although the existing studies still leave much to be desired.[33] The third term has been ignored completely, possibly because first-order approximations may well be negative (i.e., beneficial to society in dollar terms) and no economist has wished to appear to say that "air pollution is good for you," however qualified that statement would be. Actually the numerical comparison of dollar costs and benefits appears to be unimportant in comparison with the glaring omission of the first term of the three: the physical and psychic losses for which we have no convenient dollar price tags. It is not acceptable to say that these kinds of losses are not zero, or even to say that they are large but inherently unquantifiable. The problem remains, however, to estimate them quantitatively *in terms of dollars*, which is the only existing available measure of utility (or disutility).

Fortunately it is not quite accurate to say that there exists no marketplace in which the services and/or disservices provided by air pollution are exchanged. Literally speaking, this is so, but there is one market where the impact of these services/disservices is felt and can be measured: real estate. To quote Ridker,

> If the land market were to work perfectly, the price of a plot of land would equal the sum of the present discounted stream of benefits and costs derivable from it. . . . Since air pollution is specific to locations and the

> supply of locations is fixed, there is less likelihood that the negative effects of pollution can be significantly shifted onto other markets. We should, therefore, expect to find the majority of effects reflected in this market, and can measure them by observing associated changes in property value.[34]

To the above, it should be added that the real estate market, like others, is very imperfect. In this case, the crucial flaw is the lack of perfect information on the part of purchasers. It would have been equally accurate and more appropriate to say that the price of a plot of land reflects the sum of present values of *anticipated* (i.e., perceived) future benefits and costs derivable from it. The point of this remark is that the vast majority of real estate buyers have essentially no knowledge at all of the more acute medical effects of air pollution—which are still being argued in highly abstruse terms even among doctors. Hence, it is apparent that the latter are not being taken into account in land prices. What the real estate market primarily reflects is the tangible, experiential aspects of pollution: more rapid deterioration and extra cleaning and maintenance costs, the milder medical symptoms, such as shortness of breath and smarting eyes, plus bad smells and dirt. Ridker assumed—justifiably, no doubt—that these problems would be closely correlated with sulfur dioxide emissions. Eight "sulfation zones" were identified in St. Louis, and it was found by survey that average property values varied by about $250 per lot, per zone, other things remaining equal.[35]

Assuming an annual discount rate[36] of 6-8 per cent, this presumably can be interpreted to mean that the marginal utility of a shift from one sulfation level to the next is about $15-$20 for a lower middle-class or middle-class city-dweller. The marginal utility of a shift from the highest to the lowest sulfation level was evidently about $150 or $200 per year, on the basis of the rather narrow spectrum of tangible disservices (maintenance, odor, soot) mentioned above.

The amount which a fully knowledgeable real estate buyer would add to this to allow for the more serious, but rarer conditions, such as lung cancer and emphysema—whose link with air pollution is apparent statistically but not causally—is much harder to estimate. It has been observed that a human life is worth more to society than the simple discounted present value of future earnings, and acknowledged, also, that its value must nevertheless be finite, rather than infinite.[37] Limited guidance may perhaps be derived from the upper range of awards of juries in cases of accidental injury or death in cases where the negligent party is insured and can be presumed to have unlimited resources. Such awards nowadays often run above $250,000.

In the future, better information may come from sophisticated polling techniques, designed to elicit "willingness to pay." It is well known that simple questions, like "what would you be willing to pay to avoid (or gain) so and so," yield misleading answers.[38] However, there are methods of reducing, if not eliminating, some of these secondary interactions between the pollster and the person being polled. It is possible that more meaningful answers can be obtained to questions like "would you accept a 1-in-10 chance of dying within 5 years in exchange for X thousand dollars?" Indeed, there are several professions—such as bullfighting and auto-racing—which offer opportunities (but not certainties) of large rewards in exchange for very high risks of injury or death. By analyzing data from polls, together with actual statistics for risky professions, it should be possible to cast much more light into this area of ignorance.

Whether by these methods, or others, only when the problem of putting a dollar value on illness and death has been grappled with, will it be possible to estimate the costs of pollution and the benefits of pollution control.

Alternative Control Policies and Technologies

This topic is a broad one which can only be skimmed in an overview such as this. As regards basic policies, there is a continuum of possibilities, depending largely on where the policy-maker stands with respect to one basic philosophical issue: the value of the free market as a method of allocating resources and incomes in our society. If the free market is deemed to be a mechanism worth preserving and improving, then the appropriate method of minimizing the disutilities[39] arising from air pollution is to recognize the fact that most of them arise from market failures and thus to attempt to eliminate these failures or find means of compensating for them. If, on the other hand, the free market *per se* is not felt to be important, then there is no basic objection to strictly pragmatic *ad hoc* responses, even though the latter may perpetuate or worsen the fundamental market failures. As a matter of observation, existing approaches to the problem of control tend to be of the latter type.

A classic market-preserving approach essentially attempts to eliminate externalities by "internalizing" them. On the government level this approach leads to regional compacts and "super agencies." In the private sector, however, the standard method of internalization—merger—is not available in most cases.[40]

The next alternative is to eliminate the effect of the market imperfections (if not the imperfections themselves) by attaching prices to *all* services—and disservices—which are now rendered "free" by the atmosphere. This means dollar exchanges, positive or negative as the case warrants, would be imposed for:
(1) private use of air as an input for any purpose,
(2) private use of the assimilative capacity of the atmosphere, for any purpose,
(3) inadvertent or unwanted material inputs *from* the air.

A formal scheme for incorporating such exchanges in the general equilibrium theory of economics has been described elsewhere.[41] In practice, the charges for air used for breathing would be very low since the quantity available greatly exceeds any possible near-term demand for this purpose. Charges for oxygen used for combustion might be the same, per unit, but would be greater in total. Charges for accepting CO_2 might be waived (as being covered by the charge for oxygen) but there would be additional charges for using the atmosphere as a sink for other products of inefficient combustion. On the other hand, persons inadvertently receiving unwanted inputs from the atmosphere, such as smog or soot, would receive appropriate compensation.

The important point is that if all these services and disservices were exchanged on a market, there would be *finite* prices attached to them. While such a market cannot exist in actuality as long as the air is held in common as a public good, there may be means of simulating the relevant effects of such a market: namely, the exchanges of money and the adjustments in productive processes and technology which would inevitably follow. One such simulacrum is the proposed "effluent tax," which would require a residuals producer to pay the government (as a surrogate for the public) in proportion to the quantity of residuals dispersed in the environment.

Without belaboring the point unduly, an illustration may be worthwhile. At the present time, in the absence of either a market exchange mechanism or an effluent charge, an electric utility may produce any amount of soot it pleases.[42] Its products are: (1) electricity and (2) soot (disregarding other effluents for the moment). It buys fuel, sells electricity, and "gives away" its soot, and chooses the cheapest possible fuel. Suppose, however, that the utility is no longer allowed to give away its co-product, soot, but must pay its neighbors a price to accept it. Then it can do one of two things: it can continue to use the same fuel and the same combustion technology and simply charge more for the electricity, or it can shift to a cleaner fuel, use precipitators in the stacks, and reduce the output of soot. Since the demand for electricity will decrease if the price rises, profit considerations dictate that the electric utility will seek to keep the price of power low by finding cheap ways of eliminating the soot. Within a few years the "price" of eliminating soot will fall drastically, since many people will have a positive incentive to reduce it.

The *ad hoc* approach, which does not seek to preserve or improve the free competitive market, encompasses any number of variants, although the most common are the enforcement of arbitrary standards and subsidies. The first is a simple statement that emissions from such-and-such a process or engine shall not exceed a given amount, together with an appropriate amount of enforcement. Theoretically, this method might result in standards being set unrealistically low (or even at "zero"), although in practice the proposed standards are invariably modified by considerations of what the affected industry says is feasible. Unfortunately, the industry never really knows what it could do, at what price, and neither does anybody else. Worse, there is an historic tendency on the part of industry to grossly exaggerate the costs of any change whatever. The result is that standards are almost invariably much too lenient.

The most popular approach, with industry, is government subsidy, or—equivalently—tax credit. Unfortunately, by overestimating the cost, it is sometimes possible to make a sizable windfall profit.[43] On the other hand, it is the case that certain industries would be severely damaged by a strict application of an effluent tax or even by the imposition of a realistic standard of emissions. While it seems difficult to justify making exceptions in favor of established interests, it is also inequitable, in some pertinent sense, to hurt or eliminate an industry by suddenly changing the rules of the game. This problem is not hypothetical: for example, the leather industry, for one, can probably not afford to clean up and remain competitive with synthetics.[44] In time, other industries based on natural products (sugar refining, paper, etc.) may face the same problem. Thus a case could be made for a public buy-out or a temporary subsidy to ease the period of transition.

Passing from policy to technology, there are two basic approaches: symptomatic treatment and process change. The first approach comprises the gamut of smoke precipitators, stack gas absorbers, filters and washers, afterburners and catalytic mufflers for automobiles, etc. These devices add complexity and cost to residuals-producing processes. Moreover, since the quantity of residuals is not actually decreased by add-on devices, the problem is very often merely shifted from one medium to another. Thus sulfur dioxide can be removed from stack gases by "washing"—but the sulfur-laden water still constitutes a disposal problem which may not be any less serious in magnitude. However, in some cases—as in the case of seaports—disposal in this manner may be preferable to use of the the air as a sink. Disposal as a solid, as with fly ash precipitated from stacks, would virtually always be advantageous. (Indeed, this material has several potential markets, e.g., as insulation or filler). In the case of automobile exhausts, the main problem arises from inefficient combustion, rather than impurities in the fuel, and afterburners do perform a useful service if they simply reduce the amount of unburned or partially burned material which escapes.

The alternative basic approach is, in the long run, more promising, however. It is to decrease the amount of residuals produced by fundamental process changes. In the case of electric utilities, this may be done by shifting from high sulfur to low sulfur oil; or by using natural gas or gassified desulfurized coal. Conversion to electricity may also be carried out nearer the mine, thus reducing transportation costs as well as reducing residuals load (which includes heat as well as combustion waste products) on the urban airshed. A shift to nuclear power also will reduce the problem of combustion by-products, although the thermal pollution problem will be worse and a new problem of radioactive waste disposal must still be faced. Ultimately, however, controlled thermonuclear reactions (fusion power) promises to eliminate most of the presently envisaged residuals problems, including the latter.

Combustion wastes from automotive vehicles can also be drastically reduced by changing the basic technology. The least disruptive change would involve a switch from the internal combustion engine (ICE) to an external combustion engine (ECE). It has been concluded elsewhere that a modern Rankine-cycle reciprocating ECE using steam or a synthetic working fluid with appropriate characteristics—such as one of the Freons—would provide very satisfactory service in all automotive applications with no sacrifice in power, weight, effective range, smoothness of operation or fuel consumption efficiency. Indeed, the evidence suggests that such an engine, mass-produced, would be simpler, cheaper to manufacture, longer-lived, and more economical to operate than the ICE.[45]

In the longer-term, electric propulsion for vehicles may be in the cards, since there is very rapid progress in battery and fuel cell technology, under the stimulus of military and space requirements. Extrapolating the recent rate-of-change in battery and fuel cell capabilities for another decade or two suggests that by 1985 or so, an electric car, using a fuel cell for primary power and batteries for peak power needs, will be economically and technologically competitive if marketed in such a way as to take advantage of its very low operating costs.[46]

Either an external combustion engine or the battery/fuel-cell option would reduce the emissions problem very drastically even from levels contemplated for 1985 by the large automobile manufacturers. To explore the circumstances under which a process-change of this magnitude might occur in an industry as massive and entrenched as the automotive industry is a major topic in itself and cannot be undertaken here.

However, there is good reason to believe that expenditures of government money may be most effective when, and to the extent that, they help to bring about process changes or large-scale technological substitutions such as the above. Thus, the technology of utility electricity generation has begun to reflect the massive federal government support of nuclear research. The government also can exert leverage by taxing a socially "undesirable" activity, or by explicitly creating a market for a desirable one through its own purchases. Indeed, the most likely way of encouraging the creation of a modern "steam-power" industry would be to specify that procurement for government agencies, the Post Office, police and so forth must utilize external combustion engines rather than internal combustion engines for propulsion. This strategy has not yet been tested, but it appears promising enough to warrant very serious consideration.

References

[1]For instance, in the report of the President's Materials Policy (i.e., Paley) Commision in 1952, there is no mention at all of air. The same is true of H. Brown, J. Bonner & J. Weir, Man's Natural and Technological Resources (1957); and the monumental Resources in America's Future (1962) by Landsberg, Fischman, & Fisher.

[2]Carbon and oxygen combine in the ratio of 12 to 32, since the atomic weights are 12 and 16 respectively: coal and natural gas contain approximately 75 per cent carbon by weight and petroleum contains about 85 per cent carbon.

[3]*See* Winsten, *DDT Reduces Photosynthesis by Marine Phytoplankton,* 159 Science 1474 (1968).

[4]There is also the possibility that higher levels of CO_2 may result in higher worldwide temperatures, through the well-known "greenhouse effect," which, in turn, may cause shifts in precipitation patterns. The climatic effects of a temperature rise (or fall) are matters of speculation at present. However, mechanisms have been proposed which might suggest quite drastic effects, not excluding a possible new ice-age (resulting from increased precipitation in the form of snow over the arid land areas of northern Canada and Siberia). *See* Conservation Foundation, Implications of Rising Carbon Dioxide Content of the Atmosphere (1963).

[5]Presentation by W. A. Vogely and W. E. Morrison, World Power Conference, Oct. 1966, Patterns of Energy Consumption in the United States 1947-65 and 1980 Projected.

[6]R. Ayres & A. Kneese, *Environmental Pollution* in New Resources in an Urban Age (Perloff ed. 1969).

[7]W. Vogely & W. Morrison, *supra* note 5.

[8]*See* President's Science Advisory Comm., *Restoring the Quality of Our Environment* (Nov. 1965).

[9]*See* Automobile Manufacturing Association, Automobile Facts and Figures (1966 ed.).

[10]Subpanel on Air Pollution, Report on The Automobile and Air Pollution: A Program for Progress (1967).

[11]R. Ayres & A. Kneese, *supra* note 6.

[12]Automobile Manufacturing Association, *supra* note 9.

[13]R. Ayres & A. Kneese, *supra* note 6.

[14]*Id.*

[15]Particularly, the mercaptans (RHS) including hydrogen sulfide.

[16]Aerojet General Corp., California Waste Management Study, Report No. 3056 to the State of California, Dep't of Public Health (1965).

[17]R. Ayres & A. Kneese, *supra* note 6.

[18]They also may be correlated with smoking, malnutrition and other forms of stress. This makes statistical analysis extremely difficult.

[19]*See* Goldsmith, *Effects of Air Pollution on Health*, 1 Air Pollution (2d ed. 1968).

[20]Pets are valued highly once they become "part" of a family, but their value declines later on as they become elderly and decrepit.

[21]Brandt & Heck, *Effects of Air Pollutants on Vegetation*, 1 Air Pollution (2d ed. 1968).

[22]Our grandfathers' generation got around this difficulty by utilizing detachable collars, but this frugal custom has disappeared in the United States. It still survives, to some degree, in coal-burning London—where the celluloid "white collar" was once the universal badge of a clerical—and hence middle-class—job.

[23]*See* Lowrey, *The Climate of Cities,* Scientific American (Aug., 1967).

[24]This literature has been reviewed and summarized in the presentation "How Much is Air Pollution Costing Us?" by A. V. Kneese, National Conference on Air Pollution, in Washington, D.C., Dec. 12-14, 1966.

[25]The absurdity of this measure is clear if we note that according to it men are "worth" 70 per cent more than women at age 20, but men and women have equal expectations at age 60, with the relative values reversed by age 70. Again, by this measure, an individual is "worth" much more if he dies slowly and agonizingly in a hospital than if he dies at home in his sleep.

[26]The population explosion notwithstanding. Each individual only has one life to live, some threescore and ten years (give or take a few) in length.

[27]It is not impossible that the dollar benefits actually exceed the dollar costs, although this may seem a bit far-fetched at first.

[28]Of course, in principle, the reverse could also happen, which would be no less important (but with opposite implications) if true.

[29]In this context, the availability of assimilation capacity for residuals is a service rendered by the environment, for which an appropriate price should be paid, while the provision of unwanted residuals (such as soot or gaseous effluents) constitutes a disservice for which there should be a compensation corresponding to a negative price.

[30]Actually, it would necessarily be more expensive under the altered ground rules only *if* the present technology were the cheapest one available. This is probably not the case in most big cities, however, since nuclear plants are now cheaper than almost any existing fossil fuel plants, except where coal or oil is available locally. New facilities are overwhelmingly nuclear and if all doubts regarding safety and radioactive waste disposal were resolved, most existing fossil fuel plants in big cities would be replaced by nuclear power plants.

[31]Again, this refers to the fact that certain economic services rendered by the environment are exchanged at zero price, which would not be the case in a perfectly operating free competitive market.

[32]This problem is discussed in Ayres & Kneese, *Production, Consumption, and Externalities* to be published in The American Economic Review (1969).

[33]The best estimates are those by R. Ridker, Economic Costs of Air Pollution: Studies in Measurement (1965).

[34]Ridker, *Strategies for Measuring the Cost of Air Pollution*, The Economics of Air Pollution (1966).

[35]*Id.*

[36]The "discount rate" is equivalent to the average annual increase in value of alternative investments. To find the present value of a dollar-benefit to be received some years in the future one asks "what is the dollar amount which, if we invested it at 6-8%, would equal the specified amount at the appropriate time?"

[37]Notwithstanding the irreplaceable uniqueness of each personality and each soul.

[38]Since the person queried actually pays nothing to have his opinion recorded, he can make very extreme statements in the hope of indirectly influencing policy makers.

[39]As distinguished from *effects,* which are strictly physical.

[40]The most extreme example would be public ownership of all sources of pollution (which essentially means all productive facilities and all energy-converting devices). This eliminates externalities as such, by merging the producers and consumers into one unit, but it also eliminates competition—another important feature of the free market—and has a very serious problem with respect to its "internal" operation, including the question of allocation of resources. Thus public ownership essentially begs the question rather than solving it.

[41]Ayres & Kneese, *supra* note 32.

[42]Except as limited by *ad hoc* smoke control laws.

[43]A typical method is to ascribe entirely or mostly to pollution control a large capital investment which would have been made anyway. It takes a very alert and knowledgeable bureaucrat to detect this sort of cheating.

[44]However, it must be remembered that if hides had no market, they would be a disposal problem for meat packers; hence, the equilibrium market solution would involve an appropriate payment from the meat packers to the leather industry (in lieu of disposal costs), thus eliminating the need for a public subsidy, but probably raising the price of meat.

[45]*See* R. Ayres, *supra* note 8. For a more thorough exposition, *see* R. Ayres, Technology and Urban Transportation: Environmental Quality Considerations, to be published for Resources for the Future by Johns Hopkins University Press, 1969.

[46]This probably implies rental on a mileage basis in a manner analogous to the way Xerox copiers and electronic computers are rented currently. *See* R. Ayres, Technology and Urban Transportation, *supra* note 45.

Clean Air and Future Energy

E. F. SCHUMACHER

I have set myself the task to talk about my own subject, which is economics, and to study in particular how economics relates to the kind of thing in which the National Society for Clean Air is concerned, namely, the protection and conservation of the environment in which we live. I have been worried for some time about certain misunderstandings about the nature and relevance of economics, that seem to me to exist not only among laymen but also among many of the economists themselves, misunderstandings inimical to conservation. When the economist delivers a verdict to the effect that this or that activity is "uneconomic," two important and closely related questions arise: first, what does this verdict mean? And, second, is the verdict conclusive in the sense that practical action can reasonably be based on it?

Going back into history we may recall that when there was talk about founding a professorship for political economy at Oxford some 150 years ago, many people were by no means happy about the prospect. Edward Copleston, the great Provost of Oriel College, did not want to admit into the University's curriculum a science "so prone to usurp the rest"; even Henry Drummond Esq. of Albury Park, who endowed the professorship in 1825, felt it necessary to make it clear that he expected the University to keep the new study "in its proper place."[1] The

---

Source: Lecture given by E. F. Schumacher at the Annual Conference of the National Society for Clean Air in Blackpool, England, in October 1967. Reproduced by permission of the National Society for Clean Air and the author.

---

first professor, Nassau Senior, was certainly not to be kept in an *inferior* place. Immediately, in his inaugural lecture, he predicted that the new science "will rank in public estimation among the first of moral sciences in interest and in utility" and claimed that "the pursuit of wealth . . . is, to the mass of mankind, the great source of moral improvement."[2] Not all economists, to be sure, have staked their claims quite so high. John Stuart Mill (1806-1873) looked upon political economy "not as a thing by itself, but as a fragment of a greater whole; a branch of Social Philosophy, so interlinked with all the other branches that its conclusions, even in its own peculiar province, are only true conditionally, subject to interference and counteraction from causes not directly within its scope."[3] And the great John Maynard Keynes, some 80 years later, admonished us not to "overestimate the importance of the economic problem, or sacrifice to its supposed necessities other matters of greater and more permanent significance."[4]

Such voices, however, are but seldom heard today. It is hardly an exaggeration to say that, with increasing affluence, economics has moved into the very centre of public concern, and economic performance, economic growth, economic expansion, and so forth have become the abiding interest, if not the obsession, of all modern societies. In the current vocabulary of condemnation there are few words as final and conclusive as the word "uneconomic." If an activity has been branded as uneconomic, its right to existence is not merely questioned but energetically denied. Anything that is found to be an impediment to economic growth is a shameful thing, and if people cling to it, they are thought of as either saboteurs or fools. Call a thing immoral or ugly, soul-destroying or a degradation of man, a peril to the peace of the world or to the well-being of future generations; as long as you have not shown it to be "uneconomic" you have not really questioned its right to exist, grow and prosper.

But what does it *mean* when we say something is uneconomic? I am not asking what most people mean when they say this; because that is clear enough. They simply mean that it is like an illness: you are better off without it. The economist is supposed to be able to diagnose the illness and then, with luck and skill, remove it. Admittedly, economists often disagree among each other about the diagnosis and, even more frequently, about the cure; but that merely proves that the subject matter is uncommonly difficult and economists, like other humans, are fallible.

No, I am asking what *it* means, *what sort of meaning the method of economists actually produces.* And the answer to this question cannot be in doubt: something is uneconomic when it fails to earn an adequate profit in terms of money. The method of economics does not, and cannot, produce any other meaning. Numerous attempts have been made to obscure this fact, and they have caused a very great deal of confusion; but the fact remains. Society, or a group or individual within society, may decide to hang on to an activity or asset *for non-economic reasons*—social, aesthetic, moral or political—but this does in no way alter their *uneconomic character*. The judgment of economics, in other words, is an extremely *fragmentary* judgment; out of the large number of aspects which in real life have to be seen and judged together before a decision can be taken, economics supplies only one—whether a thing yields a money profit *to those who undertake it* or not.

Do not overlook the words "to those who undertake it." It is a great error to assume, for instance, that the methodology of economics is normally applied to determine whether an activity carried on by a group within society yields a profit to society as a whole. Even nationalized industries are not considered from this more comprehensive point of view. Every one of them is given a financial target—which is, in fact, an obligation[5]—and is expected to pursue this target without regard to any damage it might be inflicting on other parts of the economy. In fact, the prevailing creed, held with equal fervour by all political parties, is that the common goodwill necessarily be maximized if everybody, every industry and trade, whether nationalized or not, strives to earn an acceptable "return" on the capital employed. Not even Adam Smith had a more implicit faith in the "hidden hand" to ensure that "what is good for General Motors is good for the United States."

However that may be, about the *fragmentary* nature of the judgments of economics there can be no doubt whatever. Even within the narrow compass of the economic calculus, these judgments are necessarily and *methodically* narrow. For one thing, they give vastly more weight to the short than to the long term, because in the long term, as Keynes put it with cheerful brutality, we are all dead. And then, secondly, they are based on a definition of cost which excludes all "free goods," that is to say, the entire God-given environment, except for those parts of it that have been privately appropriated. This means that an activity can be economic although it plays hell with the environment, and that a competing activity, if at some cost it protects and conserves the environment, will be uneconomic.

Economics, moreover, deals with goods in accordance with their market value and not in accordance with what they really are. The same rules and criteria are applied to primary goods, which man has to win from nature, and secondary goods, which pre-suppose the existence of primary goods and are manufactured from them; and among primary goods no distinction is made between renewable and non-renewable goods, although from many points of view this is the most vital distinction of all. All goods are treated the same, because the point of view is fundamentally that of private profit making, and this means that it is inherent in the methodology of economics *to ignore man's dependence on the natural world.*

It is not surprising, therefore, that the idea of conservation has no home in economics. It is obviously an uneconomic idea, an impediment to the maximization of immediate profits. You may have noticed this in connection with the discovery of gas in the North Sea. In ministerial speeches and leading articles in *The Times* it was announced as an obvious and unquestionable truth that any failure to exploit this new power resource with the utmost speed and at the highest possible rate would be grossly uneconomic.

Now, there would be no need to enlarge on these points, if everyone were aware of the extreme narrowness of the base on which such judgments are built. Nor would there be any cause for criticism, for it is the acknowledged right of any specialist to specialize as narrowly as he wishes. The trouble is, however, that the words "economic" and "uneconomic" (as we have observed already) have acquired an infinitely wider meaning than they can legitimately claim: they are taken as almost synonymous with good and bad, or useful and useless.

It is a remarkable fact: the gloomy forebodings of the Oxford dons 150 years ago have come true—economics is indeed a science "so prone to usurp the rest." In spite of its palpable and obvious narrowness, it has been enthroned as universal judge. In spite of its specialization on private profit, verdicts are taken as equally applicable to the public interest. In spite of its concentration on the short term, which may be sufficient for the purposes of private persons, its doctrines are being applied to the affairs of nations whose life-spans are counted in centuries, if not millennia. Instead of using economics as a useful, if narrowly specialized, tool, modern society has embraced it as its primary religion, thereby laying itself open to dangers of an unprecendented kind.

It is obvious that the idea of conservation is more than ever in need of support, as the tempestuous advances of science and technology multiply the hazards. But as I said before, it is an uneconomic idea and has therefore no acknowledged place in a society under the dictatorship of economics. When it is occasionally introduced into the discussion, it tends to be treated not merely as a stranger but as an undesirable alien, probably dishonest and almost certainly immoral. In the past, when religion taught men to look upon Nature as God's handiwork, the idea of conservation was too self-evident to require special emphasis. But now that the religion of economics lends respectability to man's inborn envy and greed and Nature is looked upon as man's quarry to be used and abused without let or hindrance, what could be more important than an explicit theory of conservation? We teach our children that science and technology are the instruments for man's battle with nature, but forget to warn them that, being himself a part of nature, man could easily be on the losing side.

Modern economic thinking, as I have said, is peculiarly unable to consider the long term and to appreciate man's dependence on the natural world. It is therefore peculiarly defenceless against forces which produce a gradual and cumulative deterioration in the environment. Take the phenomenon of urbanization. It can be assumed that no-one moves from the countryside into the city unless he expects to gain a more or less immediate personal advantage therefrom. His move, therefore, is economic, and any measure to inhibit the move would be uneconomic. In particular, to make it worthwhile for him to stay in agriculture by means of tariffs or subsidies, would be grossly uneconomic. That it is done none the less is attributed to the irrationality of political pressures. But what about the irrationality of cities with millions of inhabitants? What about the cost, frustration, congestion and ill health of the modern monster city? Yes, indeed, these are problems to be looked at, but (we are told) they do not invalidate the doctrine that subsidized farming is grossly uneconomic.

It is not surprising, therefore, that all around us the most appalling malpractices and malformations are growing up, the growth of which is not being inhibited, because to do so would be uneconomic. Something like an explosion has to occur before warning voices are listened to, the voices of people who had been ridiculed for years and years as nostalgic, reactionary, unpractical and starry-eyed. No-one would apply these epithets today to those who for so many years had raised their voices against the heedless economism which has turned all large American cities into seedbeds of riots and civil war. Now that it is almost too late, popular comments are outspoken enough: "Throughout the U.S., the big cities are scarred by slums, hobbled by inadequate mass transportation, starved for sufficient finances, torn by racial strife, half-choked by polluted air." And yet: "The nation's urban population is expected to double by the beginning of the next century."[6] You might be tempted to ask, Why? The answer would come back: Because it would be uneconomic to attempt to resettle the rural areas. The American economist, John Kenneth Galbraith, has brilliantly shown how the conventional wisdom of economics produces the absurdity of "private opulence and public squalor."[7]

Other changes, equally destructive or even more so, are going on all around us, but they must not be talked about because to do so might cause alarm and even impede economic growth. All the same, we cannot claim that we have not been warned. For instance, in spite of enormous advances in medicine, on which we do not fail to congratulate ourselves, there is a relentless advance in the frequency of chronic illness. The U.S. Public Health Service states that "About 40.9 per cent of persons living in the United States were reported to have one or more chronic conditions. While some of these conditions were relatively minor, others were serious conditions such as heart disease, diabetes, or mental illness."[8] "We are exchanging health for mere survival," writes Lewis Herber in his comprehensive and invaluable book on *Our Synthetic Environment*. "We have begun to measure man's biological achievements, not in terms of his ability to live a vigorous, physically untroubled life, but in terms of his ability to preserve his mere existence in an increasingly distorted environment. Today, survival often entails ill health and rapid physical degeneration."[9] Even the achievements in prolonging life are not impressive, except for the very young. In America, the life expectancy of a white male aged 45 years has increased by only 2.9 years since 1900, and that of a 65-year-old man by only 1.2 years. Considering the enormous economic advances in America since the beginning of this century, these results are astonishingly small. "Almost any improvement in social conditions or medical techniques," comments Lewis Herber, "would have rescued large numbers of people from premature death and added substantially to their life span... Nevertheless, most of the increase in longevity is due to the fact that more children survive the diseases of infancy and adolescence today than two generations ago. What this means, in effect, is that if it weren't for the extraordinary medical advances and great improvements of the material conditions of life, today's adult might well have a much shorter life span than his grandparents had. This is a remarkable indication of failure."[10] At the same time, the expenditure on medical services in the United States now amounts to some 50,000 million dollars a year, or about *five dollars a week* for every man, woman, and child, on average.

It is not my purpose to investigate the causes of this extaordinary development. It is well known that the infectious diseases, which were the principal causes of death in 1900, have been reduced almost to vanishing point; but that deaths from the so-called degenerative diseases have greatly increased, particularly deaths from cancer, heart disease, and diabetes, involving increasing numbers of children and young adults. "Many individuals seem to be succumbing to degenerative diseases long before they reach the prime of life. Not only is cancer a leading cause of death in childhood and youth, but... many American males between 20 and 30 years of age are on the brink of a major cardiac disease... If diseases of this kind represent the normal deterioration of the body, then human biology is taking a patently abnormal turn. A large number of people are breaking down prematurely."[11] Deaths from infectious diseases are now so low that further medical advances in this field cannot have a large impact; yet the growth of the degenerative diseases continues. The time may not be far off when death rates overall start rising in the most "advanced" countries. The real costs of a deteriorating environment are heavy indeed.

Developments of this kind are invariably the result of imbalance and disharmony. In the blind pursuit of immediate monetary gains, modern man has not only divorced himself from nature by an excessive and hurtful degree of urbanization, he has also abandoned the idea of living in harmony with the myriad forms of plant and animal life on which his own survival depends; he has developed chemical substances which are unknown to nature and do not fit into her immensely complex system of checks and balances; many of them are extremely toxic, but he none the less applies them or discharges them into the environment, as if they would be out of action when they had fulfilled their specific purpose or could no longer be seen.

The religion of economics, at the same time, promotes an idolatry of rapid change, unaffected by the elementary truism that a change which is not an unquestionable improvement is a doubtful blessing. The burden of proof is placed on those who take the "ecological viewpoint": unless *they* can produce evidence of marked injury to man, the change will proceed. Common sense, on the contrary, would suggest that the burden of proof should lie on the man who wants to introduce a change; *he* has to demonstrate that there *cannot* be any damaging consequences. But this would take too much time, and would therefore be uneconomic. Ecology, indeed, ought to be a compulsory subject for all economists, whether professionals or laymen, as this might serve to restore at least a modicum of balance. For ecology holds:

> that an environmental setting developed over millions of years must be considered to have some merit. Anything so complicated as a planet, inhabited by more than a million and a half species of plants and animals,

> all of them living together in a more or less balanced equilibrium in which they continuously use and re-use the same molecules of the soil and air, cannot be improved by aimless and uninformed tinkering. All changes in a complex mechanism involve some risk and should be undertaken only after careful study of all the facts available. Changes should be made on a small scale first so as to provide a test before they are widely applied. When information is incomplete, changes should stay close to the natural processes which have in their favour the indisputable evidence of having supported life for a very long time.[12]

Of all the changes introduced by man into the household of nature, large-scale nuclear fission is undoubtedly the most dangerous and profound. As a result, ionizing radiation has become the most serious agent of pollution of the environment and the greatest threat to man's survival on earth. The attention of the layman, not surprisingly, has been captured by the atom bomb, although there is at least a chance that it may never be used again. The danger to humanity created by the so-called peaceful uses of atomic energy is hardly ever mentioned. There could indeed be no clearer example of the prevailing dictatorship of economics. Whether to build conventional power stations, based on coal or oil, or nuclear stations, is being decided solely on economic grounds, with perhaps a small element of regard for the "social consequences" that might arise from an over-speedy curtailment of the coal industry. But that nuclear stations represent an incredible, incomparable, and unique hazard for human life does not enter any calculation and is never mentioned. People whose business it is to judge hazards, the insurance companies, are not prepared to insure nuclear power stations anywhere in the world for third party risk, with the result that special legislation has had to be passed whereby the State accepts all liabilities.[13] Yet, insured or not, the hazard remains, and such is the thraldom of the religion of economics that the only question that appears to interest either governments or the public is whether "it pays."

It is not as if there were any lack of authoritative voices to warn us. The effects of alpha, beta, and gamma rays on living tissues are perfectly well known: the radiation particles are like bullets tearing into an organism, and the damage they do depends primarily on the dosage and the type of cells they hit.[14] As long ago as 1927, the American biologist, H. J. Muller, published his famous paper on genetic mutations produced by X-ray bombardment,[15] and since the early 'thirties the genetic hazard of exposure to ionizing radiation has been recognized also by non-geneticists.[16] It is clear that here is a hazard with a hitherto unexperienced "dimension," endangering not only those who might be directly affected by this radiation but their offspring as well for all future generations.

A new "dimension" of hazard is given also by the fact that while man now can—and does—create radioactive elements, there is nothing he can do to reduce their radioactivity once he has created them. No chemical reaction, no physical interference, only the passage of time reduces the intensity of radiation once it has been set going. Carbon-14 has a half-life of 5,900 years, which means that it takes nearly six thousand years for its radioactivity to decline to one-half of what it was before. The half-life of strontium-90 is 28 years. But whatever the length of the half-life, some radiation continues almost indefinitely, and there is nothing that can be done about it, except to try and put the radioactive substance into a safe place.

But what is a safe place, let us say, for the enormous amounts of radioactive waste products created by nuclear reactors? No place on earth can be shown to be safe. It was thought at one time that these wastes could safely be dumped into the deepest parts of the oceans, on the assumption that no life could subsist at such depths.[17] But this has since been disproved by Soviet deep-sea exploration. Wherever there is life, radioactive substances are absorbed into the biological cycle. Within hours of depositing these materials in water, the great bulk of them can be found in living organisms. Plankton, algae, and many sea animals have the power of concentrating these substances by a factor of 1,000 and in some cases even a million. As one organism feeds on another, the radioactive materials climb up the ladder of life and find their way back to man.[18]

No international agreement has yet been reached on waste disposal. The conference of the International Atomic Energy

Organization at Monaco, 16th to 21st November, 1959, ended in disagreement, mainly on account of the violent objections raised by the majority of countries against the American and British practice of disposal into the oceans.[19] "High level" wastes continue to be dumped into the sea, while large quantities of so-called "intermediate" and "low-level" wastes are discharged into rivers or directly into the ground. An A.E.C. report observes laconically that the liquid wastes "work their way slowly into ground water, leaving all or part [sic!] of their radioactivity held either chemically or physically in the soil."[20]

The most massive wastes are, of course, the nuclear reactors themselves after they have become unserviceable. There is a lot of discussion on the trivial economic question of whether they will last for 20, 25, or 30 years. No-one discusses the humanly vital point that they cannot be dismantled and cannot be shifted but have to be left standing where they are, probably for centuries, perhaps for thousands of years, an active menace to all life, silently leaking radioactivity into air, water and soil. No-one has considered the number and location of these satanic mills which will relentlessly accumulate in these crowded islands, so that, after a generation or two, there will be no habitation in Britain outside the "sphere of influence" of one or more of them. Earthquakes, of course, are not supposed to happen, nor wars, nor civil disturbances, nor riots like those that infested American cities. Disused nuclear power stations will stand as unsightly monuments to unquiet man's assumption that nothing but tranquility, from now on, stretches before him, or else—that the future counts as nothing compared with the slightest economic gain now.

Meanwhile, a number of authorities are engaged in defining "maximum permissible concentrations" (MPC's) and "maximum permissible levels" (MPL's) for various radioactive elements. The MPC purports to define the quantity of given radioactive substance that the human body can be allowed to accumulate. But it is known that *any* accumulation produces biological damage. "Since we don't know that these effects can be completely recovered from," observes the U.S. Naval Radiological Laboratory, "we have to fall back on an arbitrary decision about how much we will put up with; i.e. what is 'acceptable' or 'permissible'—not a scientific finding, but an administrative decision."[21] We can hardly be surprised when men of outstanding intelligence and integrity, like Albert Schweitzer, refuse to accept such administrative decisions with equanimity: "Who has given them the right to do this? Who is even entitled to give such a permission?"[22] The history of these decisions is, to say the least, disquieting. The British Medical Research Council noted some 12 years ago that

> The maximum permissible level of strontium-90 in the human skeleton, accepted by the International Commission on Radiological Protection, corresponds to 1,000 micro-micro-curies per gramme of calcium (=1,000 S.U.). But this is the maximum permissible level for adults in special occupations and is not suitable for application to the population as a whole or to the children with their greater sensitivity to radiation.[23]

A little later, the MPC for strontium-90, as far as the general population was concerned, was reduced by 90 per cent and then by another third, to 67 S.U. Meanwhile, the MPC for workers in nuclear plants was raised to 2,000 S.U.[24]

We must be careful, however, not to get lost in the jungle of controversy that has grown up in this field. The point is that very serious hazards have already been created by the "peaceful uses of atomic energy," affecting not merely the people alive today but all future generations, although so far nuclear energy is being used only on a statistically insignificant scale. The real development is yet to come, on a scale which few people are capable of imagining. If this is really going to happen, there will be a continuous traffic of radioactive substances from the "hot" chemical plants to the nuclear stations and back again; from the stations to waste processing plants; and from there to disposal sites. The slightest accident, whether during transport or production, can cause a major catastrophe; and the radiation levels throughout the world will rise relentlessly from generation to generation. Unless all living geneticists are in error, there will be an equally relentless, though no doubt somewhat delayed, increase in the number of harmful mutations. K. Z. Morgan, of the Oak Ridge Laboratory, emphasizes that the damage can be very subtle, a deterioration of all kinds of organic qualities, such as mobility, fertility, and the efficiency of sensory organs. "If a small dose has any effect at all at any stage in the life cycle of an organism, then chronic radiation at this level can be more damaging that a single massive dose... Finally, stress and changes in mutation rates may be produced even when there is no immediately obvious effect on survival of irradiated individuals."[25]

Leading geneticists have given their warnings that everything possible should be done to avoid an increase in mutation rates;[26] leading medical men have insisted that the future of nuclear energy must depend primarily on researches into radiation biology which are as yet still totally incomplete;[27] leading physicists have suggested that "measures much less heroic than building... nuclear reactors" should be tried to solve the problem of future energy supplies—a problem which is in no way acute at present;[28] and leading students of strategic and political problems, at the same time, have warned us that there is really no hope of preventing the proliferation of the atom bomb, if there is a spread of plutonium capacity, such as was "spectacularly launched by President Eisenhower in his 'atoms for peace' proposals of 8th December, 1953."[29]

Yet all these weighty opinions play no part in the debate on whether we should go immediately for a large "second nuclear programme" or stick a bit longer to the conventional fuels which, whatever may be said for or against them, do not involve us in entirely novel and admittedly incalculable risks. None of them are even mentioned: the whole argument, which may vitally affect the very future of the human race, is conducted exclusively in terms of immediate economic advantage, as if two rag and bone merchants were trying to agree to a quantity discount.

I wonder how Dr. Des Voeux would have reacted to such an absurdly improbable situation. What, after all, is the fouling of air with smoke compared with the pollution of air, water, and soil, with ionizing radiation? Not that I wish in any way to belittle the evils of conventional air and water pollution; but we must recognize "dimensional differences" when we encounter them; radioactive pollution is an evil of incomparably greater "dimension" than anything mankind has known before. One might even ask: what is the point of insisting on clean air, if the air is laden with radioactive particles? And even if the air could be protected, what is the point of it, if soil and water are being poisoned?

Even an economist might well ask: What is the point of economic progress, a so-called higher standard of living, when the earth, the only earth we have, is being contaminated by substances which may cause malformations in our children or grandchildren? Have we learned nothing from the thalidomide tragedy? Can we deal with matters of such a basic character by means of bland assurances or official admonitions that "in the absence of proof that [this or that innovation] is in any way deleterious, it would be the height of irresponsibility to raise a public alarm"?[30] Can we deal with them simply on the basis of a short-term profitability calculation?

"It might be thought," wrote Leonard Beaton, "that all the resources of those who fear the spread of nuclear weapons would have been devoted to heading off these developments for as long as possible. The United States, the Soviet Union and Britain might be expected to have spent large sums of money trying to prove that conventional fuels, for example, had been underrated as a source of power . . . In fact . . . the efforts which have followed must stand as one of the most inexplicable political fantasies in history. Only a social psychologist could hope to explain why the possessors of the most terrible weapons in history have sought to spread the necessary industry to produce them . . . Fortunately, . . . power reactors are still fairly scarce."[31] In fact, a prominent American nuclear physicist, A. W. Weinberg, has given some sort of explanation: "There is," he says, "an understandable drive on the part of men of good will to build up the positive aspects of nuclear energy simply because the negative aspects are so distressing." But he also adds the warning that "there are very compelling personal reasons why atomic scientists sound optimistic when writing about their impact on world affairs. Each of us must justify to himself his preoccupation with instruments of nuclear destruction (and even we reactor people are only slightly less beset with such guilt than are our weaponeering colleagues)."[32]

Our instinct of self-preservation, one should have thought, would make us immune to the blandishments of guilt-ridden scientific optimism or the unproved promises of pecuniary advantages. "It is not too late at this point for us to reconsider old decisions and make new ones," says a recent American commentator. "For the moment at least, the choice is available."[33] Once many more centres of radioactivity have been created, there will be no more choice, whether we can cope with the hazards or not.

It is clear that certain scientific and technological advances of the last 30 years have produced, and are continuing to produce, hazards of an altogether intolerable kind. At the Fourth National Cancer Conference in America in September, 1960, Lester Breslow of the California State Department of Public Health reported that tens of thousands of trout in western hatcheries suddenly acquired liver cancers, and continued thus:

> Technological changes affecting man's environment are being introduced at such a rapid rate and with so little control that it is a wonder man has thus far escaped the type of cancer epidemic occurring this year among the trout.[34]

To mention these things, no doubt, means laying oneself open to the charge of being against science, technology, and progress. Let me therefore, in conclusion, add a few words about future scientific research. Man cannot live without science and technology any more than he can live against nature. What needs the most careful consideration, however, is the *direction* of scientific research. We cannot leave this to the scientists alone. As Einstein himself said,[35] "almost all scientists are economically completely dependent" and "the number of scientists who possess a sense of social responsibility is so small" that they cannot determine the direction of research. The latter dictum applies, no doubt, to all specialists, and the task therefore falls to the intelligent layman, to people like those who form the National Society for Clean Air and other, similar societies concerned with *Conservation.* They must work on public opinion, so that the politicians, depending on public opinion, will free themselves from the thraldom of economism and attend to the things that really matter. What matters, as I said, is the *direction* of research, that the direction should be towards non-violence rather than violence; towards an harmonious co-operation with nature rather than a warfare against nature; towards the noiseless, low-energy, elegant and economical solutions of our immature sciences.

The continuation of scientific advance in the direction of ever increasing violence, culminating in nuclear fission and moving on to nuclear fusion, is a prospect of terror threatening the abolition of man. Yet it is not written in the stars that this must be the direction. There is also a life-giving and life-enhancing possibility, the conscious exploration and cultivation of all relatively non-violent, harmonious, organic methods of co-operating with that enormous, wonderful, incomprehensible system of God-given nature, of which we are a part and which we certainly have not made ourselves.

References

[1] *Cf.* A. Dwight Culler, *The Imperial Intellect*, Yale University Press, 1955, p. 250.
[2] Nassau Senior, *An Introductory Lecture on Political Economy*, delivered before the University of Oxford on the 6th of December, 1826, London, 1827, pp. 1 and 12.
[3] John Stuart Mill, *Autobiography*, 1924 ed., pp. 165-6.
[4] John Maynard Keynes, *Essays in Persuasion*, London, 1933, p. 373.
[5] *Cf. The Financial and Economic Obligations of the Nationalised Industries*, Command, 1337, H.M.S.O., London, 1961.
[6] *Time*, Aug. 26, 1966, p. 11.
[7] John Kenneth Galbraith, *The Affluent Society*, Penguin, 1962, p. 211.
[8] U.S. Public Health Service, Health Statistics from the *U.S. National Health Survey*, Series C, No. 5, Washington, D.C., 1961, p.1.
[9] Lewis Herber, *Our Synthetic Environment*, London, 1963, pp. 198-9.
[10] *Ibid.* pp. 197-98.
[11] *Ibid.* pp. 8-9; *Medical Tribune*, Vol. 2, No. 29 (1961), p. 16.
[12] Ralph and Mildred Buchsbaum, *Basic Ecology*, Pittsburgh, 1957, p. 20. (Quoted by Herber, *op. cit.*).
[13] *Cf.* C. T. Highton, "Die Haftung für Strahlenschäden in Grossbritannien," *Die Atomwirtschaft, Zeitschrift für wirtschaftliche Fragen der Kernumwandlung*, 1959, p. 539.
[14] *Cf.* Jack Schubert and Ralph Lapp: *Radiation: What it Is and How it Affects You*, New York, 1957. Also Hans Marquardt and Gerhard Schubert, *Die Strahlengefährdung des Menschen durch Atomenergie*, Hamburg, 1959. And Volume XI of *Proceedings* of the International Conference on the Peaceful Uses of Atomic Energy, Geneva, 1955; and Volume XXII of *Proceedings* of the Second United Nations International Conference on the Peaceful Uses of Atomic Energy, Geneva, 1958.
[15] *Cf.* H. J. Muller, "Changing Genes: Their Effects on Evolution," in *Bulletin of the Atomic Scientists*, Chicago, 1947.

[16] *Cf.* Statement by G. Failla, Hearings before the Special Subcommittee on Radiation, of the Joint Committee on Atomic Energy, 86th Congress of the United States, May 5-8, 1959, *Fallout from Nuclear Weapons*. Washington, D.C., 1959, Vol. II, p. 1577.

[17] R. Revelle and M. B. Schaefer, "Oceanic Research Needed for Safe Disposal of Radioactive Wastes at Sea"; and V. G. Bogorov and E. M. Kreps, "Concerning the Possibility of Disposing of Radioactive Waste in Ocean Trenches." Both in Vol. XVIII of *Proceedings*, Geneva Conference 1958 (see Note 14 above).

[18] *Ibid.*, B. H. Ketchum and V. T. Bowen, "Biological Factors determining the Distribution of Radioisotopes in the Sea," pp. 429-33.

[19] Conference Report by H. W. Levi, in *Die Atomwirtschaft*, 1960, pp. 57 *et. seq.*

[20] U.S. Atomic Energy Commission, Annual Report to Congress, Washington, D.C., 1960, p. 344.

[21] U.S. Naval Radiological Defence Laboratory Statement, in *Selected Materials on Radiation Protection Criteria and Standards, their Basis and Use*, p. 464. (Quoted by Herber, *op. cit.*)

[22] Albert Schweitzer, *Friede oder Atomkrieg*, 1958, p. 13.

[23] British Medical Research Council, *The Hazards to Man of Nuclear and Allied Radiations*, p. 68. (Quoted by Herber, *op. cit.*)

[24] Lewis Herber, *op. cit.*, p. 181.

[25] K. Z. Morgan, "Summary and Evaluation of Environmental Factors that must be considered in the Disposal of Radioactive Wastes," in *Industrial Radioactive Disposal*, Vol. 3, p. 2378 (Quoted by Herber, *op. cit.* p. 193.).

[26] *Cf.* H. Marquardt, "Natürliche und künstliche Erbänderungen," *Probleme der Mutationsforschung*, Hamburg, 1957, p. 161.

[27] *Cf.* Schubert and Lapp, *op. cit.*

[28] A. M. Weinberg, "Today's Revolution," in *Bulletin of the Atomic Scientists*, Chicago, 1956.

[29] Leonard Beaton, *Must the Bomb Spread?* Penguin Books in association with the Institute of Strategic Studies, London, 1966, p. 88.

[30] W. O. Caster, "From Bomb to Man," in *Fallout*, ed. by John M. Fowler, New York, 1960, pp. 48-9.

[31] *Op. cit.*, pp. 88-90.

[32] *Op. cit.*, pp. 299 & 302.

[33] Walter Schneir, "The Atom's Poisonous Garbage," in *Reporter*, March 17, 1960, p. 22 (Quoted by Herber, *op. cit.*, p. 194.)

[34] Lewis Herber, *op. cit.*, p. 152.

[35] Albert Einstein, *On Peace*, ed. by O. Nathan and H. Norden, with a Preface by Bertrand Russell, New York, 1960, pp. 455-6.

The Effects of Air Pollution on Health

A. J. de VILLIERS

A discussion of health effects should be based on an understanding, however incomplete, of the fundamental meaning of "health". It may be pertinent, therefore, to reflect that the very process of living is characterized by the interplay between the individual and the stresses to be found in his external environment. To "counterbalance" these stresses, highly complex physiological or internal adaptive mechanisms are evoked in order to maintain an optimal equilibrium (or homeostasis). Fitness or "health" of the individual depends, therefore, on the effectiveness of these counterbalancing forces. Maladjustment, on the other hand, may lead, as Hatch[1] pointed out in his concept of the multiple factors in the etiology of disease (Fig. 1), to failure of the normal defences, disturbed function, disease and/or death.

Our total environment does not remain constant but is in a continual state of change: a state influenced increasingly by man's rapidly-growing technology, the harnessing of all forms of energy and the development and use of our natural resources.

Associated with these changes, and those in medical science and technology which accompanied them, is a changing pattern and distribution of health effects or diseases. By reducing

---

Source: A. J. de Villiers, "The Effects of Air Pollution on Health", *Occupational Health Review*, Vol. 20, No. 3-4, 1968-69, pp. 25-44. Minor deletions in the original text have been made. This article will also appear as part of the Banff Conference on Pollution Proceedings, to be published by Pergamon Press. Reprinted by permission of the publishers and author.

---

the toll of the acute diseases, for example, we have increased the life-expectancy of man, but in doing so, we have increased the incidence of the chronic degenerative diseases among the elderly. The early emphasis on the single or relatively simple predo-

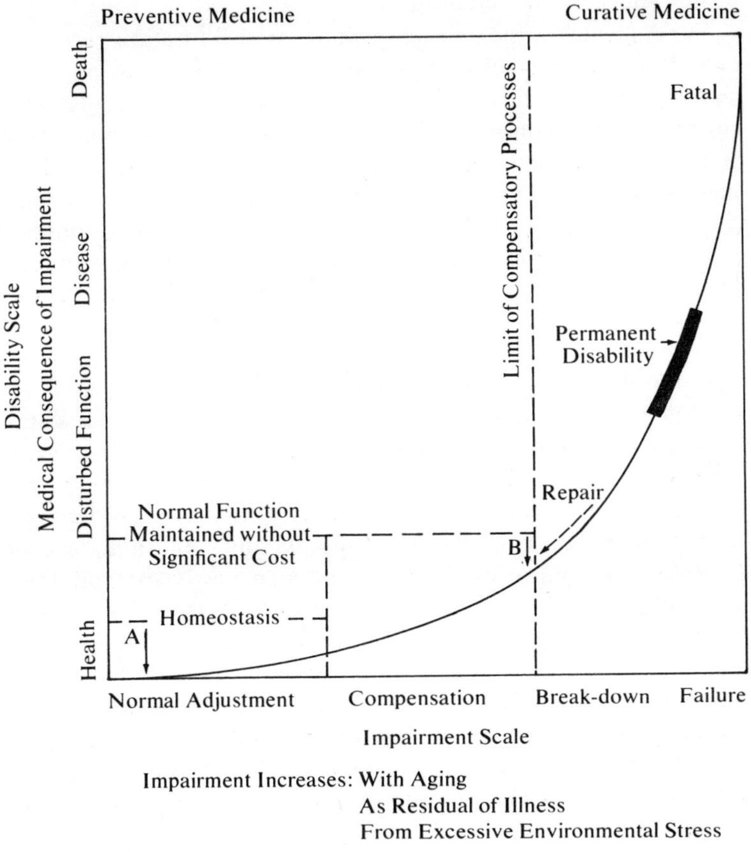

Fig. 1. Multifactor relationships in the etiology of disease

minant causes of illness and death, such as the pneumococci and the tubercle bacilli—the two leading causes of death at the turn of the century—has shifted to diseases of multiple causation exemplified by the chronic cardiovascular-respiratory diseases and malignant neoplasms. These are the leading causes of death on the North American continent today and also those affecting the target organs involved in the conflict between man and the noxious elements in his atmospheric environment. They are, therefore, of central interest to our discussion of the health effects of air pollution.

Fundamental to these developments are the questions: to what extent the chronic respiratory diseases are becoming manifest as a normal uncontrollable accompaniment of the aging process; to what extent the quality of the air in our larger cities may significantly influence the occurrence of deaths, the development of sickness and shorten the life expectancy of urban dwellers. In more practical terms—to what extent may polluted air be responsible for the toll taken in terms of human misery by chronic ill health which places an enormous burden on the economy of the country, in cost of medical care and lost national productivity caused by absenteeism and disablement.

To establish the significance of a pollution-effect relationship, it would be necessary to demonstrate excess risk, a dose-response relationship, consistency of the association and, where possible, the production of similar effects in susceptible experimental animals. This has been difficult where human populations are exposed to community air pollution, largely because of an imprecise, cumbersome and costly methodology and the presence of a multiplicity of factors operating at very low doses and dose rates. Specific pollutants in low concentrations do not often exceed the threshold limits established as guidelines for use in industry. At such low dose rates, discernible biological or health effects may not become apparent for long periods of time. Furthermore, most of the information available to date has been reported in terms of the general factor "urban pollution". This factor comprises the effects of individual pollutants or their combinations, the effects of greater population density with the consequent greater incidence and likelihood of respiratory infections, and other less specific urban factors. These are, in addition, complicated by various occupational, climatic and personal pollution (or smoking) factors and the problems of additivity, enhancement (synergism) or the development of tolerance.

Normal Defence Mechanisms and Results of Failure

Before discussing the known health effects of air pollution, it would be of interest to review briefly some of the basic processes involved in the interplay between the atmospheric environment and the internal environment of man.

Air normally contains approximately 20% oxygen, 80% nitrogen, with trace amounts of other gases, of which carbon dioxide (0.3%) is the most important. Suspended in air are particulates and droplets dispersed from natural sources or by man's industries and activities. Relatively clean air may contain up to 70,000 particles per cubic foot, but counts vary depending on the environment and nature of industry or activity. The atmosphere of our cities may contain a large number of added liquids, gases and solids as by-products of combustion processes and chemical reactions in the air. The quality and quantity of "pollutants" added in this manner is directly proportional to the amount and type of fuel burnt, the efficiency of the combustion process, the size of the community, the density of housing, industry, and motor vehicle traffic, and is notably influenced also by topographic and meteorologic factors (inversion, etc.).

The average man moves approximately 8,000 litres of air in and out of his lungs per day in order to provide for the exchange of gases (O_2 and CO_2) necessary to sustain life. Much of the particulate and droplet material, together with minute quantities of gases absorbed onto it or dissolved in it, may be deposited in the respiratory tract. The amounts so deposited will depend upon the particle size of the aerosols, the concentration to be found in the air and the duration of exposure. Particles below 1 micron usually penetrate the deep lung regions. In this way, toxic materials dissolved in, or absorbed onto, aerosols may reach the deep portions of the lung where they may exert deleterious effects over a potentially vast lung surface area.

Under ordinary circumstances, the cleansing mechanisms of the lungs are highly efficient. The larger solid particles and droplets are screened out by nasal hair or the mucous secretions of the upper respiratory tract. Particles which reach and are deposited in the deeper portions of the lungs are normally conveyed towards the throat—where they are swallowed or expectorated. A continuously moving blanket of mucus acts as a conveyor-belt for deposited material and is, in turn, propelled by the hair-like processes ("cilia") characteristic of the cells lining the air passages. This movement is facilitated by respiratory excursions, coughing and sneezing. Particles may also be engulfed and removed by scavenger or phagocytic cells or remain embedded in the interstitial tissues of the lungs. It is only when these defenses are damaged or overwhelmed by high concentrations and/or repeated exposure to deleterious substances that changes or deviations from the physiological or normal occur.

The biological effects vary, depending upon the severity of the insult or of subsequent and repeated insults and a number of individual susceptibility or host factors. These may manifest themselves as local irritation and inflammation of the air passages; injury to the lining cells of the alveoli and the underlying vasculature causing pulmonary edema and predisposing to invasion by pathogenic micro-organisms; reversible bronchial constriction; or as biochemical lesions which may result in the morphological or pathological manifestations of fibrosis, destruction of tissue (as in emphysema) or cell mutation or neoplasia. These effects can be elicited by a bewildering range of substances to be found in the atmospheric environment.

Measurable Air Pollution Health Effects

To understand the measurable effects of pollution on health, we need to distinguish between effects on the natural development of chronic respiratory disease in the previously healthy individual, and the effects of polluted atmospheres on the health status of the individuals with an altered threshold of reaction; notably, the individual with an already existing chronic respiratory or cardiac disease. These aspects are embodied in the suggestion made by Anderson[2] on the basis of accumulated epidemiological evidence that the measurable effects of air pollution should be considered to operate in seven stages as listed in Table I. These stages are consistent with the multiple factor etiology, referred to earlier, and provide a convenient structure for the consideration of health effects in relation to the different types and intensities of polluted atmospheres.

Table I: Stages in the measurable effects of air pollution on health[2]

Stage 0	No measurable effect
Stage 1	Awareness of pollution at a level sufficient to lead individuals to change residence or place of employment
Stage 2	Reversible alteration in physiological functions
Stage 3	Untoward symptoms of bodily dysfunction
Stage 4	Irreversible alteration in vital physiological functions
Stage 5	Chronic disease
Stage 6	Acute sickness or death in debilitated persons
Stage 7	Acute sickness or death in healthy persons

Generally, two major types of community air pollution occur —a *"reducing" form* consisting largely of soot, fly ash, other material and sulphur dioxide—an atmosphere characteristic of London-type "smog"; and an *oxidising form* containing carbon monoxide, hydrocarbons and photochemical decomposition products such as oxides of nitrogen, ozone, peroxyacetyl nitrate and olefine characteristic of the Los Angeles-type "smog". The combustion of sulphur-containing fossil fuels for industrial and domestic purposes largely contributes to the former, and automotive exhausts in association with an abundance of sunlight to the latter. Various mixtures of these predominant types may occur but it is essential to note, from the health point of view, that the quality and quantity of pollutants in the atmosphere may vary from city to city or region to region, each of these delimitations constituting its own kind of local ecosystem.

Effects of Reducing-type Atmospheres: The most dramatic effects of pollution have been reported in association with the reducing types of atmospheric pollution. These effects are examples of Anderson's stages six and seven and include the well-known episodes or *disasters*. Characteristically, these episodes occurred during the fall or winter months, in the Northern temperate zones; and unusually high concentrations of pollutants were associated with certain meteorological or inversion conditions. These conditions usually lasted three to five days with effects attributable to the smog following after an initial delay of one to two days.

*Table II: Air pollution episodes**

Date		Place	Attributed Mortality
February	1880	London, England	1000
December	1930	Meuse Valley, Belgium	63
October	1948	Donora, Pennsylvania	20
November	1950	Poza Rica, Mexico	22
December	1952	London, England	4000
November	1953	New York	220[4]
January	1956	London, England	1000
December	1957	London, England	700-800
December	1962	London, England	700
January	1963	New York	300[5]
November	1966	New York	168

**Adapted from Anderson*[3]

The first documented fatal fog occurred during the week of February 7, 1880. During the week of the fog, deaths due to diseases of the respiratory organs rose to exceed the corrected weekly averages of the previous two weeks by 1118.[3]

By far the best known episode, however, was the disaster that hit London in December 1952.[6,7] The cause of this disaster was a temperature inversion which occurred over the southeastern part of England. It lasted four days and was particularly severe in the London area. During these four days, a number of people became acutely ill and died. So many were affected that it resulted in an excess over expected mortality of approximately 4,000 deaths. The majority of these deaths, and the greatest number of illnesses, occurred among the elderly and in those with preexisting cardiorespiratory diseases or disabilities (Stage 6 effect). Deaths due to pneumonia and bronchitis increased almost four- and ten-fold, respectively, over those of the previous week. Smog analyses revealed increases of the sulphur dioxide and particulate levels several orders of magnitude over those previously reported. Despite these increased concentrations, however, the general levels of these pollutants, observed during the episode, were not such that conventional toxicologic data would have predicted the resulting illnesses and deaths.

As an hypothesis, Amdur[8] suggested that the air pollution effects were due probably to a potentiation of the toxic propensities of sulphur dioxide (converted to sulphuric acid in the presence of fog droplets and catalysts) which had penetrated the deep-lung regions, dissolved in or attached to submicronic particles in the fog aerosol. This suggestion has been supported in part by the observation during more recent episodes, that the lesser severity of the later episodes appeared to correlate well with the much more marked reduction in the particulate content (over that of the sulphur dioxide concentrations), achieved since the implementation of the Clean Air Act in Great Britain. However, a consideration of sulphur dioxide and particulates alone in relation to the health effects of the above episodes, undoubtedly over-simplifies the problem and it will remain to be seen what other pollutants (including various catalytic substances) may be implicated in the future. It is interesting to note, nevertheless, that advance warning, based on these measurements of increased levels of pollution, may also have helped to reduce the mortality in the later episodes. During the 1962 episode, for example, cardio-respiratory patients were specifically advised to remain indoors.

The Meuse Valley incident occurred during the first six days of December 1930. A heavy mist lay over this industrialized valley in Belgium and became particularly severe on the second day when illnesses started to occur. It was estimated that several thousand illnesses occurred; there were sixty deaths. Again, as in other disasters associated with this kind of pollution, the illnesses and deaths attributed to the fog occurred chiefly among the elderly and those with pre-existing heart or lung disease.

A combination of industrial effluent, topographic and meteorologic factors was also responsible for the 1948 episode in Donora,[9] a small town on the Monongahela River south of Pittsburgh, Pennsylvania. The fog lasted about six days and, as in the other disasters, excess fatalities were among the elderly and debilitated. A large number of presumably normal individuals were also affected as it was estimated that 6,000 of the 13,000 residents were affected by the fog, with a case fatality rate of 3.33 per 1,000 cases.[10] Post-mortem examination suggested that the deaths were due to asphyxia caused by changes in the stiffness of the lungs, brought about by an inflammatory response to the irritant aerosol. In discussing this, Anderson has suggested that a "smog disease" may indeed exist as an entity among respiratory cripples in heavily polluted urban areas.

The Poza Rica, Mexico, incident occurred in 1950 and was due to a coincident but accidental release of hydrogen sulphide at the time of severe atmospheric inversion conditions. It is listed and discussed as an air pollution episode but should, perhaps, more appropriately be considered as accidental pollution by a more specific chemical agent. The comparatively brief period of the episode, nevertheless, claimed 22 lives; 320 persons were hospitalized (Stage 7 effect).

Apart from these excesses of death during pollution episodes, positive correlations between an urban factor including, of course, air quality, with *mortality* and a number of causes of death, have now been well established. Earlier studies described the excess urban over rural deaths in the United Kingdom, as well as the association among city dwellers of an increased risk of lung cancer presumed to be related to the carcinogenic polycyclic hydrocarbons present in urban atmospheres.[11] A long-term study of the relationships between residents, occupations and smoking habits and the mortality from chronic diseases among Canadian veterans[12] has also indicated a higher death rate among those persons who had lived five or more years in a city with a ratio of 1:12. This association between urban residents and mortality rates in excess of those of rural residents was independent of smoking habits. The urban-rural ratio in the above study for lung cancer mortality was 1.5. In the United States, Manos,[13] reviewing mortality for 163 areas in the United States for the years 1949-51 inclusive, by degrees of urbanization, was also able to demonstrate the association of an urban factor and an urban-rural gradient in association with an increased incidence of lung cancer and a number of other disease categories. In a later work, Manos and Fisher[14] reported a high frequency of positive correlations between a number of different indices of air pollution, taking into account also city characteristics, and socio-economic factors, and the following causes of death: malignant neoplasms of the esophagus and stomach; trachea, bronchus and lung; arteriosclerotic heart disease, including coronary disease; and chronic endocarditis, not specified as rheumatic. They pointed out, however, that more critical tests would be required before assuming a definite causal relationship.

Much of the demonstrated excess of mortality may be due to a *higher frequency or prevalence* of respiratory diseases occurring under higher intensity pollution conditions in certain urban communities. Many investigators, using a standard respiratory questionnaire in conjunction with simple lung function tests, have been able to demonstrate significant relationships between the prevalence of chronic respiratory diseases and urban pollution (Stage 5 effect). There is also some evidence that the prevalence is directly related to the intensity of pollution and the size of the community. At lower levels of pollution, as found in the smaller communities in North America, however, the differences between relative pollution levels may not always be large enough to demonstrate an effect on the frequency distributions of these diseases or overcome the overwhelming influence of such added variables as personal pollution or smoking.

The findings of the Windsor-Detroit health study[15] carried out under the aegis of the International Joint Commission during the years 1951-54, were inconclusive for the above and other reasons. In this study, the sickness incidence was compared between each sample of 200 randomly-selected families in each high and low pollution area defined for the purpose of the study on either side of the border. These families were interviewed on a bi-weekly basis during the period of the study in order to obtain the necessary sickness information. While some health effect was demonstrated on the Detroit side, where sickness rates were generally at a higher level in the more polluted area, the study, on the whole, was inconclusive. Some of the reasons for this became clear during the course of the study. In the Windsor area, for example, the high pollution area did not have consistently high pollution readings and when pollution levels increased, a concomitant increase in pollution level occurred in the low pollution area.

Bates[16] discussed differences in the severity of bronchial disease among a group of Canadian veterans resident in the four Canadian cities Toronto, Winnipeg, Montreal and Halifax, and indicated that the cases from Winnipeg, by far the cleanest of the cities in respect of industrial dustfall and SO_2 levels, appeared to be less severe than the groups from the other three cities. Caution was, however, expressed about the possible influence of medical treatment and climatic factors, as well as the adequacy of the air quality information available at the time of the study.

Ferris and Anderson[17] studied the prevalence of respiratory disease in Berlin, New Hampshire, a moderately polluted city and later made comparisons[18] with that observed in Chilliwack, B.C., a city of comparable size. Chilliwack had a much lower dustfall and sulphur dioxide pollution exposure during the period of the study (ratios of 6.6 and 10.0, respectively[19]), and comparisons made indicated a tendency towards a slightly lower respiratory disease prevalence than in Berlin, N.H., but the differences were small.

In his recent review of the subject, Ferris[20] compared the New Hampshire findings with those of the United Kingdom and found that the U. S. prevalence was very similar to that of rural England. However, while an age gradient could be demonstrated to occur for various symptoms in the United Kingdom, this could only be demonstrated for the symptom breathlessness in New Hampshire, suggesting that the type of response or health effect may differ in quality. When comparing the symptom groupings, simple bronchitis and complex bronchitis, it was clearly demonstrated that with increasing levels of pollution, more severe effects were to be found. Simple bronchitis refers to chronic phlegm production whereas complex bronchitis includes, in addition, some evidence of breathlessness and a period of increased cough or phlegm, lasting at least three weeks for two or more winters.

From the clinical point of view, real differences appear to exist. The findings of Reid[21] and others suggest that there is a higher incidence of recurrent disabling chest infections or so-called complex bronchitis in England than in the United States. Further, when the mortality rate due to chronic bronchitis in Great Britain was compared with that in Denmark,[22] it was found that the rate for Denmark was only 1/6 of that for the rural areas of Great Britain and that in Denmark, rural-urban differences could not be demonstrated.

Of considerable interest in these studies, then, is the fact that the biological effects may differ qualitatively and quantitatively from region to region and country to country. Chronic respiratory disease is much more evident in England than the United States. Men between the ages of 45 and 54, for example, living in Britain have five times the death rate for certain chronic respiratory disease and twice the lung cancer death rate, as compared with those in North America.

Some of the above differences, as seen earlier, are attributable to higher pollution levels in the United Kingdom, and some are undoubtedly due to differences in diagnosis—chronic bronchitis having been more commonly quoted as a cause of death in England. In the United States, the chronic respiratory disease component of the individual's cause of death often appears with emphasis on emphysema as a contributory cause of death only. Dean[23] pointed to another possible factor when he suggested that the British-born migrant carries with him a greater liability to lung cancer or to be deleteriously affected by factors in his ambient air environment. He also carries with him his smoking habits.

Other approaches to the establishment of positive correlations between pollution and health have included the use of such indices as the *utilisation of medical services*, the *day-by-day reporting of untoward symptoms*, and the study of special indicator or sensitive population groups (such as panels of chronic bronchitics, asthmatics, school children and identical twins) and *pulmonary function studies*. Positive correlations have, for example, been established between peaks in SO_2 concentrations and the particulate content of the atmosphere and hospital admissions and/or the occurrence of certain symptoms [24,25] (Stage 3 effect) among exposed populations. Minor ventilatory function changes have also been described among normal (Stage 2 effect) and chronic respiratory disease subjects exposed to a variety of environmental factors.[26] Previous studies have correlated the incidence of asthmatic attacks among adults with intensities of pollution.[27] Another recent study of asthma in children in Philadelphia revealed a nine-fold greater incidence of bronchial asthma during days of stagnant air and high air pollution than on control days of cleaner and less stagnant air.[28] The irritant and inflammatory effect of SO_2 in conjunction with the existence of a chronic respiratory disease component as, e.g., in the elderly, is said to be operative in these cases.

Sulphur dioxide is formed during the combustion of sulphur in fossil fuels and is a common constituent of polluted air. Small amounts of SO_3 are also formed, but together with the quantities produced by oxidation of SO_2 in the atmosphere (photochemical, catalytic), are rapidly converted to sulphuric acid. The associated presence of sulphuric acid and sulphate salts is the reason for the purported health effects, some of which are reviewed in Table III. The threshold value set for SO_2 in industry is at 5.0 ppm, at which level exposure can occur without serious health effects during an eight-hour day, forty-hour week. The highest value obtained for SO_2 during the 1952 London disaster was only 1.3 ppm, but it was accompanied by a high smoke of particulate loading, optimal conditions for the conversion of SO_2 into sulphuric acid and/or a particular combination of a number of different factors operative on a twenty-four hour dose-time relationship or dose rate.

In addition to a combined action of different environmental factors, it appears that concentration (and, therefore, also dose-rate) and duration of exposure at higher dose rates, may also be of special importance. This is suggested by the data available for one pollutant—sulphur dioxide. Short-term levels of 0.2 ppm SO_2 and higher have been implicated in apparently increasingly severe pollution episodes. Values of 0.20-0.86 during three consecutive days were reported for the 1953 New York episode during which 220 excess deaths occurred; a twenty-four hour average of 0.25 ppm was associated with increases in total death rates in London; a fifteen-day average of 0.40 ppm was said to be responsible for 406 excess deaths among men 45 years of age and older and the 1952 London episode was related to average values of 0.5 or slightly more during the five days of the disaster period. These values quoted for SO_2 alone do not, of course, reflect the degree of hazard accurately, and must be considered in conjunction with the degrees of particulate loading and other factors. The clarification of the role played by these other factors is essential to our understanding of the effects on health of reducing types of polluted atmospheres.

Table III: Summary of sulphur dioxide concentration and suggested health effects

(Other Associated Pollutants Not Specified)

Conc. in ppm	*Time-Dose Relationship*	*Effect*
0.015 -0.15	Annual average	Increased morbidity [24,29,15]
0.20-0.86	3 consec. days	Air Pollution Episode; N.Y. 1953 [4]
0.25	24-hour average	Increased total death rates, London 1963 [30]
0.3-1.0		Can be detected by average individual (taste) [31]
0.46	Average for 15 days	406 excess deaths; pop. 45 years + [32]
0.5		Damage to sensitive parts [33]
0.5-0.7		Odour threshold; highly sensitive persons [34]
0.57	5-day average	Air Pollution Episode; London 1952 [6,7]
0.5-2.0	Calculated for 3-4 days	Air Pollution Episode; Donora, Pa. 1948[9]
1.6	10 minutes	Threshold for bronchoconstriction; healthy man [35]
3.0		Odour threshold; average individual [31]
5.0	8-hr day; 40-hr week	T.L.V. for industrial exposure [36]
6-12	immediate	Irritation to nose and throat [31]
20.0		Least amount irritating to eyes [31]
50-100	30-60 minutes	Maximum permissible; short exposure value [31]
400-500		Immediately dangerous to life [31]

Exposure to Oxiding Atmospheres: Unlike the pollution found in Britain and parts of the eastern United States, the oxidizing type of pollution, found characteristically in Los Angeles, has not been correlated with marked excesses of deaths, nor with excesses of lung cancer. Instead, much of the earlier emphasis was placed on the occurrence of a time-associated relationship between daily oxidant levels and the mean daily frequency of eye discomfort[37] (Stage 3 effect), the demonstration of certain disturbances in pulmonary function among chronic respiratory[38] disease patients and a low positive correlation between chemical measures of air pollution and the number of attacks of asthma among asthmatics.[39]

Of, perhaps, considerably greater significance and potential portent are the reports of Brant,[40] who found increased respiratory dysfunction and, in a later study,[41] increased hospital admissions for cardiovascular diseases, under sustained high oxidant; low relative humidity; low temperature conditions, related on a post-exposure basis of four weeks. He suggested that these conditions constituted a formidable and potentially catastrophic danger to public health in Los Angeles. In their recent study, Sterling[42] and others, in essence, confirmed these findings when they found a definite correlation between pollution and fluctuations in rates of admission to hospitals for respiratory diseases and heart and other conditions thought to be relevant or possibly affected by air pollution. With, again, the exception of eye irritations and allergies, these ailments were primarily those that affected individuals with a low threshold or pre-existing disease or debility.

It is possible, therefore, that the oxidizing form of pollution is a lower intensity stress causing ill effects in debilitated individuals only after a delay of days to weeks. It appears, at any rate, to have a different mechanism of action than the reducing smogs, one which has not yet been shown to be clearly associated with the development of irreversible changes (Stage 4 effect) in the previously healthy individual.

Of considerable current interest is the role of carbon monoxide present as an important constituent in automobile exhaust gases. It has been suggested[43] that carbon monoxide may well be the most underestimated pollutant of this era and evidence is gradually accruing in support of this contention.

The quantity present in automobile exhaust gases varies, as we know, with the air/fuel ratio and may, under certain conditions, amount to between 5,000 and 70,000 ppm. As a product of incomplete combustion, it is very widely encountered and is, as such, also an important component of inhaled cigarette smoke which may contain between 200-800 ppm. The current threshold limit value for industrial exposure is set at 50 ppm for an eight-hour day. Values up to 50 ppm or more are found on Los Angeles freeways and downtown areas for short periods of time and have also been reported in Montreal during last year's bus strike and, hence, the increase in automobile traffic. Levels in underground garages may reach 80-100 ppm (one-hour average) or up to 200 ppm (20-minute average) for short periods.

Carbon monoxide has a much greater affinity for hemoglobin than oxygen and exerts its effect by interrupting the normal oxygen supply to the tissues (anoxia). The gas is released, but slowly, and continued exposure leads to increasing degrees of saturation of the blood. Overt symptoms do not normally appear until a saturation of 10-20% has been reached. Individuals with existing lung or heart disease, associated with low grades of oxygen deficiency, are particularly prone to be deleteriously affected by increases in carbon monoxide. The heart muscle itself is an avid user of oxygen and heart pain (angina) may be induced or be made more severe with small concentrations of carbon monoxide. Repeated long-term exposure has been found to have an effect on the blood-forming tissues as well, resulting in an increased packed-cell volume. This has the tendency to thicken the blood and to increase the likelihood of clot formation and growth—yet another mechanism associated with morbidity and mortality from cardiovascular disease. It is, however, the extra work-load imposed on the heart muscle of cardio-respiratory patients, by levels of 5-10% carboxyhemoglobin that is of immediate concern to the health of these subjects.

Carboxyhemoglobin concentrations of below 5% may, in addition, affect task performance[44] and levels of 5-10% saturation may dangerously affect the alertness of automobile drivers.[45] These are levels that can be attained by cigarette-smoking or work in traffic tunnels. Blood taken from drivers responsible for traffic accidents revealed substantially higher levels of CO-hemoglobin than individuals who thought they had been exposed to carbon monoxide or workmen who had some exposure to the gas at work. It has been pointed out that laboratory tests used in assessing the effects of CO on psychomotor activity may not reliably predict the influence of increased blood levels of CO-hemoglobin on mental alertness, since attention of the subject during testing may affect the test result, but be absent at the time of accidents when, indeed, attention is distracted.

It is clear that much more emphasis should be placed on the measurement and evaluation of the effects of this widely dispersed gaseous pollutant.

Other important constituents of the Los Angeles-type smog include the oxides of nitrogen, and ozone. Automobiles are responsible for approximately thirty-to-sixty per cent of the nitrogen oxides present in urban atmospheres. Nitrogen dioxide in high concentrations is a most toxic gas causing severe degrees of pulmonary edema but whilst the threshold level for eight-hour daily exposure in industry is set at 5 ppm, these values are never found in urban atmospheres.

Ozone, used as one of the indicators of the level of oxidizing pollution, is another important and potentially toxic component. It is an irritant to the eyes and mucous membranes and, at high concentrations, is a dangerous lung irritant. The recommended threshold limit value in industry is 0.1 ppm,[46] a level at which plant damage is said to occur. Pulmonary function has been shown to be affected at levels of 0.6-0.8 ppm for two hours and tolerance may develop at these and slightly higher levels. Animal experiments have indicated that, at levels of 0.7 to 0.9 ppm, ozone may predispose or aggravate a response to bacterial function.[47]

Effects of Personal Pollution

No discussion of the health effects of polluted atmospheres can ignore the considerable effect of personal pollution or smoking. Smoking is of particular importance to the natural history of the chronic respiratory diseases. Considerable differences occur between smokers and non-smokers concerning crude mortality and mortality from lung cancer[48,49] and cardiovascular disease, the prevalence of certain symptoms indicative of chronic non-specific respiratory disease and measurable ventilatory function. An increasing risk of developing lung cancer with an increasing daily consumption of cigarettes has been demonstrated; so, too, has the fact that elimination of the hazard considerably reduces this risk.

So overwhelming and powerful is the influence of smoking as a factor in respiratory disease that it bears repeating that Anderson found the effects of smoking eliminated differences in the prevalence of respiratory disease between two cities, despite significant differences in air quality. It may be argued—with some justification, that the levels of pollution in these two communities were not sufficiently high to affect the prevalence of respiratory disease. However, a recent study[50] of another North American community in New Jersey showed quite clearly that when smokers were compared with non-smokers in a heavily polluted area, the cigarette smokers had a prevalence of chronic productive cough 8.3 times greater than the non-smokers.

It is also notable that pulmonary emphysema, as reported from the autopsy room, occurs primarily in those with a long history of smoking. Ishikawa[51] and his colleagues in Winnipeg have recently reviewed the incidence of emphysema in a series of 300 routine autopsies from St. Louis, Mo., and Winnipeg, respectively. This study revealed not only a higher prevalence, an earlier age distribution and a more severe form of the disease in the more highly polluted area of St. Louis, but also a much greater prevalence of emphysema among smokers when compared with non-smokers. While demonstrating additivity of effect, smoking in this case—if these comparisons can be made—did not overshadow the effect of pollution and other urban factors presumably operative at a higher level of intensity than those of the Berlin-Chilliwack comparisons. These studies confirm not only a dose-response relationship for air quality but also the important additive effects of smoking.

It has recently been reported that individuals who do not smoke enjoy an advantage in prolonged life.[52] This was demonstrated in studies of the non-smoking Seventh Day Adventists in California, who live longer than smokers and who have a lower probability of developing lung cancer, pulmonary emphysema, other diseases of the respiratory tract as well as coronary artery disease. At age 40, their life expectancy is 6.1 years greater than that for other California men.

The Influence of Climatic, Socio-Economic and Other Factors

The role of *climatic factors* (other than inversion conditions) on the prevalence of respiratory disease, is less well-defined. Climatic factors have been implicated in the effects of pollution on asthmatic attacks and appear to be integrally related to health effects of oxidizing pollution in Los Angeles. Tromp[53] and others in Holland demonstrated the influences of changing meteorological conditions, e.g., changes in temperature on the frequency and severity of episodes among a group of asthmatics. The above data indicate that climatic factors should be considered and controlled in future epidemiologic studies. Such studies should also consider the effects of *socio-economic factors*, selective migration and the competing effects of occupational exposures. With regard to *occupational* influences, Anderson has indicated that one should not "assume that persons employed in occupations where they will be exposed to respiratory irritants" will necessarily have more respiratory disease as selection factors are operative within industry and that these may preclude such populations from epidemiological studies. Nevertheless, certain industrial environments unquestionably contribute to the development of acute, chronic and often disabling occupational lung disease.

Health Effects and Trace Elements: Of growing importance to health are the concentrations of trace elements to be found in urban environments. Of particular interest among these is lead, to be found in almost all gasolines used in North America. Almost 300,000 tons of the compounds are used each year and the element is, therefore, continually being returned to the atmosphere, constituting a source of lead absorption by inhalation. Lead is also deposited on city streets, washed down in sewers and, in certain cases, it gains access into drinking water supplies and, hence, into the food cycle (average daily consumption is 320 micrograms). Drinking water may contain 10 micrograms per litre on the average.[54]

Large city atmospheric levels naturally vary with the amount of traffic and report of average values range from a few tenths of micrograms per cubic metre to as much as 15 micrograms per cubic metre of lead in a few cities. The average for urban atmosphere in the United States is estimated at 1.4 micrograms per cubic metre. Lead is, in addition, present in cigarette smoke (an average of 0.3 micrograms per puff).

"Normal" blood lead values are approximately 0.02 milligrams per cent (.2 ppm). At 0.08 mg % and over, clinical symptoms may occur. Although there is no real evidence that so-called "normal" blood values are increasing, the margin between safe and symptom-inducing levels appears slight and may require further reviews in years to come.

Other trace elements of importance to health include elemental nickel which, at low concentrations, may interfere with normal metabolism of inhaled polycyclic hydrocarbons;[55] cadmium, which, on the basis of the average concentrations found in 28 cities, has been correlated with death rates from hypertension and arteriosclerotic heart disease;[56] vanadium, which acts as a respiratory irritant; and asbestos.

Asbestos has given rise to considerable concern since the demonstration by Thomson[57] and others that "asbestoid" bodies can be found in the lungs of approximately 50% of city dwellers and since the demonstration by Wagner,[58] Selikoff,[59] Newhouse[60] and others of the association between exposure to asbestos and the incidence of mesothelial tumours of the pleura and peritoneum. Asbestos is used in many building materials and is an important component in the brake linings of automobiles. As such, this mineral has become ubiquitous, certainly as far as our urban atmospheres are concerned. Since the full significance of exposure to asbestos fibres, at the minimal concentrations to be found in urban atmospheres, is as yet undetermined, consideration should be given to including the monitoring of asbestos in air pollution control programmes. Other factors of considerable but, as yet, not clearly defined importance, are the polycyclic hydrocarbons and various bacterial agents. Much has been written about the presence of the polycyclic hydrocarbons in urban atmospheres, many of them with known carcinogenic activity. Despite this, however, "there is, as yet, no clear indication that their presence is significant, though their interaction with biological and physical substances might indeed be the mechanism of carcinogenesis". It is in regard to this that the role of the microbiological agents also may indeed be of particular importance. It has been shown, for example, that exposure to Los Angeles smog can induce squamous cell carcinomata in experimental animals treated with PR-8 influenza virus.[61] The role of bacterial infections in the natural history of the non-specific chronic respiratory diseases requires further clarification as well.

Trends and Costs

It has been the purpose of this paper to discuss some of the measurable health effects of air pollution, to focus attention on some of the difficulties encountered in defining health effects and to show the essentially long-term or insidious nature of their onset. It has not been possible to review all aspects of health in the broad sense of the term, including welfare and the growing awareness of individuals of the disagreeable aspects of air pollution (at the perception or Stage 1 effect level). This type of effect is, nevertheless, of growing and of fundamental importance to the development of acceptable air quality criteria.

It has not been the purpose to discuss the problems of health in the future as it may be affected by the atmospheric environment against a background of increasing industrialization and population growth. However, it would be of interest to examine the present status with regard to discernible trends in diseases of interest to air pollution. The simplest—although crude—indicator of present trends is the mortality index.

On the basis of the premise that the quality of the atmosphere in larger urban communities is deleterious to health, particularly in terms of the diseases that affect the target organs—the cardio-respiratory diseases—it would not be unreasonable to use as a yardstick trends in mortality from diseases such as lung cancer, chronic bronchitis and emphysema and degenerative heart disease. In Canada, the trend in mortality for these diseases has been steadily upward (*Fig. 2*). While it must be emphasized that not all the increases are due to influence of atmospheric pollution, since diagnostic factors and changes in cigarette smoking habits and many other competing risks may play a part, the trend is, undoubtedly, important.

An increasing incidence of disease has also brought a spiralling of the monetary cost of ill health. So many direct and intangible factors are involved that it is obviously not possible to prepare an accurate cost-accounting for the ill health attributable to the various forms of atmospheric pollution. Nevertheless, air pollution is an important contributor to the natural history of the chronic respiratory diseases which, in turn, are responsible for about one-quarter of all in-hospital patient days for all respiratory diseases per year. In 1965, for example, 3.2 million in-hospital days were recorded in Canada for all diseases of the respiratory

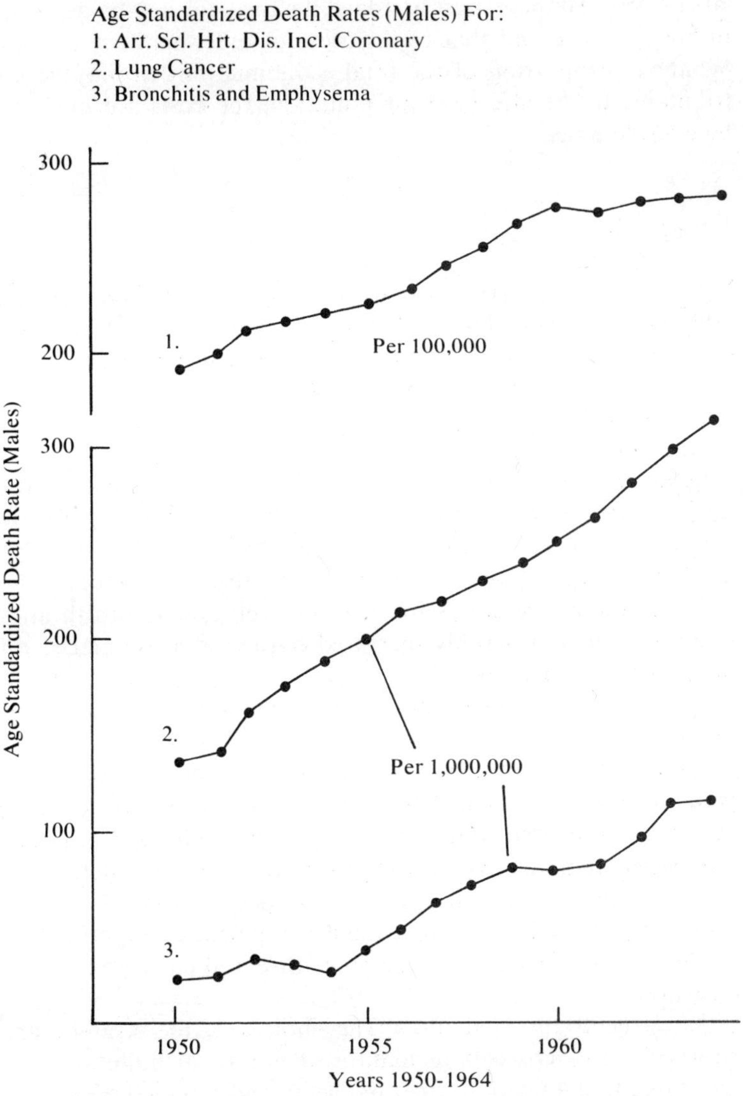

Fig. 2

system at an estimated cost of approximately 123 million dollars. Lost wages and losses in productivity due to these diseases were estimated at approximately one billion five hundred million dollars in 1967. To these must be added the costs for day-to-day out-of-hospital care and that of a variety of other indirect factors. Whatever proportion of the total economic burden may be attributable to the effects of air pollution, the costs are likely to be considerable.

Conclusion

Sufficient evidence is available to indicate that atmospheric pollution in varying degrees does affect health adversely. It contributes to excesses of deaths, increased morbidity and the earlier onset of chronic respiratory diseases. There is evidence of a relationship between the intensity of the pollution and the severity of attributable health effects and a consistency of the relationship between these environmental stresses and the diseases of the target organs. While experimental results were not reviewed in detail, there is, nevertheless, a considerable body of knowledge available to support and explain the effects observed in man.

The trend, at present, is towards more chronic ill health and, as a result, a considerably increased burden is being placed on the economy of the country.

It would not be unreasonable to say, therefore, that we are already behind in our efforts to control and alleviate the effects of air pollution on health. We shall, accordingly, need renewed impetus and efforts of the highest order directed at the development of new and improved control measures; better indicators of pollution based on more ongoing and prospective studies to determine health effects, more research for the elucidation of mechanism of toxic action of pollutants, and the development of experimental models to serve as the basis for preventive and corrective health measures.

As Sargent[62] pointed out, "The choices in the strategy are between costs—costs of regulation of output of pollutants, of selection of alternative sources of energy and raw materials, and of new technological design—and risks—risks of economic loss through environmental and material deterioration, of increased discomfort, dysfunction, morbidity and mortality in the biosphere, and of reducing renewable natural resources in the ecosystem that can meet man's subsistence requirements". "Whereas much is known about the costs of regulation, relatively little is known about the risks. For this reason, it is imperative that greater attention be given to environmental biology and particularly human adaptability".

References

[1]Hatch, T. F., *Changing Objectives in Occupational Health.* Amer. Industr. Hyg. Assoc. J., 23:1, 1962.

[2]Anderson, Donald O., *The Effects of Air Contamination on Health*: Part III. Can. Med. Assoc. J., *97*, Sept. 23, 1967, 802.

[3]Anderson, Donald O., *The Effects of Air Contamination on Health*: Part I. Can. Med. Assoc. J., *97*, Sept. 2, 1967, 528.

[4]Greenberg, Leonard and others, *Report of an Air Pollution Incident in New York City*, November 1953, Public Health Reports, *77*, 1, January 1962, 7.

[5]Greenberg, L., Field, F., Erhardt, C. L. and Reed, J. I., *Air Pollution, Influenza and Mortality in New York City During January-February 1963.* Presented at the 58th Annual Meeting, APCA, Toronto, June 22, 1965.

[6]Abercrombie, G. F., *December Fog in London and the Emergency Bed Service.* Lancet, *I*, January 31, 1953, 234.

[7]Wilkins, E. T., *Air Pollution and the London Fog of December 1952.* J. Roy. San. Inst., *74*, 1, January 1954, 1.

[8]Amdur, Mary O., *The Influence of Aerosols Upon the Respiratory Response of Guinea Pigs to Sulphur Dioxide.* Am. Ind. Hyg. Assoc. Quarterly, *18*, 1957, 149.

[9]Hemeon, W. C. L., *The Estimation of Health Hazards from Air Pollution.* Arch. Industr. Health, *11*, 1955, 397.

[10]Schrenk, H. H., *Air Pollution in Donora, Pa., Epidemiology of the Unusual Smog Episode of October 1948*: Preliminary Report by H. H. Schrenk and others. Federal Security Agency. Public Health Service, Bureau of State Services, Division of Industrial Hygiene, Public Health Service Bulletin No. 306, United States Government Printing Office, Washington, D.C., 1949.

[11]Stocks, P., *Recent Epidemiological Studies of Lung Cancer Mortality, Cigarette Smoking and Air Pollution With Discussion of a New Hypothesis of Causation.* Brit. J. Cancer, XX, 4, December 1966, 27.

[12]*A Canadian Study of Smoking and Health*, Department of National Health and Welfare, Ottawa, 1966.

[13]Manos, Nicholas E., *Comparative Mortality Among Metropolitan Areas of the United States, 1949-51. 102 Causes of Death.* U.S. Department of Health, Education and Welfare, Public Health Service, Bureau of States Services, Division of Special Health Services, Air Pollution Medical Programme, October 1957, Public Health Service Publication No. 562.

[14]Manos, N. E. and Fisher, G. F., *An Index of Air Pollution and Its Relation to Health*. Air Pollution Control Assoc. J., *9*, May 1959, 5.

[15]Report of the International Joint Commission, United States and Canada, on the Pollution of the Atmosphere in the Detroit River Area. Washington, Ottawa, 1960.

[16]Bates, D. V., Gordon, C. A., Paul, G. I., Place, R. E. G., Snidal, D. P. and Woolf, C. R., *Chronic Bronchitis*. Report on the Third and Fourth Stages of the Co-ordinated Study of Chronic Bronchitis in the Department of Veterans Affairs, Canada. Med. Serv. J. Can. *XXII*, 1, January 1966, 5.

[17]Ferris, Benjamin G. and Anderson, Donald O., *The Prevalence of Chronic Respiratory Disease in a New Hampshire Town*. Am. Rev. Resp. Dis., *86*, 2, August 1962, 165.

[18]Anderson, Donald O., Ferris, Benjamin G. and Zickmantel, Rosalie, *The Chilliwack Respiratory Survey, 1963*: Part III. *The Prevalence of Respiratory Disease in a Rural Canadian Town*. Can. Med. Assoc. J., *92*, May 8, 1965, 1007.

[19]Anderson, D. O. and Ferris, B., *Community Studies of the Health Effects of Air Pollution—A Critique*. Can. J. of Public Health, 1966, 209.

[20]Ferris, B. G., *Epidemiological Studies on Air Pollution and Health*. Arch. Env. Health, *16*, 4, April 1968, 541.

[21]Reid, D., *Diagnostic Standardization in Geographic Comparisons of Morbidity*. Amer. Rev. Resp. Dis., *86*, 1962, 850.

[22]Christensen, O. W. and Wood, C. H., *Bronchitis Mortality Rates in England and Wales and in Denmark*. Brit. Med. J., *1*, 1958, 620.

[23]Dean, G., *Lung Cancer in Northern Ireland*. Brit. Med. J., *1*, 1966, 1506.

[24]Sterling, T. D. et al., *Air Pollution and Urban Morbidity*: A First Report. Arch. Env. Health, *13*; 158, August 1966.

[25]McCarroll, James, Cassell, Eric J., Wolter, Doris W., Mountain, Joseph D., Diamond, Judith R. and Mountain, Isabel M., *Health and the Urban Environment*. V. *Air Pollution and Illness in a Normal Urban Population*. Arch. Env. Health, *14*, 1, January 1967, 178.

[26]Spicer, William S., *Air Pollution and Meterologic Factors*. Arch. Env. Health, *14*, 1, January 1967, 185.

[27]Doerner, Alexander A., *Air Pollution and Chronic Lung Disease*. Annals of Allergy, *23*, October 1965, 475.

[28]Girsh, Leonard S., Shubin, Elliot, Dick, Charles and Schulaner, Frederic A., *A Study on the Epidemiology of Asthma in Children in Philadelphia*. Journal of Allergy, *39*, 1967, 347.

[29]Seidberg, L. D., Prindle, Richard A. and Landau, Emanuel, *The Nashville Air Pollution Study*, III: *Morbidity in Relation to Air Pollution*. Am. J. Pub. Health, *54*, January 1964, 85.

[30]Lawther, P. J., *Compliance with the Clean Air Act*. Medical Aspects. J. Inst. Fuel, *36*: 341, August 1963.

[31]Patty, Frank A., *Industrial Hygiene and Toxicology*, II: *Toxicology*. Second Revised Edition, Interscience Publishers, 1967.

[32]Greenburg, L., Field, F., Erhardt, C. L. and Reed, J. I., *Air Pollution, Influenza and Mortality in New York City During January-February, 1963*. Presented at the 58th Annual Meeting, APCA, Toronto, June 22, 1965.

[33]Goldsmith, John R., Greenburg, Leonard, Altshuller, A. P., Spicer, William S., Cassell, Eric J. and Landsberg, H. E., *Air Pollution and Health*, American Thoracic Society. Medical Section of the National Tuberculosis Association, 1966. 302

[34]Dubrovskaya, F. I., *Hygienic Evaluation of Pollution of Atmospheric Air of a*

Large City With Sulphur Dioxide Gas. In: *Limits of Allowable Concentrations of Atmospheric Pollutants*. Book 3. Ryazanov, V. A., ed. Levine, B. S., Trans. U.S. Dept. of Commerce. OTS. Washington, D.C., 1957, pp. 37-51.

[35]Tomono, Y., *Effects of SO_2 on Human Pulmonary Functions*. Japan J. Ind. Health, *3*: 77, February 1961.

[36]Threshold Limit Values for 1967. Recommended and Intended Values. Adopted at the 29th Annual Meeting of the American Conference of Governmental Industrial Hygienists, Chicago, Illinois, May 1-2, 1967.

[37]Hammer, D. I., Portnoy, B., Massey, F. M., Wayne, W. S., Oelsner, T. and Wehrle, P. F., *Los Angeles Air Pollution and Respiratory Symptoms*. Arch. Env. Health, *10*, March 1965, 475.

[38]Motley, H. L., Smart, R. H. and Leftwich, C.L., J.A.M.A., *171*, 1469, 1959.

[39]Schoettlin, Charles E. and Landau, Emanuel, *Air Pollution and Asthmatic Attacks in the Los Angeles Area*, Public Health Reports, *76*, June 1961, 545.

[40]Brant, John W. A. and Hill, Stanley R. G., *Human Respiratory Diseases and Atmospheric Air Pollution in Los Angeles, California*. Int. J. Air. Wat. Poll., *8*, Pergamon Press, 1964, 259.

[41]Brant, John W. A., *Human Cardiovascular Diseases and Atmospheric Air Pollution in Los Angeles, California*. Int. J. Air. Wat. Poll., *9*, Pergamon Press 1964, 219.

[42]Sterling, T. D., Pollack, S. V. and Phair, J. J., *Urban Hospital Morbidity and Air Pollution*. A Second Report. Arch. Environ. Health, *15*, September 1967, 362.

[43]Goldsmith, J. R., *Report of Meeting on Carbon Monoxide*. Science, *157*, August 18, 1967, 842.

[44]Schulte, J. H., *Effects of Mild Carbon Monoxide Intoxication*. Arch. Environ. Health, *7*, 524, 1963.

[45]Lawther, P. J., Abstracted in Notes and Comments. *Motor Exhausts and Health*. The Medical Officer, Feb. 25, 1966, 101.

[46]Brant, John W. A. and Hill, Stanley R. G., *Human Respiratory Diseases and Atmospheric Pollution in Los Angeles, California*. Int. J. Air. Wat. Poll., *8*, Pergamon Press, 1964.

[47]Coffin, D. L. and Blommer, E. J., J. Air. Pollut. Contr. Assoc., *15*, 523, 1965.

[48]Doll, R. and Hill, A. B., *Mortality in Relation to Smoking. Ten Years' Observations of British Doctors*, Brit. Med. J. Nos. 5395 and 5396, 1399-1410 and 1460-1467, May and June 1964.

[49]*Smoking and Health, Report of the Advisory Committee to the Surgeon-General of the Public Health Service*, P.H.S.P. No. 1103.

[50]Gocke, T. M., *Factors which Aggravate Chronic Bronchitis. Emphysema in Industry*. Indus. Hyg. Foundation of Am., Inc. Medical Series Bulletin No. 10, 1966, 57.

[51]Ishikawa, S., Personal communication. University of Manitoba.

[52]APHA Conference Report 1967, *Lifespan of Adventists Prolonged by Not Smoking*. Public Health Reports, *83*, 3, March 1968, 225.

[53]Tromp, Solco. W., *Biometeorological Aspects of Respiratory Diseases*. Reports Biometeorological Research Centre No. 3, March 8, 1966.

[54]*Public Health Service Drinking Water Standards*, U.S.P.H.S. Publication No. 956, 1962.

[55]Stokinger, H. E., Mountain, J. T. and Dixon, J. R., *Newer Toxicologic Methodology*. Arch. Environ. Health, *13*, Sept. 1966, 296.

[56]Carrol, Robert E., *The Relationship of Cadmium in the Air to Cardiovascular Disease Death Rates*. J.A.M.A., *198*, 3, October 17, 1966, 177.

[57]Thomson, J. G., *Asbestos as a Modern Urban Hazard*, S. Afr. Med. J., *31*, Jan. 19, 1963, 77.

[58]Wagner, J.C., Sleggs, C.A. and Marchand, P., Brit. J. Industr. Med., *17*, 1960, 260.

[59]Selikoff, I. J., Churg, J. and Hammond, E. C., J. Amer. Med. Assoc., *188*, 1964, 22.

[60]Newhouse, Muriel L. and Thompson, Hilda, *Mesothelioma of Pleura and Peritoneum Following Exposure to Asbestos in the London Area*. Brit. J. Industr. Med. Vol. 22, p. 261, 1965.

[61]Kotin, P. and Falk, H. L., Dis. Chest. *45*, 236, 1964.

[62]Sargent, Frederick, *Air Pollution: A Problem for Human Ecology*. Arch. Environ. Health, *14*, 1, January 1967, 35.

New Restrictions Ruled on DDT

KENNETH MAYALL

DDT is at last on the way out in Ontario, and indeed in all of Canada.

For those who care about our polluted environment, there were just two red-letter days in 1969. The first was September 18. On that day an important regulation was approved by the Provincial Government. Under this regulation, as of January 1st, 1970, the housewife and the cottage owner in Ontario will no longer be able to buy or be *allowed to use* compounds containing DDT for the control of flies, mosquitoes and other insect pests. The spraying of DDT on forests and individual trees to control insect pests will also be illegal. Spraying of DDT will be retained only for three specific uses, for which there is at present no suitable substitute. The general ruling is contained in a new Regulation under The Pesticides Act, 1967, which is administered by the Ontario Department of Health. The exceptions allowed in the use of DDT are its use for the control of bats, many of which carry rabies, its use in greatly diluted form for cutworm control in tobacco (a crop of great economic importance in Ontario) and, under special circumstances, for plant "bug" extermination on apples. Permits will have to be obtained before DDT is bought or used for any purpose.

Source: Kenneth Mayall, "New Restrictions Ruled on DDT", from *Watersheds* magazine, volume 4, numbers 3 and 4, 1969, published by The Conservation Authorities Branch of the Ontario Department of Energy and Resources Management. Reprinted by permission of the publisher and author.

Research is now world-wide concerning the dangers of pesticides. In Canada the Federal Government sets the conditions for labelling and *annual* registration of every pesticide. The Department of National Health and Welfare ensures that food offered for sale for human consumption contains no undesirable levels of chemicals. Under the Ontario Department of Health's regulations, records have for several years been compulsory of the use of DDT and other pesticides sold in lots of four pounds or more in a single sale. It is thought that 90 per cent of the DDT used in Ontario falls into this category. Thus a good estimate of the amounts used in the various counties is available. The counties where tobacco is a major crop have been using about 80 per cent of the DDT used in the province. The maximum dosage permitted per acre on tobacco now will be approximately 25 per cent of what it was in 1969.

Even before the new Regulation was approved, Ontario had taken the lead in Canada in reducing the total load of DDT in use. The Ontario Water Resources Commission decided in 1968 not to approve the commercial spraying of DDT in watercourses or lakes, and the Department of Lands and Forests also discontinued the use of it in any of its projects on Crown lands in 1968.

Now why is there all this fuss about the use of DDT? After 1874, when it was first synthetized by a German chemist, it remained a substance of merely scientific interest for more than 60 years. The Swiss chemist who discovered in 1939 that it was a powerful insecticide received the Nobel prize for his discovery. It was extensively used by various armies during the Second World War and became popular for insect control in Canada in 1946. It is cheap and easy to make and its sales rocketed. But DDT is an exceptionally stable member of the now dreaded chlorinated hydrocarbons, which include aldrin, dieldrin and chlordane. It is virtually insoluble in water, but may vaporize from the ground without losing its dangerous potential. (Incidentally, it is estimated that about one billion pounds of DDT is now circulating through the water and air of the earth.)

A Frightening Fatality Rate

DDT in soil or water is ingested and concentrated in very small quantities by the smallest animal life, but proceeds through the food chain until it appears in very much higher concentrations in fish or other predators including mammals.

When used for forest spraying in 1954, DDT killed nearly all of the salmon in the famous Miramichi River in New Brunswick, along with their foods. It was estimated recently by the United States Public Health Service that the average American by 1969 had already gathered 12 parts per million of DDT into his human tissues. This would roughly apply to the people of southern Ontario as well. Nobody knows what the effect of 12 parts per million in human tissue means in the long run. Its cumulative effect on humans after several generations is of course not known, but the mere fact that DDT concentrates in and attacks the liver, causing the liver enzymes to break down the sex hormones in mammals, makes research scientists view it with suspicion.

So far as we know there has been no human fatality due solely to DDT. But we do know that DDT in Ontario is almost certainly the cause of an alarming decline in successful reproduction of lake trout in some of the Muskoka lakes. There is now overwhelming evidence that DDT in fish, the prime food of the Bald Eagle, is the single reason for the rapid decline in numbers of this species, which is now virtually sterile in eastern North America. In addition, many other kinds of birds now lay eggs which cannot hatch.

The world-wide movement of the air over the earth and the waters surrounding the continents makes DDT a problem for the whole planetary surface. DDT has already been found in Antarctic seals which do not move more than a thousand miles from their breeding grounds. It has also been found in the new ice of glaciers in Alaska. There is no end to problems man has caused in tampering with his environment.

DDT is already withdrawn from sale in the States of Michigan and Arizona, and from the whole of Sweden. But it is estimated that it will take 30 years for Lake Michigan to flush its DDT into the international water of Lake Huron.

As industry has so far denied its responsibility in finding out what effects pollutants such as DDT and many others have on our environment, the responsibility fell by default upon the scientific community of university and government personnel, whose findings were needed to formulate public policy.

The second red-letter day in 1969 was November 3 when Prime Minister Trudeau announced in the House of Commons that *throughout Canada* the use of DDT would be greatly reduced beginning January 1, 1970. While Canada does not go quite as far as Ontario in reducing DDT, the maximum tolerance will be reduced from seven parts per million to one part per million on 61 common vegetables and fruits, either Canadian or imports. This is a great advance.

The stage is now set for a concentrated attack on other chlorinated hydrocarbons. One group of these now attracting great attention is the polychlorinated biphenyls (PCB) which are used in some plastics, paints and resins. Deadly quantities of these pass into fresh and salt water in industrial effluents. Their effects may be as grave as or graver than those of DDT. These constitute the next great challenge, which industry should be and definitely is not now facing. PCB may be harder to control than DDT. It should be remembered that DDT is still being passed into the world environment through exports from many parts of the United States and other countries. Ontario has made an auspicious start in environmental control, but to this writer it seems that our overall environment will probably be worse before it is better.

Pesticide Pollution of Our Environment

C. R. HARRIS

How serious is the problem of environmental pollution with pesticides? Most scientists who are really knowledgeable in the field concede that in terms of over-all environmental pollution, pesticides are pollutants of minor importance yet over the past few years, the question of pesticide pollution has received such great publicity that an attitude bordering on hysteria has developed far out of proportion to the actual problem. The reasons behind this furor are two-fold. First, in contrast to many other pollution problems, where analytical methods are rudimentary, almost unbelievably sensitive methods of analysis have been developed for some insecticides which allow us to measure residues not in grams, or tenths of grams, but in billionths and even trillionths of grams. Second, the publication of a book called *Silent Spring* by Rachel Carson in 1962 drew public attention to the fact that pesticides were not only controlling pests, but were also resulting in serious environmental side effects. *Silent Spring* served its purpose in that it forced an appraisal of the adequacy of information on pesticide residues and their persistence in the environment, but many of the statements in it were inaccurate and the conclusions based on emotion rather than true facts. Needless to say some segments of the pesticide industry responded with salvo after salvo in an attempt to refute Miss Carson. The end result has been that the public has become

Source: C.R. Harris, "Pesticide Pollution of Our Environment", taken from a speech presented to the Maple City Kiwanis Club, London, Ontario, January 26, 1970. Reprinted by permission of the author.

utterly confused as to the assets and liabilities of pesticide use. This confusion is best demonstrated by the fact that the urban dwellers, who on the one hand question the use of pesticides in agriculture, are on the other hand, responsible for the huge consumption of these same materials for home and garden use.

In 1945 a compound, now famous, by the name of DDT became available for general use. It was the first of a series of highly effective, broad-spectrum poisons, commonly known as the chlorinated hydrocarbons. Others in this category include aldrin, dieldrin, heptachlor, and endrin. These materials were fantastically effective against nearly all species of insect pests and naturally they were used extensively, often at excessive rates or by methods of application which were both wasteful and detrimental. We needlessly contaminated huge sections of our environment. More recently, two other major groups of compounds have become available for use—the organophosphorus and carbamate insecticides. These materials are generally less persistent, but also less effective than the chlorinated hydrocarbons. Our major concern with regard to environmental pollution at present is with DDT, aldrin, dieldrin, and heptachlor.

In one way or another insecticide residues generally end up in the soil regardless of whether they are applied directly to the soil or to crops from which they are washed down into the soil by rainfall. The persistence of these materials in soil has been examined quite extensively. Both aldrin and heptachlor are relatively volatile and disappear quite rapidly from the soil. Unfortunately, soil microorganisms convert small amounts of aldrin and heptachlor to dieldrin and heptachlor epoxide, both of which are toxic, persistent compounds. DDT is also highly persistent in soil, but is slowly degraded by microorganisms to DDE. *From the available evidence, it would appear that residues of dieldrin and DDT will persist in soils for many years.*

DDT, aldrin, and to a lesser extent, heptachlor have been used extensively in Ontario and soils in many of our agricultural areas are contaminated with residues of these materials. In tobacco and vegetable soils, residues of all insecticides average 3 and 10 ppm respectively. A part-per-million incidentally is an amount equivalent to digging up all the soil to a depth of 3 inches over an acre of land and mixing 1 pound of insecticide with it.

In orchard soils DDT residues are quite high, averaging 62 ppm. However, on an over-all basis our soils in Ontario would average less than 1 ppm of insecticide residues. It is of interest to note here that arsenic, which is far more poisonous in many ways than DDT, occurs naturally in soils at concentrations as great as 10 ppm.

Although residues are present in our soils, this does not necessarily mean that they constitute a pollution problem. This will depend entirely on the side effects which are occurring as a result of this residue buildup. Without going into great detail I would like to discuss some of these possible side effects and the data which we have at present. Side effects may be of two types —direct and indirect. The direct side effects are primarily those relating to the soil organisms themselves. Indirect side effects may result from movement of the insecticide from one sector of the environment to another.

What of the effects of insecticides on the soil organisms? The first to be considered must be the soil microorganisms which are of major importance in maintaining soil fertility. *Extensive evidence obtained in our own laboratory and at numerous other laboratories throughout the world clearly indicates that the chlorinated hydrocarbon insecticides have little, if any, effect on soil microorganisms.*

In addition to microorganisms, earthworms are also important in maintaining soil fertility. However, experiments have shown that with one or two exceptions (heptachlor, chlordane), the chlorinated hydrocarbon insecticides have little effect on earthworm populations. Unfortunately, earthworms are capable of absorbing relatively large amounts of the chlorinated hydrocarbons from soil. When these contaminated worms are fed on by birds in sufficient quantities, it can result in serious side effects.

As would be expected, the soil insects are killed by the chlorinated hydrocarbons and in addition to controlling pest species of insects, beneficial species are also affected, including the parasites and predators of the pests. However, this broad-spectrum effect is not confined to the chlorinated hydrocarbons—the organophosphorus and carbamate insecticides may be even more toxic to soil animals. However, some interesting work in England has indicated that the effect of insecticides on beneficial soil animals is of less importance than normal soil cultivation.

While residues of the chlorinated hydrocarbons do not appear to be influencing soil fertility there have been some detrimental side effects. One of these has been the development of insecticidal resistance by soil insects. In many areas of the world, including Canada, soil insects have become resistant to materials such as aldrin and heptachlor and the search for alternative materials has been both expensive and time consuming.

Another side effect which has caused concern is the fact that residues of some insecticides, such as dieldrin, are absorbed from soils by some crops. *DDT, incidentally, is not absorbed to any significant extent by crops.* Generally speaking root crops are the greatest "absorbers." Other vegetable crops also absorb dieldrin and heptachlor epoxide from the soil. *However, the residues in these crops are not exceeding the tolerances for direct human consumption which have been established by the Food and Drug Directorate of the Department of National Health and Welfare.*

A potentially more serious aspect of this problem involves the absorption of residues of insecticides such as dieldrin by crops used for animal feed. Here we become involved with the problem of "magnification." When small amounts of dieldrin are absorbed by crops which are in turn fed in large quantities, continuously, to animals, the animals tend to store the insecticide in their fatty tissue. With continuous feeding of a contaminated crop, perhaps 10-25 x the concentration of dieldrin found in the plant may be found in milk or other animal products. Thus a residue of 20 ppb in feed may result in a residue of 0.2 ppm in milk—an unacceptable level. We have found that crops such as alfalfa, oats, corn, sugar beets, potatoes, and turnips all absorb dieldrin and heptachlor epoxide from soil. Information from various areas in Canada indicates that we have fairly extensive low-level contamination of milk and to a lesser extent, other animal products with residues of dieldrin and other chlorinated hydrocarbons. *However, residues of the chlorinated hydrocarbon insecticides in milk and animal products, are, in the vast majority of cases, well within the acceptable limits recognized by Federal Agencies. The evidence indicates that insecticide residues in our crops, milk, and other animal products do not constitute a hazard to human health.*

From the discussion so far, it is apparent that the direct side effects resulting from the accumulation of chlorinated hydrocarbon insecticide residues in soil are not sufficiently serious to merit major concern. Those problems which do exist, e.g. toxicity to earthworms, insecticide resistance, and absorption and translocation of residues by crops are limited to one or 2 insecticides. DDT has caused remarkably few direct side effects when one considers the amount of material which has been used over the past 25 years, and the residue levels present in the soil.

But what of the indirect side effects? Are the organochlorine insecticide residues in soil being transferred by one method or another to other sectors of the environment? On preliminary examination it would appear that this is highly unlikely. The so-called "hard" insecticides, DDT, dieldrin, and heptachlor epoxide are virtually non-volatile and insoluble in water. They are strongly adsorbed by soil and do not move to any significant extent through the soil to the ground water. Yet, it is becoming apparent that relatively small amounts of these materials are indeed being transported from soil to water and air. Presumably this is occurring because of very limited volatilization, and because of erosion of topsoil by both wind and water. Because of its widespread use, the major offenders are DDT and its degradation product DDE. Although the extent of contamination of water or silt with these materials may only be at the ppb or even ppt level, these minute concentrations can, because of magnification, result in serious effects on the upper levels of the biological chains in the ecosystem. For example minute concentrations of DDT–DDE adsorbed on suspended colloids in water can be absorbed and concentrated by microorganisms. The microorganisms are consumed by plankton-eating fish, which are in turn consumed by larger predatory fish, which are then consumed in turn by predatory birds such as cormorants, mergansers, and ospreys. In one situation in Long Island Sound it is claimed that the concentration of DDT increased from 3 ppt in water to 25 ppm in the predatory birds—an astounding 8.3 million fold increase over the original amount. While such a concentration might not be toxic to the birds there is evidence that DDT interferes with calcium metabolism and hence the "thin-shell" phenomenon which is apparently common in predatory birds. More recently, the research results have indicated that it is not DDT which is so much responsible for the upset in calcium metabolism in birds or the toxicity to fish embryos, but rather its degradation product DDE, which for many years was considered a "harmless" residue.

While the evidence that DDT–DDE can result in serious side effects in the ecosystem is generally accepted it is difficult at present to quantitatively estimate its importance relative to other pollutants. Unfortunately, much of the data on fish and wildlife is subject to question. Analysis by gas liquid chromatography which is the general method now in use is a difficult, exacting task. Interpretation of the data is extremely important and, unless one is careful, artifacts or contaminants can often be mistaken for DDT or DDE. Complicating the picture is a group of common industrial pollutants, related to DDT, which, it is now recognized, are in themselves highly toxic (more so than DDT–DDE) and produce similar physiological effects on fish and wildlife. These pollutants, known as PCB's (polychlorinated biphenyls), occur commonly in industrialized areas. *The picture with regard to these materials is not yet clear, but it seems likely that future work will show that the PCB's are pollutants of equal or even greater importance than DDT–DDE.*

Pesticides, particularly DDT, can under certain circumstances unquestionably result in serious environmental side effects. But what is the situation in Canada and more specifically in Ontario? The extent to which environmental pollution will occur is directly proportional to the amount of pesticide used. In all of Canada, less pesticide is used, than in the State of California. Obviously, the extent of pollution in this country will then be only a fraction, and a small fraction at that, of what is occurring in the United States. What of the situation in Ontario? As I have already pointed out, the problem in soils is not particularly serious. We do have residues, some side effects have occurred, but the problem is well in hand. Other data obtained in Provincial and Federal laboratories indicates that residues in milk and animal products are well within acceptable levels.

Of some 10,000 farms in Ontario, tests in the last 3 years or so have indicated that less than a dozen have had residues of dieldrin or DDT in milk above the acceptable levels. In lakes adjacent to agricultural areas only traces of DDT or dieldrin are present in the water and residues in fish are not at serious levels. Bird populations do not appear to be decreasing rapidly, with the possible exception of those at the top of the biological chains, i.e. the predatory birds. Generally speaking, the data available indicates that *the use of pesticides in agriculture in Ontario has not created any insuperable problems.* Nevertheless, we do have some pollution problems in Ontario and it is interesting to see where they have occurred. In some fishing areas in Ontario, residues of DDT in fish are significantly higher than in other locations. The location—not adjacent to agricultural areas—but in the Muskoka region. Pesticide use in that area—not agricultural—but applied for pleasure purposes for mosquito and black fly control by resort and cottage owners. Another example of gross misuse of pesticides has been the massive use of DDT by municipalities to control Dutch Elm Disease. Combine the runoff into storm sewers from this and other homeowner use of DDT and other pesticides in cities and you can begin to see the picture. *Pesticide Pollution has arisen from Pesticide Misuse and I submit to you that it is not agriculture which is primarily to blame, but those same urban dwellers who now profess to be concerned about environmental contamination by pesticides.*

Obviously there is reason for concern over the side effects which pesticides are causing and in recent months the opponents of pesticide use have mounted a tremendous campaign to have the so-called "hard" chlorinated hydrocarbon insecticides banned for use. In Ontario they have convinced the Provincial Government that this is the best course of action and as a result aldrin, heptachlor, and dieldrin have been completely banned, while DDT has been severely restricted for use.

In recent weeks I have been quoted and extensively misquoted by the local newspaper as to my position on the restrictions on the use of insecticides and I would like to take this opportunity today to clearly state my position. First, *I do not oppose restricting the use of pesticides which are potential pollutants.* In fact

I have strongly advocated for the past several years, restrictions in the use of a number of insecticides including DDT. However, *I do feel that it is a mistake to ban useful materials such as aldrin and heptachlor on the mistaken assumption that there are less dangerous alternative materials available as replacements.* I say this for a number of reasons. First, there is a popular misconception that the substitute materials are less persistent in soil than the so-called "hard" chlorinated hydrocarbons and this is not necessarily the case. Second, while most chlorinated hydrocarbons have limited solubility in water many of the newer materials are slightly to moderately soluble, and we run the risk of contaminating ground water as well as streams and lakes. Third, most of these new materials are volatile and the reason that they disappear quickly is because they are evaporating in the air. Is air pollution any more preferable than water pollution? Fourth, in many instances, these new materials are being applied at 5-6 times the rate that we applied the chlorinated hydrocarbons. Fifth, these materials are more toxic to handle and can be as, or more toxic, to beneficial soil animals, fish, and wildlife. At least with DDT, aldrin, and heptachlor we know some of the side effects which can occur. Little, if anything, is known as to the environmental side effects which the substitute materials will cause. Surely in attempting to control the pesticide pollution problem, we should insure that the cure is not worse than the disease!

Rather than becoming completely hysterical about the pesticide problem, it is obvious that we should attempt to develop a moderate approach. How can we bring this about? The following are a few suggestions.

1. *Research*: We cannot do without pesticides; at the same time we do not want to use materials which will result in serious environmental pollution. There is a drastic requirement for expansion of our research programs on pesticide application, efficacy, and persistence and degradation in the environment. Research programs on integrated control should also be expanded. More research requires more funds both at federal and provincial levels.
2. *Legislation*: At the Federal level the requirements for registration of pesticides should be and are being tightened. In

addition to information on efficacy and hazard to human health, much more emphasis should be placed on the effects of pesticides on environmental quality. Once a material is registered it should be mandatory that in-depth reviews of the registered uses be conducted periodically. Sufficient qualified staff should be provided to enable the CDA to conduct these reviews.

At the Provincial level the Government should ensure that qualified staff are available to administer the Pest Control Act. At present the number of qualified pesticide specialists within the provincial civil service is shockingly small and decisions are being made by civil servants and boards who are not qualified to do so. The Provincial Government should consider appointment of a highly qualified pesticide coordinator responsible for coordination of pesticide work within the Provincial Government and for liaison with the Federal Government.

3. *Control of Pesticide Use*: Banning useful pesticides is not the answer. However, at present, if a pesticide is registered for use, there is little further control over its use. As you all know, anyone can buy pesticides in drugstores, supermarkets, hardware stores, seed stores, and nurseries. Surely this is the key to the problem. If the majority of pesticides were sold under a system of permits or prescriptions, misuse could be kept to a minimum and consequently pollution could be held within acceptable limits.

Pesticides are with us to stay, whether we like it or not. Properly utilized, their assets greatly outweigh their liabilities. We must simply learn how to control their use.

Significance of Pesticide Residues in Foods in Relation to Total Environmental Stress

H. F. KRAYBILL

Through the utilization of pesticide chemicals man has achieved a more abundant supply of food and fibre and enhanced the control of pest-vectored diseases. Associated with such pest control procedures is the problem of chemical contamination of the environment of man, animals and aquatic organisms. An awareness of this problem by the general public and environmental health scientists has led to the promulgation of new statutes by groups of nations to govern the control of chemical residues in the food supply and the total environment. This concern for environmental pollution evolved from earlier recognition of the hazards of fallout radioactivity, bacterial toxins and, more recently, by the presence of fungal metabolites in certain food crops.

A balanced account of the overall problem of environmental pesticide contaminants and residues was portrayed in the President's Science Advisory Committee Report on "Use of Pesticides."[1] Regulatory and legislative procedures advanced for enforcement of standards of safety or other standards have not been restricted to national scope but indeed have become a matter of international co-operation and agreement.

Source: H. F. Kraybill, "Significance of Pesticide Residues in Foods in Relation to Total Environmental Stress", *The Canadian Medical Association Journal*, 100: 204, 1969. Minor deletions in the original text have been made. Reprinted by permission of the publisher and author.

It is no longer appropriate or desirable to view the pesticide contamination problem relevant to man's total exposure and human health in terms of one environmental component, such as food, but rather an overview must prevail encompassing the total environment. Reinforcement of these considerations necessitates recognition of the potentiating role of multiple pesticide chemical exposure and the interaction of other chemical stress agents and drugs from which man may receive a constant challenge. It is, therefore, incumbent upon local, state and federal agencies that regulatory programs prevail and legislation be enacted for control, elimination or minimization of the presence of pesticides and pesticide residues in food, water, air, and other parts of man's environment.

Exposure Assessment

Man and animals are exposed over their entire lifetime to various atmospheric contaminants, water pollutants and toxic residues in food. In consideration of the risk involved and safety measures to be implemented, the impact is first viewed in terms of exposure of the general population. In this context the greatest exposure to pesticides of most consumers in the general population results from residues in food. The author has stated[2] that for individuals in the general population 90% of the total persistent pesticide exposure arises from pesticide intake in food. This statement is further corroborated by data presented by Campbell, Richardson and Schafer.[3] In Fig. 1 the data presented demonstrate the need for considering environmental factors other than food. A recalculation of the data from the above referenced sources has been made and the estimated annual environmental exposure to DDT + DDE through ingestion, absorption and inhalation routes of exposure is reflected in Fig. 1. For the general population organochlorine insecticide ingestion, represented by DDT + DDE in food, would be approximately 85% of the estimated total exposure. It is recognized that precise data are lacking on the component environmental exposure to pesticides from sources other than food and water. The magnitude of the concentration of pesticides contributed by potable water supply can be accurately measured since broad surveillance programs in the United States have been designed for that purpose. Determination of the exact exposure levels in air has been somewhat more difficult owing to lack of adequate collection instruments. Only recently have some significant advances been made in this area according to Yobs.[4]

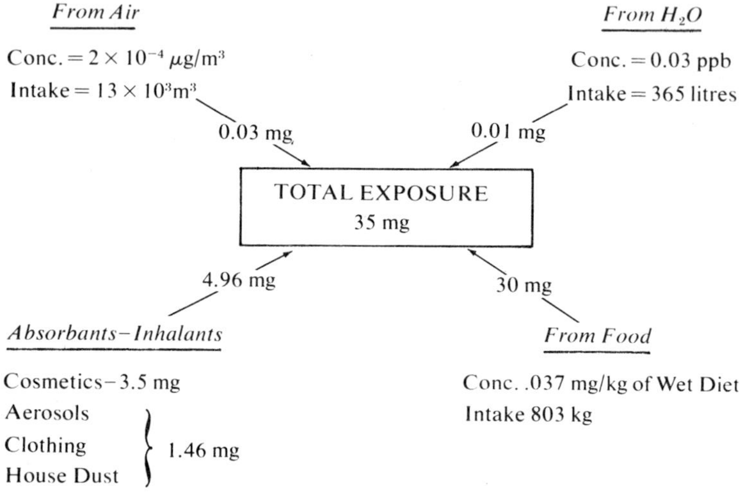

Fig. 1. Sources of pesticide exposure

The "general population" in those geographical regions where aerial spraying for crop and forest insects or mosquito abatement programs takes place receives, of course, higher atmospheric levels of pesticide exposure. Another example of atmospheric exposure for the general population is the excessive and continuous use of aerosol spraying for insect control in homes and institutions and of Vapona (DDVP) strips for fly control. In such instances the above figures for proportionate levels of total exposure to pesticides from foods would have to be revised downward. Blood levels of DDE in selected members of the general population have suggested the importance of considering the environmental insult from aerosol spraying and other domestic applications. Studies in south Florida by Davies *et al.*,[5] conducted on persons having no recent or remote history of being occupationally exposed to pesticides, have revealed DDE levels in the blood of a combined population of male and female whites in the range of 1.8 to 19.4 ppb or a mean of 8.0 ppb. Similarly, among non-white males and females the range in DDE levels in the blood was 3.6 to 54.2 ppb or a mean of 16 ppb. No explanation was given for the ethnic differences in blood levels of DDE other than that one can assume variant chronic environmental exposure. Further consideration is being given to environmental exposure to pesticide chemicals in various other substrates. For example, residues in clothing, rugs, blankets (for mothproofing), in dust from vacuum sweepers, and on contact surfaces such as pesticide-treated and painted walls, may become absorbed by the skin on contact or inhaled by volatilization or dispersion into the air. To our knowledge no measurements have been made on residues in drugs from plant materials treated with pesticides. However, levels of chlorinated insecticides in cosmetics have been determined by Edmundson *et al.*[6]

Since many of the cosmetics are labelled as containing lanolin, analyses were made and various organochlorine insecticides were determined in the lanolin cosmetic products. It might be expected that organochlorine insecticide chemicals would be taken up by natural oils and fats, including wool fat, especially since sheep are treated with these pesticides for control of ectoparasites. Analyses were made for BHC (α, β and γ isomers), dieldrin, p,p′-DDT, p,p′-DDD and p,p′-DDE. The products examined were eye shadow, lipstick, hair spray and dressing, and creams and lotions. The following levels of DDT + DDE were found in (a) hair dressing—3.83 ppm total DDT + DDE (DDT—3.5 ppm, DDE—0.33 ppm); (b) lipstick—8.50 ppm DDT; (c) hair lotions and sprays—3.1 ppm DDT + DDE (DDT—2.8 ppm, DDE—0.3 ppm); and (d) eye shadow—0.16 ppm DDE. All products but eye shadow contained BHC, dieldrin, DDT and DDE. Based on some rough quantitative estimates of usage by men and women, the annual DDT + DDE exposure (largely absorption) contributed by these products was approximately 3.5 mg. per person (Fig. 1).

Thus far no mathematical models have been constructed to integrate the component contributions of all these sources of exposure. Ultimately this will be necessary to provide an accurate measurement of the stress from pesticides in not only food but also those other environmental components which challenge the general population. In current epidemiological studies conducted by the U.S. Public Health Service, a surveillance of these exposure sources is being made for evaluation of the relative contribution of pesticide exposure from all these environmental contributors.[7]

Another segment of the population that is considered at high risk relevant to pesticide exposure are those who are occupationally exposed, such as formulators, aerial spray pilots, pest control operators, agricultural applicators and chemical manufacturing plant employees. These members of the population receive exposure to pesticides by one or all three routes of entry into the body—inhalation, absorption and ingestion. It may seem irrelevant to consider this population group in relation to evaluation of the potential hazard from the usual environmental exposure of the general population to food, water and air. However, from epidemiological considerations their exposure and the magnitude of their exposure must be recognized in considering whatever limitations are imposed for this group since their total exposure reflects a summation of all exposures, including the maximal exposure experienced by the general population under all conditions. A diagrammatic representation of types of pesticide exposure of various population groups is shown in Fig. 2.

The residue problem ultimately focalizes on the so-called persistent pesticides of which the organochlorine insecticides, such as DDT (with the metabolites DDE and TDE), aldrin, dieldrin, gamma BHC, chlordane and heptachlor and its epoxide are notable examples. None of the current legislation attempts to define persistent pesticides. However, in recent years, because of concern over persistent pesticides, repeated bills have been introduced in Congress which, in effect, would practically eliminate or greatly restrict the use of persistent organic chemicals.

These pesticides may be present in high concentration as residues on food crops at harvest time because their chemical nature imparts some resistance to biodegradability. If not completely removed, and in some cases this is impossible, these compounds appear as residues in the somatic tissue of man and animals from ingestion of food and feeds in which such residues

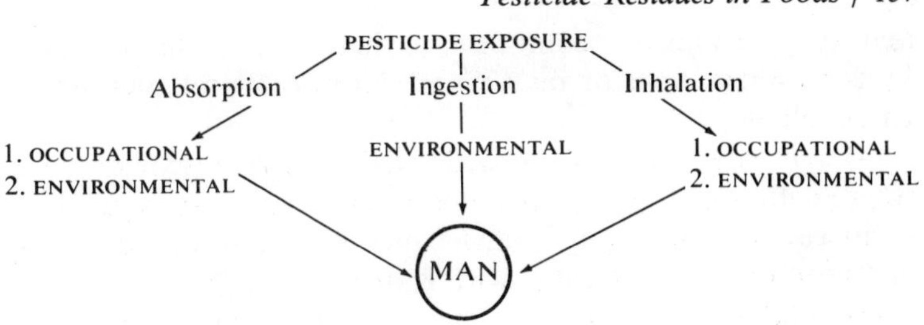

Occupational Exposure

1. Pest Control Operations
2. Agricultural Applications
3. Formulation Operations
4. Mosquito Abatement Operations
5. Pesticide Manufacturing

Environmental Exposure

1. Air
2. Water
3. Food
4. Cosmetics–Drugs
5. Contact Surfaces
6. Aerosol Uses
7. Persistence in Soils
8. Automatic Dispensing Devices
9. Pesticide Strips

Fig. 2. Types of pesticide exposure of various population groups

appear. Because of this situation some of the compounds may require a high tolerance. One of the incongruities of the persistent pesticide problem is that these persistent pesticides, since they are resistant to environmental degradation (air, light and water) and are therefore efficacious in insect control, do contribute to the appearance of residues in substrates such as food and human adipose tissue, where they are not desired. It has been suggested and considered that perhaps application of persistent pesticides should be limited to early phases of crop maturation whereas during the later stages of crop development a non-persistent or degradable pesticide might be used. Such a procedure, utilizing both types of compounds, might achieve the goal of reduction or partial elimination of persistent pesticides, as recommended in the PSAC Report on Use of Pesticides.

As useful as the persistent pesticides are in insect control, they have a long residence time in the soil and are capable of contaminating crops in successive years after initial application, either through direct entry into root crops, such as potatoes, carrots, sugar beets, etc., or by translocation to the leafy and stem portions of a plant or crop that is later to be consumed by domestic animals or man. Some illustrations of such occurences follow:

(a) soybeans containing endrin—this crop was grown in soil where cotton had been grown and treated with endrin;

(b) carrots containing endrin—grown in soil where a crop had been previously treated with endrin;

(c) alfalfa containing dieldrin and heptachlor epoxide—alfalfa was grown in soil where a previous crop had been treated with these pesticides;

(d) dried sugar beet pulp from sugar beets contaminated with dieldrin—this crop was grown in soil which had previously been treated with aldrin for several years.

The tolerances in feed crops have been purposely established to minimize or preclude transfer of pesticides as residues into meat, poultry, eggs and dairy products. Remarkable progress is being made in this direction under current uses of persistent pesticides in agricultural practices. The previously mentioned products are the types of foods that present the highest pesticide residues, but detailed reference to this matter will be made later.

The quantity of pesticides actually consumed by man has relevance to health significance. For this reason one might consider the setting of tolerances for pesticide residues on the processed foods or the "ready-to-eat prepared food" as the ideal practice. However, the objection to such a proposed procedure in establishment of tolerances is that one could not adequately refer residues above tolerances in the food at this point in the distribution system to appropriate corrective action. Hence, this system is impractical for a control program. The tolerance establishment makes use of data from experimental animals on "no effect" levels, cumulative potential of the pesticide, metabolic fate and maximal contribution to the total diet which might be expected if all commodities for which tolerances are sought have residues at the tolerance levels—all of which is extrapolated to potential effects on man. The tolerance level that is set permits an adequate margin of safety between that level and the "no effect" level obtained from animal experimental data, keeping in mind the proportion of the total diet contributed by the food crop which man would consume and from which the particular pesticide residue might be anticipated.

Another factor in the consideration of the applicability of tolerances in terms of safety is that the tolerance must be at such a level as to ensure safety for the consumer, if an individual did consume a particular raw food which contained residues at the tolerance level. As previously stated, however, in such deliberations the amount of food consumed in the raw state is compared with the proportion consumed in the processed state where residue reduction occurs.[8]

In the United States the Food and Drug Administration examines some 25,000 samples of food annually to ascertain the adequacy of compliance and the practices used in pesticide application to the end that food and feed crops are within the established tolerances. During a four-year period about half of the samples examined contained residues of one or more pesticide chemicals. Only 3% of these samples exceeded legal tolerances or, if no legal tolerances had been established, were beyond the guidelines for excessive residues. Of the samples containing residues, 75% of the individual pesticide residues found were below 0.11 ppm and 95% of the residues were below 0.51 ppm.[8]

In order to acquire definitive data on pesticide residues in foods as actually consumed, various systems have been employed. One of these systems is the total diet study or "market basket survey" used by the Food and Drug Administration. Detailed description of this procedure has been referred to elsewhere,[9] but, in essence, samples of food obtained bi-monthly at retail stores in five geographical regions are prepared for consumption and composited into 12 classes of similar foods for more reliable analysis and minimization of the dilution factor. The food intakes are those selected for a 16- to 19-year-old male group reflecting maximal consumption of about 4 kg. (8.8 lbs.) of food and beverage daily. This is almost twice the intake in the standard adult diet of an individual at moderate activity, which provides approximately 2.2 kg. (4.8 lbs.) daily. Hence, the intake of pesticide associated with this high food consumption should present the maximal exposure for a general population group. Other studies on total diet pesticide content have

Table I: Average Daily DDT and DDE Content of Total Diets or Prepared Meals

(U.S. Public Health Service Studies)

	Years	DDT mg.	DDE mg.
PHS household meals (Wenatchee, Wash.)[10]	1962-64	0.314	0.173
PHS restaurant meals (Wenatchee, Wash.)[10]	1962-64	0.038	0.044
PHS restaurant meals (Wenatchee, Wash.)[11]	1953-54	1.178	0.026
PHS institution study*[11-14]	1953-60	0.136	0.039
Mean of PHS studies		0.199	0.122
FDA total diet study**[15,16]	1963-64	0.026	0.015
FDA total diet study[8,9]	1965-67	0.028	0.021

*Mean of four studies including meals of meat abstainers (0.041 mg. DDT and 0.024 mg. DDE). Meals taken at Tacoma and Walla Walla, Wash., Tallahassee, Fla., and Anchorage, Alaska.

**Assuming intake of 3.78 kg. of diet as compared with PHS study where intake was 2.1 kg.

been conducted by the U.S. Public Health Service covering the period 1953-1964. These studies were based on complete, prepared meals taken in prisons, hospitals, restaurants and a college where meat was not a component of the diet.[10-14] In the Public Health Service studies the average daily intake of food was about 2.1 to 2.2 kg., which was considerably less than the total diet intake represented in the Food and Drug Administration studies for the 18- to 19-year-old male. Earlier diet studies conducted by FDA have been reported by Mills[15] and Williams.[16]

In Table I a summation of the data for all these studies is presented, reflecting the average daily DDT and DDE content of total diets or prepared meals during the period 1953-1967. The pesticide residues in household meals during 1962-1964 were somewhat higher than those in restaurant meals taken at Wenatchee, Washington, even though the total weight of food consumed was about the same. Home-grown foods or specialty produce which could have been used in the household meals and which may have been unprocessed or eaten raw, containing higher residues, may have accounted for this difference. In any event, it was assumed that the restaurant meals more nearly typify the average DDT and DDE intake for the general population in the United States. If one compares the DDT and DDE content of restaurant meals for the period 1953-54 with that of 1962-64 there is noted a decrease in daily DDT intake from 0.178 to 0.038 mg. and for DDE intake a slight increase from 0.026 to 0.044 mg. Studies in the institutions, including prisons and hospitals, during the period 1953-1960, reflected from the mean DDT value of four studies a slightly higher value for this pesticide than that in the restaurant study of 1962-64, but were comparable in DDT value to the restaurant study for 1953-54. The mean value for DDT daily intake in institutions for the period 1953-1960 was about 0.167 mg., but the value of 0.136 mg. given in Table I represents the inclusion of values from food samples taken at a college in Walla Walla, Washington, where there were meat abstainers. It is of interest to note that the diet for meat abstainers contributed only a daily intake of 0.041 mg. of DDT and 0.024 mg. of DDE.

For comparative purposes data from the Food and Drug Administration total diet studies are also included in Table I. It is of interest to note the general agreement in values of the daily DDT and DDE content of prepared meals and diets. The FDA total diet values for DDT and DDE content are slightly lower than any of the total diet values presented in the Public Health Service studies.

The amount of DDT in the diet (PHS restaurant study 1962-64) at a level of 0.038 mg. per day would represent a mean concentration of 0.018 ppm in the total wet diet. A level of 0.026-0.028 mg. per day (FDA total diet studies) would represent a mean concentration of 0.0065 ppm in the total wet diet, which is a considerably lower value than that for the PHS restaurant study. If one assumes a daily DDT intake of 0.038 mg., this would be equivalent to a daily dosage rate of about 0.0005 mg. per kg. for a man weighing 70 kg.

For the period 1965-67 in the U.S.A., residues of chlorinated organic pesticide chemicals have been found in all diet samples and all food classes within samples with the possible exception of beverages.[8] The average daily intake for this class of compounds, encompassing some 12 food classes in the total diet, was 0.0013 mg. per kg. of body weight in the general population. Meat, fish and poultry contribute about 40μg. or 40% of the total daily dietary intake of these pesticide residues (Fig. 3). If one combines this class of foods with dairy products, then over half of the daily intake (55.2%) of pesticide residues arises from these food items (Fig. 3). These pesticide chemicals are not applied directly to these food products but are carried through as metabolites of the parent compound and are deposited in tissue or excreted in the milk and thus indirectly become sources of the pesticides. Garden fruits, fruits and grain-cereal products provided approximately 10% each of the intake of chlorinated pesticides. The levels of pesticides ingested in these products are lower than in the animal, marine and dairy products since control is exercised over the direct application of chemicals to the raw agricultural commodities. DDT and analogs (DDE + TDE) plus dieldrin, lindane and heptachlor epoxide account for approximately 85% of the total intake of the chlorinated pesticides;[9] DDT alone, one of the major persistent pesticides, accounted for one-third.

For the three-year span 1965-67, the daily dietary intake of organic phosphate pesticide chemicals has been reported at 0.00013 mg. per kg. of body weight. Malathion alone accounts for about 77% of the daily intake of this group of "OP" compounds. Other "OP" compounds, such as parathion, diazinon, ethion and ronnel, were reported in such low frequency and quantity that they do not represent any significant contribution.[9]

Herbicide chemicals, such as 2,4-D, PCP, MCP, 2,4,5-TP and others, represented a level of residue exposure to the general population of about the same order as the "OP" compounds or 0.00013 mg. per kg. of body weight for the daily dietary intake.[9] Of this total, the common herbicide 2,4-D contributed one-third of the intake and MCP and PCP combined represented about one-half of the daily intake of herbicides.[9]

The carbamate-type pesticides are found infrequently in the total diet samples. Carbaryl, one of the primary carbamate insecticides, when detected in root crops, fruits, sugars and adjuncts, represented a total daily dietary intake of 0.0009 mg. per kg. of body weight for the general population.

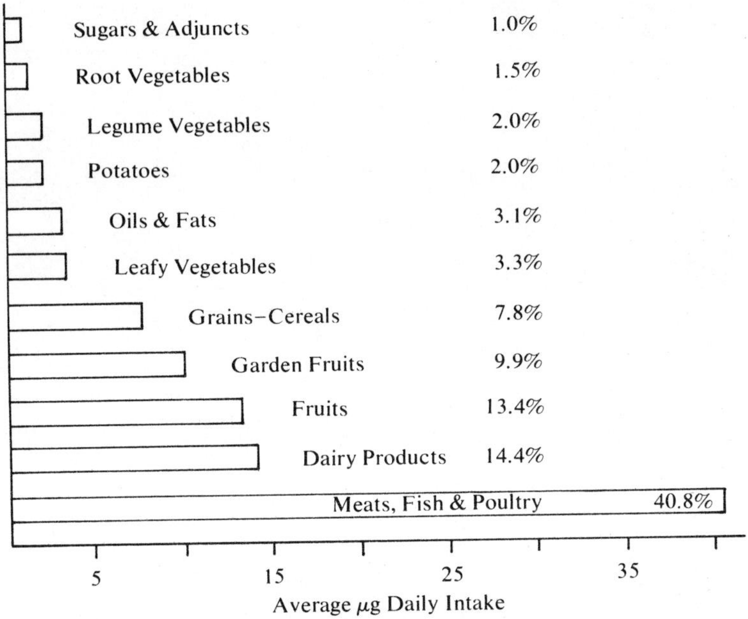

Fig. 3. Intake of pesticide residues in average total daily diet[9]

It appears that corrective measures implemented for minimizing the indirect sources of pesticides through reduction and/or cancellation of approved uses and patterns of use of some of the more persistent chlorinated organic pesticides in forage crops, pastures and animal feeds, have brought about a lower average level of dieldrin and heptachlor epoxide in 1967. Although the persistent and non-persistent pesticide chemicals appear, for example, in raw vegetables before preparation, peeling, processing and cooking removed all but 5 to 25% of the residue, depending upon the vegetable and the pesticide that is to be removed.[17]

Refined analytical procedures have improved the surveillance programs and the ability to detect organophosphate pesticides, and these changes may account for the increase in detectable levels and reporting of these chemicals in foods and total diet. However, there may be some increases in the "OP" compound utilization due to gradual replacement of the persistent "OC" (organochlorine) pesticides.[8]

The proportion of food containing residues at or above the

tolerance level is indeed quite small. In fact, the current legally adopted tolerances for raw agricultural commodities are considerably above the average levels found in a significant proportion of the food under surveillance for residues in the United States. Some low-level residues of pesticides in food have been reported for which tolerances have not been established. These chemical residues probably appear as normal environmental contaminants rather than as residues accruing in foods from improper uses in agricultural practices.[8]

Criteria for Safety Assessment

Establishment of finite levels for environmental contaminants, such as pesticides in the human food supply, is predicated on information and data relevant to safety. This assessment of safety eventuates in the setting of permissible levels of tolerances for the various pesticides. The tolerances must be established on the basis of toxicological studies in at least two species of experimental animals, one of which may be a non-rodent. Delineation of the toxicological procedures and requirements for such studies are beyond the scope of this report and are discussed elsewhere. However, such studies on experimental animals usually provide data on acute, subacute and chronic toxicity of the chemical pesticides examined. Further indications and knowledge of safety may be provided through information and data on these chemicals after a tolerance has been set and the pesticide has been in extensive use. This type of additional evidence on safety may be furnished through more extensive toxicological research using newer, sophisticated approaches or from direct or indirect extrapolation of findings regarding human exposure to these chemical pesticides. The clinical, biochemical, pharmacological and epidemiological data on human exposure to these pesticide chemicals may be generated from studies on occupational or industrial exposure, accidental exposure, controlled clinical and human toxicological investigations, or from comprehensive epidemiological studies using retrospective and prospective approaches on various populations. The latter studies may provide direct or presumptive evidence on these chemicals with respect to disease induction which may necessitate a reconsideration of previously established tolerances.

From the preceding discussion it is apparent that various procedures are required for quantification of the level of intake and the magnitude of the total exposure. An estimate of the actual ingestion in man is provided through the *total diet studies*, previously alluded to, which have been carried out in the United States by the Food and Drug Administration and the U.S. Public Health Service. Comparable studies have been carried out in Great Britain and other countries. The international concern about the potential dangers of pesticide residues in food is evidenced by the Food and Agricultural Organization of the United Nations through their standards for *acceptable daily intake* for several pesticides. Pesticides not currently covered by such standards may ultimately be covered through continued toxicological research. The acceptable daily intake established by the FAO Committee on Pesticides in Agriculture and the World Health Organization (WHO) Committee on Pesticide Residues reflects a range of pesticide residue levels for some of the more commonly used pesticides.[18] For comparative purposes the maximal value of this range may be used in an attempt to arrive at some measurement of the problem of potential hazard and the degree to which current levels of pesticide occurrence reflect a hazard reduction. These criteria for safety assessment may be referenced as MADI or maximal acceptable daily intake.[19] In utilizing the MADI this assumes that pesticide levels above the maximum would constitute a hazard to the general population. Such an index is used in the absence of any threshold or finite value above which the level of ingestion is clearly a hazard and below which it is clearly safe.

Another criterion that may be employed in projections on probable intakes of pesticides for which toxicological data are available is the so-called ETI or estimated tolerance intake. In this index there is incorporated an estimate of the percentage of specific foods in a normal diet which would contain a specific pesticide residue and then, utilizing the tolerance level for that specific pesticide, the total dose of pesticide from foods at the tolerance level is calculated.[20] Unfortunately, losses in residue due to preparative procedures, such as washing, trimming and cooking, are not taken into consideration.

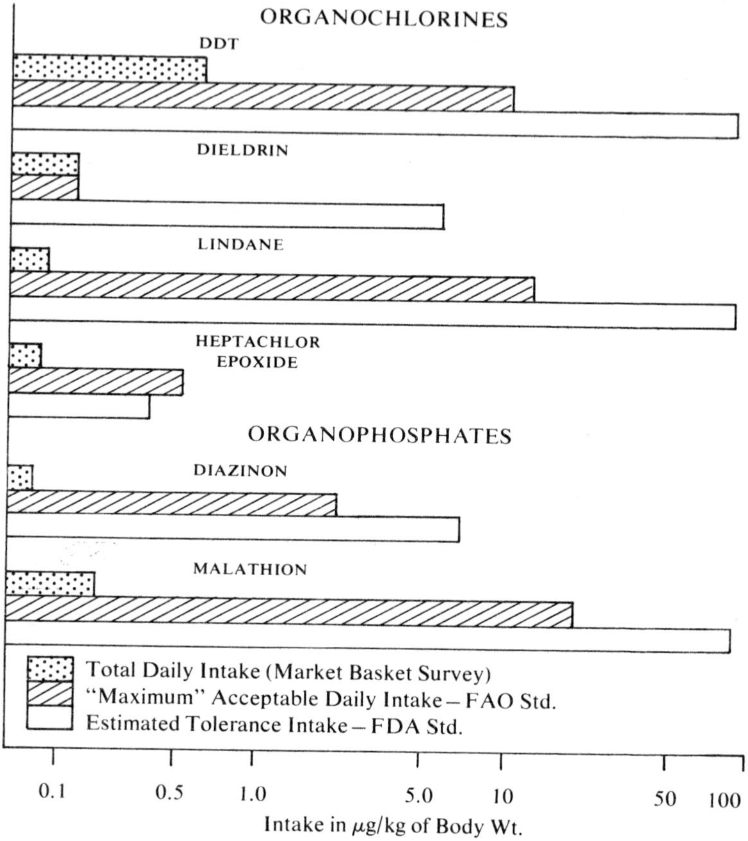

Fig. 4. Actual pesticide intake compared with FAO acceptable intake and FDA standard of estimated tolerance intake

From the three criteria described: (a) Actual Intake "Total Diet"—market basket survey, (b) FAO Acceptable Daily Intake —MADI, and (c) FDA Estimated Tolerance Intake, it is possible to make comparative evaluations of total intake and to determine how close these actual ingestions approach the toxicological guidelines or safety standards established by FAO/WHO and FDA. In Fig. 4 actual pesticide intake (from total diet assay) is compared with the FAO acceptable intake (using maximal value of MADI) and the FDA standard of ETI or estimated tolerance intake. It is apparent that the values for actual intake of pesticides from total diet assay are only a small fraction of the standards or critical levels promulgated by FAO and FDA. There are some exceptions, such as dieldrin, where the actual total intake approaches the maximal acceptable daily intake (FAO standard) but is only about 2% of the FDA estimated tolerance intake. Heptachlor plus heptachlor epoxide yield an actual residue value in the total diet which is 10% of the maximal

Table II: Most Frequently Detected Pesticides

Chemical pesticide	*Frequency of detection* %**
DDT	26.7
DDE***	25.5
Dieldrin	17.8
TDE***	10.0
Heptachlor epoxide	7.5
Lindane	4.8
BHC	2.8
Endrin	2.5
Aldrin	2.0
Toxaphene	1.5

**Some samples contain more than one residue.
***Metabolites of DDT, usually combined as a group.

allowable daily intake or FAO standard but exceeds the FDA standard of estimated tolerance intake (ETI) by 125%. Lindane and DDT levels in total diet samples appear to be well below any of the standard values. Diazinon, an organophosphate insecticide, appears in total diets at a level of 10% of the FAO–MADI standard.

From data of Duggan and Dawson[21] and Taylor and Favors[19] a ranking, on the basis of frequency of detection, of the first 10 pesticides is presented in Table II. In this instance the persistent organochlorine insecticides, such as DDT and its analogs and dieldrin, are the most frequently detected. The first 10 pesticides are ranked relevant to raw food samples containing residues over FDA tolerances and the percentage of food samples with above-tolerance residues (1966-67) as follows: toxaphene—5.4%; dieldrin—4.0%; diazinon—3.7%; DDT—2.8%; parathion—2.6%; chlordane—2.3%; BHC—2.0%; heptachlor epoxide—1.4%; TDE —0.9%, and malathion—0.6%.

Significant efforts must be made by industry and government to achieve a substantial reduction in the danger from pesticide residues. For example, if intensive education and compliance programs are instituted, an estimate can be made of the reduction in dietary intake of a pesticide residue that would result if all over-tolerance shipments of agricultural products were reduced to the tolerance level. Of those pesticides appearing in foods as residues which are over tolerance some do not rank close to the FAO or FDA critical levels in terms of actual ingestion in total diets appearing as prepared and cooked foods. In essence, from toxicological considerations the persistent organochlorine pesticides should receive highest priority in control programs since they have the capacity for sustained biological challenge to the somatic tissue due to their long residence time which may contribute to potential damage. The organophosphate compounds, commonly recognized as extremely hazardous during occupational exposure, at the low level exposure encountered through ingestion in foods are not readily stored in organs and tissues and *in vivo* are readily metabolized and eliminated.

Measurement of Biological Effects

BODY STORAGE

Human exposure to the environmental stress of pesticides evokes certain biochemical-pharmacological responses, one of which is the inevitable accumulation and storage in the tissues, the major reservoir being the adipose tissue. There is a dynamic equilibrium between the level of pesticide ingested, absorbed and inhaled and the level of pesticide that is ultimately deposited or metabolized and eliminated. In addition to the depot fat, pesticides have been found in the brain, liver, kidney and gonads. The levels observed are usually in direct relationship to the fat content of these organs and the magnitude of exposure. Fiserova-Bergerova *et al.*,[22] for example, noted a twofold increase in the levels of DDT and analogs in liver, brain, kidney, gonads and adipose tissue of 10 persons who died accidentally and who were occupationally exposed to pesticides in the course of their work as migrant labourers on vegetable farms in southern Florida. These investigators also observed that concentrations of these non-polar pesticides in the liver were approximately 10 times the levels found in kidney, brain and gonads, and may, in part, reflect the function of the liver as a target organ and organ of metabolism and excretion. The levels found in adipose tissue are approximately 10 times those in liver and 100 times the levels found in the kidney, gonads and brain. In the developing fetus the levels of DDT and its metabolites and dieldrin were greater than in the 0 to 5 year age group and more closely resembled concentrations noted in the older age groups. The finding, corroborated by other investigators, focuses attention on the aspect of placental transfer and the hazards of pesticide insult to neonatal groups of the general population. Evidence of placental transfer was noted as early as the 22nd week of gestation. Significantly lower levels of DDT and DDE were observed in children under 5 years of age but beyond that no correlation of age with tissue pesticide levels was observed.[22]

As previously indicated, the level of exposure can be correlated with concentration of storage of persistent organochlorine insecticides, such as DDT and dieldrin. Durham, Armstrong and Quinby[10] have plotted, on a log-log basis, the dosage levels of DDT in milligrams per man per day versus storage levels of DDT in body fat in ppm and obtained a linear relationship (Fig. 5). The lower part of the curve represents values for DDT intake from total diet surveys (intake—0.038 mg. per day; storage—3.9 ppm) including values for meat abstainers (0.041 mg. intake; storage—4.9 ppm) and a general population sampling in 1954 (0.164 mg. intake; storage—4.9 ppm). The higher values on the curve represent intake-storage relationships in prisoner volunteers who received know amounts of DDT ranging from 3.5 to 35 mg. per man per day. As more information and data accrue on the levels of organochlorine pesticides in the diet of the general population and comparable values for tissue storage, the

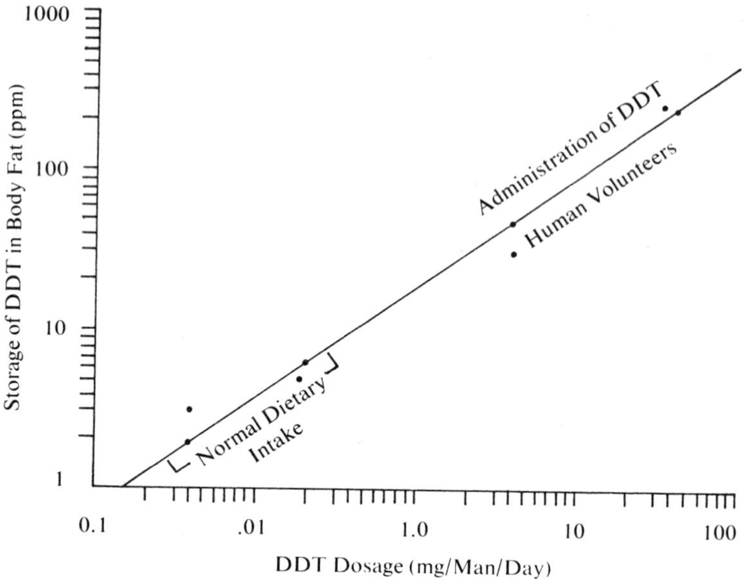

Fig. 5. Dosage levels of DDT (mg per man per day) versus storage levels of DDT in body fat in ppm[10]

lower portion of this curve can be plotted so as to provide a more comprehensive curve for computation of pesticide intake-storage relationships. These relationships have been studied by Lehman,[23] who determined in rats the storage ratios between dietary levels of the various pesticides (DDT, methoxychlor, lindane, dieldrin, endrin and isodrin) and the levels stored in the body fat. It was noted in these studies that as the dietary level of DDT decreases a greater proportion of the ingested insecticide is stored. For example, there is a ratio of 12 to 1 at a dietary level of 50 ppm whereas at 0.12 ppm the ratio is 57 to 1. If one extrapolates these findings to humans, assuming that man stores DDT at a rate comparable to that of the rat, then a total dietary intake of 0.02 ppm of DDT, with a DDT fat deposition of 5 to 7 ppm (Table III) would represent a ratio of approximately 350 to 1.

Table III: DDT and DDE Storage Levels in Various Types of Exposure

Exposure status	*No. of persons*	*DDT storage*	*DDE storage*
		ppm	*ppm*
Environmental	110	6.0 ± 0.26	8.6 ± 0.48
Occupational	30	14.0 ± 1.5	19.0 ± 2.2
General population	61	4.9 ± 0.35	6.1 ± 0.42

The storage levels of the organochlorine insecticides are dependent upon the exposure levels which man and animals encounter. Durham[24] has reported the DDT and DDE storage levels in individuals who were occupationally exposed, environmentally exposed (receiving pesticide exposure from community fogging operations, aerial spraying, etc.) and those of the general population who received the usual continuous exposure. These values, reported in Table III, reflect the effect of exposure on body storage of DDT and DDE.

The introduction of organochlorine insecticides for pest-vectored disease control and crop protection in 1941 resulted in an increase in environmental levels of these pesticides. Accordingly, this was reflected in the appearance of these chemicals in the body tissues and a gradual increase in the storage levels of these pesticides as shown in Fig. 6. It has been maintained by some investigators that peak concentrations were reached in 1950, after which there was a steady decline and then a plateau in pesticide levels. However, others have claimed that the maximal concentration in human adipose tissue was reached in 1955, followed by a decline and formation of a plateau in pesticide levels, representing the presence of these environmental contaminants continuously during the last 10 years. The values represented in Fig. 6 would appear to support the validity of the latter concept.[25-27]

During the period 1958 to 1965 various surveys in Europe, Asia, the Middle East and the United States have been made to determine the average concentration of DDT-derived materials

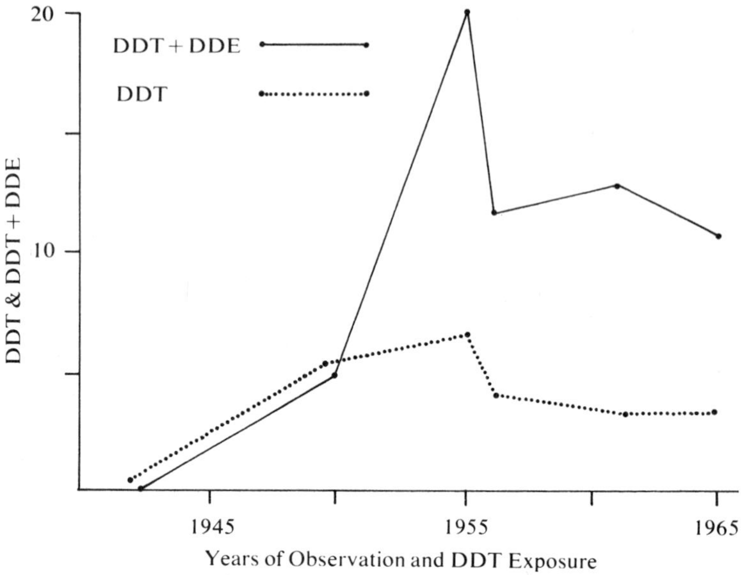

Fig. 6. Storage levels of pesticides between 1941 and 1965[27]

in the adipose tissue of the general populations in various countries (Fig. 7). England appears to incur the lowest body burden for DDT + DDE, whereas several areas in India revealed 25 to 30 ppm of DDT + DDE in the body fat of the general population. In the latter case these higher body fat levels for DDT + DDE are certainly a reflection of higher environmental contamination enhanced by vigorous pest control programs, such as mosquito abatement projects. The lower levels of DDT + DDE in body fat of Europeans are indicative of the stringent controls on the use of persistent organochlorine insecticides in those countries which, moreover, are reflected in decreased environmental levels and diminution of residues in locally grown food and forage crops.[27]

As indicated previously, the persistent pesticides have been identified in various organs and tissues. The British have found some of the organochlorine insecticides in gallstones at the following levels for these specific pesticides: γ BHC—0.03 ppm; dieldrin—0.005 ppm; pp′-DDE—0.04 ppm and p,p′-DDT—0.007 ppm.[28] DDA, the urinary metabolite of DDT, has been

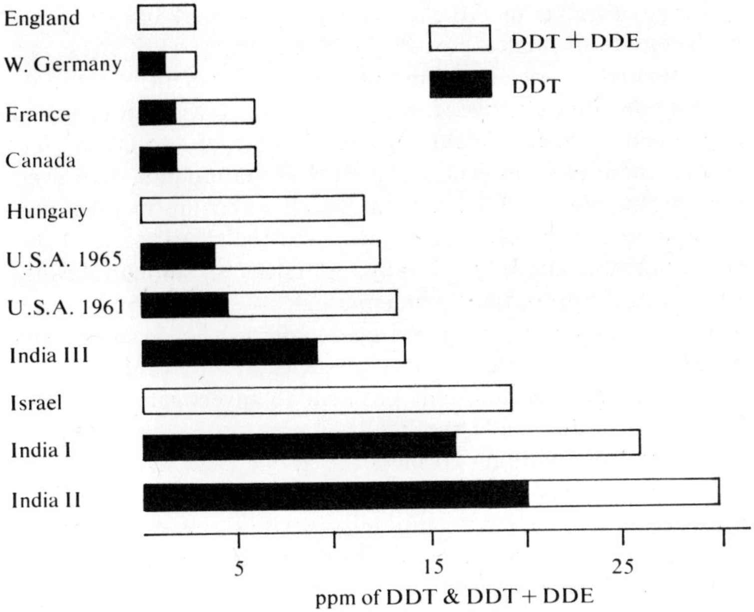

Fig. 7. Average concentration of DDT-derived materials in adipose tissue of general populations in various countries between 1958 and 1965[27]

identified in the urine of people occupationally exposed to high levels of DDT. DDE has been frequently identified in the blood of those people environmentally exposed (aerosol spraying, mosquito abatement, populations living in proximity to high-use areas of agricultural pesticides) and during occupational exposure. It is apparent that such biochemical indicators will provide useful measurements of pesticide exposure and hence are useful in assessment of the epidemiological impact of pesticides in relation to human health.

Chemical Epidemiology

Considerable attention has been given in national and international health programs to the requirement for detection and measurement of environmental exposure to pesticides, and of food residues. These programs encompass the establishment of tolerances and regulatory actions to eliminate, control, or reduce the level of the environmental exposure. Certainly, the level of stress can be evaluated and decisions on safety and assessment of response are founded on extensive toxicity studies on a wide spectrum of experimental animals including the estimate of "no effect" levels for these environmental chemical contaminants. However, the chronic effects of low-level pesticide exposure in man continue to be a problem for resolution, and the significance of this environmental challenge, if any, in terms of human health, necessitates appropriate epidemiological studies on variant groups of the population in selected geographical locations and of different ethnic origin, who experience a wide range in total exposure. The most difficult problem to investigate epidemiologically is undoubtedly the low-level exposure encountered by the general population. To meet the above objectives the U.S. Public Health Service, in 1963, mounted a full-scale epidemiological program called "Community Studies" in an attempt to establish a cause-and-effect relationship between pesticide exposure and human disease.[2]

The literature is replete with data on the magnitude of exposure of occupational workers and residents adjacent to locations where pesticides are applied for agricultural and public health purposes. Such data provide a measurement of stress, as has been previously shown, relevant to the body burden of pesticides in the general population. There is lacking, however, information on the relationship of this measured exposure to development of clinical signs or symptoms of poisoning or of demonstrable abnormalities of physiological function for the general population which receives chronic microinsults. Such data are available on controlled studies with human volunteers and those workers occupationally exposed who receive doses of pesticides above those of environmental exposure experienced by the general population.

It can be stated that poisoning from pesticides can be expected to appear most quickly, most frequently, most diversely and most severely in those people most extensively exposed. A wide array of biochemical, physiological and pathological aberrations have been observed from heavy exposure. Some of the interesting physiological effects studied involve kidney dysfunction, placental transmission of pesticides and electroencephalographic dysrhythmia.[29] The influence of certain nephrotoxic insecticide agents, such as parathion, resulting in kidney tubular dysfunction with a lowered phosphorus reabsorption index and the ultimate development of aminoaciduria and aminoacidemia, has been one of the most intriguing recent biochemical clinical studies; it was conducted in Florida on people occupationally exposed.[30] Other investigators have shown that workers exposed to chlorinated hydrocarbon and organophosphorus insecticides show characteristics of premature ageing and certain behavioural responses such as defects in memory, inability to concentrate and other aberrant neurological functions.[31]

DuBois[32] has studied the impact of prolonged exposure to organophosphorus insecticides. Although the levels of organophosphates permitted in foods may be below the levels which would cause inhibition of cholinesterase activity, somewhat higher levels on prolonged exposure may result in acquired resistance to the action of acetylcholine. This finding may explain the fact that various investigators failed to detect marked cholinesterase depression after prolonged feeding of organophosphates as may have been noted from a single exposure to the same pesticide at the same level of administration. Hence reliability of cholinesterase depression as an index for chronic exposure may be questioned. Furthermore, there may be such an adaptation by the body with development of a physiological effect on another target organ or system elsewhere.

Previous reference has been made to the correlation of blood DDT-DDE levels in certain groups of the population environmentally exposed. The levels of DDT-DDE have been found to correlate positively with random serum triglyceride levels and with left subscapular skinfold thickness. There does not appear to be any correlation with serum cholesterol level or any selected disease syndromes.[33]

Repeated references have been made to the effect of environmental exposure to pesticides on persons with respiratory diseases.[34] Although this association of pesticide exposure to chronic respiratory disease has been previously dismissed, recent studies in Hawaii have shown that there is a significant difference at the 5% level of confidence in the combined rates of reported asthma and chronic bronchitis in two population groups where household use of pesticides was frequent. Repeated attacks of sinus trouble were also reported.[35]

The total environmental exposure to pesticides from various sources, including diet, air, water, cosmetics, clothing, etc., may present to the general population a continuous low-level challenge which, in the case of the more persistent pesticides, manifests itself by an observed equilibrium between the environmental exposure and the resultant retention in human tissues and organs. Although the levels of pesticides measured in tissues and blood and as pesticide metabolites in urine reflect a response to such a challenge, the significant implications of this low-level chronic exposure in terms of well-defined clinical symptomatology or aberrant physiological function upon the general population are not well delineated at this time and must await findings from retrospective and prospective studies now in progress. Special attention is being given to those persistent pesticides which have the potential for chronic cellular insult and the induction of chronic disease.

References

[1]United States President's Science Advisory Committee: *Use of pesticides*; a report, Superintendent of Documents. U.S. Government Printing Office, Washington, 1963.

[2]Kraybill, H. F.: *Pesticides in public health.* Paper presented at the Michigan State Medical Society Centennial, Detroit, Michigan, September 24, 1965.

[3]Campbell, J. E., Richardson, L. A. and Schafer, M. L.: *Arch. Environ. Health (Chicago)*, 10: 831, 1965.

[4]Yobs, A.: *Report to United States Federal Committee on Pest Control, Subcommittee on Pesticide Monitoring*, 1967 (unpublished).

[5]Davies, J. E. *et al.*: *Amer. J. Public Health.* In press.

[6]Edmundson, W. F. *et al.*: *Industr. Med. Surg.*, 36: 806, 1967.

[7]Kraybill, H. F.: *The Public Health Service program on pesticides.* Paper presented at the Idaho Annual Health Conference on Pesticides. People and Problems, Sun Valley, Idaho, May 25-27, 1965.

[8]United States Department of Agriculture and Food and Drug Administration: Joint report on the regulation of pesticides in the United States; report as basis for discussion with the Federal Republic of Germany and the Benelux Countries, Washington, December 18-21, 1967 (unpublished).

[9]Duggan, R. E. and Weatherwax, J. R.: *Science*, 157: 1006, 1967.

[10]Durham, W. F., Armstrong, J. F. and Quinby, G. E.: *Arch. Environ. Health (Chicago)*, 11: 641, 1965.

[11]Walker, K. C., Goette, M. B. and Batchelor, G. S.: *Journal of Agricultural and Food Chemistry*, 2: 1034, 1954.

[12]Hayes, W. J., Jr. *et al.*: *A.M.A. Arch. Industr. Health*, 18: 398, 1958.

[13]Hayes, W. J., Jr., Durham, W. F. and Cueto, C., Jr.: *J.A.M.A.*, 162: 890, 1956.

[14]Durham, W. F. *et al.*: *Science*, 134: 1880, 1961.

[15]Mills, P. A.: *Journal of the Association of Official Agricultural Chemists*, 47: 74, 1964.

[16]Williams, S.: *Ibid.*, 47: 815, 1964.

[17]Farrow, R. P. *et al.*: *Journal of Agricultural and Food Chemistry*, 16: 65, 1968.

[18]Food and Agriculture Organization of the United Nations, Committee on Pesticides in Agriculture and World Health Organization Expert Committee on Pesticide Residues: Evaluation of the toxicity of pesticide residues in food: report of a joint meeting, Geneva, September 30-October 7, 1963. Food and Agriculture Organization of the United Nations, Rome, 1964.

[19]Taylor, R. J. and Favors, J.: *Food—Bacterial contamination model*, staff paper, F.D.A., September 28, 1967.

[20]Lehman, A. J.: *Summaries of pesticide toxicity*, Associate Commissioner for Planning and Evaluation (unpublished), Association of Food and Drug Officials of the U.S., Topeka, Kansas, 1965.

[21]Duggan, R. E. and Dawson, K.: *FDA Papers*, 1: 4, June 1967.

[22]Fiserova-Bergerova, V. *et al.*: *Industr. Med. Surg.*, 36: 65, 1967.

[23]Lehman, A. J.: *Quarterly Bulletin of the Association of Food and Drug Officials of the U.S.*, 20: 95, March 1956.

[24]Durham, W. F.: *Arch. Environ. Health (Chicago)*, 10: 842, 1965.

[25]Quinby, G. E. *et al.*: *J.A.M.A.*, 191: 175, 1965.

[26]Davies, J. E., Welke, J. O. and Radomski, J. L.: *Epidemiological aspects of pesticides in the South.* Report to the 22nd annual meeting of the American Association of Industrial Nurses, Miami Beach, Fla., April 6-8, 1965.

[27]Kraybill, H. F.: *Pesticide residues in mammalian tissues: problems, incidence and controls.* Paper presented at the 19th annual Reciprocal Meat Conference of the American Meat Science Association, Ithaca, N.Y., 1966.

[28]Great Britain, Laboratory of the Government Chemist: Report of the Government Chemist, 1966. Her Majesty's Stationery Office, London, England, 1967, p. 91.

[29]Upholt, W. M., Kraybill, H. F. and Davis, R. S.: *New leads in health pesticides research.* Report to the 5th Interamerican Conference on Toxicology and Occupational Medicine, Miami, Fla., August 1-4, 1966.

[30]Davies, J. E., Mann, J. B. and Tocci, P. M.: *Ann. N.Y. Acad. Sci.*, in press.

[31]Holmes, J. and Metcalf, D. R.: *Ibid.*, In press.

[32]DuBois, K. P.: *Arch. Environ. Health (Chicago)*, 10: 837, 1965.

[33]Weiner, B. P., Worth, R. M. and Shimatsu, F. Y.: Personal communication.

[34]Ganelin, R. S., Cueto, C., Jr. and Mail, G. A.: *J.A.M.A.*, 188: 807, 1964.

[35]Klemmer, H. W.: Personal communication.

Human Needs and Inhuman Cities

EDWARD T. HALL

The United States today finds itself in the midst of four interrelated crises. The first is political and is particularly critical overseas in Vietnam. The second concerns the macroecological system as defined by Barbara Ward in *Spaceship Earth*. The third crisis is the population explosion, and the fourth is the urban crisis. Additional subcrises which are byproducts of our rapid economic growth complicate the distressing state of the culturally deprived in "the other America." I think history may show that, in spite of the urgency and the seriousness of our political-military involvement in Vietnam, the last three crises will require our greatest expenditure of energy and wisdom, and a far greater concentration of total effort than that demanded in this war. From my own point of view, I find it impossible to separate these three crises: ecological-systems, population explosion, and urban deterioration. All of them bear directly on the topic of this symposium.

One does not shape and maintain the physical environment independent of the spatial experience which may range from the most intimate—like the physical touching of bodies—to reveries of future excursions to lakes and mountain streams. The sense of crowding—or its obverse—is so subtle and so complex

Source: Edward T. Hall, "Human Needs and Inhuman Cities", published originally under Smithsonian Institution copyright in *The Fitness of Man's Environment*. Reprinted by permission of the publisher. This entire work is now in the Harper & Row Torchbook edition.

that I am continually amazed by some newly-identified facet of the subject. I was once discussing spatial needs with a psychiatric colleague, and he pointed out the relationship of unused distant space to one's immediate feelings about life in the city. He phrased it as follows: "If I were to hear that the people of the United States no longer had access to our national parks —the forest and the mountains and the great outdoors—even though I might never visit them again, my anxiety rate would be very considerably increased. The important thing is to know that they are there and available." When someone says that his anxiety rate has risen, this is only another way of saying that he is under stress and that his adrenals are working overtime. There are, of course, a great many individuals who, having lived all of their lives in cities, have no conscious need for open space and, in fact, may even be quite threatened by the outdoors. There is great danger, however, in allowing a large segment of our population to grow up without ever experiencing the complex relationships that make up ecological systems: we could develop a citizenry so uninformed as to permit the destruction of its own biotope. I'm not certain that we have not already done so. As recently as five years ago, it was difficult to interest people in the significance of John Calhoun's work with rats or John Christian's studies of the consequences of animal crowding. Today, one can hardly pick up a newspaper without reading about a new study on the effects of crowding. This recent preoccupation with crowding is symptomatic of our times, and our growing awareness of its consequences is extremely encouraging. There is also an increased awareness of the fact that each species inhabits its own biotope, and that each biotope constitutes part of a complex of interrelated ecosystems. All too many Americans, however, still demand specific answers to specific problems. In considering the human environment we are not dealing with the kind of phenomena in which one can identify specifics. Rather, we are dealing with systems that require a holistic approach, a point made repeatedly and elegantly by René Dubos. The ethological evidence is overwhelming: as populations build up, so does stress. Eventually, the animals' capacity to withstand stress begins to diminish, and the population collapses for a variety of reasons.[1]

Man has confounded the issue considerably and in a number of different ways. Not only has he produced a variety of extensions—like automobiles and factories—but his evolution is now primarily *by means* of his extensions. Man has conditioned himself to respond in quite different ways to the environmental pressures of crowding. In a sense, people of different ethnic groups respond differently to crowding because they perceive space differently. Man, as a culture-producing and culture-internalizing organism, has created a number of different types of biotopes for himself. There is no standard way of measuring spatial adequacy for man. What is crowded to an Englishman would be impossibly controlled or understimulating to an Arab. Because of such cultural differences, it is necessary to introduce an added dimension that will make it possible to equate space needs of different cultures according to some sort of self-anchoring scale. We have this instrument in the various theories of sensory deprivation and information overload. Man can suffer from both, and an excess of either can destroy him.[2] An adequate environment balances sensory inputs and provides a mix that is congenial as well as consistent with man's culturally conditioned needs. This principle applies to housing standards for our own socioeconomic groups in the United States. I mention this by way of introduction because the hidden structure of culture is one of the most consistently ignored features of our 20th-century life.

What are we facing today in our cities? In the summer of 1966, Joseph Alsop devoted three columns to cities. In his first column he wrote: "The problem of the cities, in the form it is now assuming, is the most urgent, the most difficult, and the most frightening American domestic problem that has emerged in all the years of this country's history since the Civil War."[3] In a recent *Fortune* article, Edmund Faltermayer states: "Two things are common to all the great cities: an exciting and beautifully designed downtown section, and a large middle-class population living close to the central core. Most American cities fail miserably on both counts. Only New York, Chicago, and San Francisco can even make claims to greatness."[4] Elsewhere I have stated: "the implosion of the world's population into cities everywhere is creating a series of destructive behavioral sinks more lethal than the hydrogen bomb. Man is faced with a chain reaction and practically no knowledge of the structure and the cultural atoms producing it."[5] The current urban crisis is sufficiently acute that its seriousness is widely recognized by laymen and specialist alike.

In the last thirty years, the character of our major cities in the United States has changed radically.[6] Our cities have been bombed by urban renewal in as devastating a way—and just as effectively—as though they had been bombed by an outside enemy. The difference is that if the bombing had come from an enemy, we would have recognized the crisis and would have done something about it. As it is, there is no coherent program for our cities. People are moved about, neighborhoods destroyed, whole viable social groups disrupted, and the fabric of life disintegrated—all in the name of progress. Fried's and Gleicher's studies of the Boston West End are particularly relevant.[7] For the first time we have documentation on an impressive scale of what happens when the members of a dominant ethnic group and class look at the biotope of another group and fail to see its structure. Seeing no structure, they then proceed to destroy. The same thing has happened in many other American cities.

Lewis Mumford accustomed us to thinking of the city as a process. He showed the city as the focus of the activities that make up what we have come to know as civilization. It is not too farfetched to think of a society as a living organism. Using a physiological analog, the city can be compared to various parts of the nervous system. If we were, therefore, to perceive in a human body the wild and uncontrolled growth of cells in the central nervous system or in an important ganglion of nerves controlling the functions, we would know that there was a serious crisis and act accordingly. In considering the plight of our cities, I do not detect signs of the kind of urgent action that the symptoms warrant. In fact, Vice President Humphrey observed recently that if the war in Vietnam were to end tomorrow he questioned whether the United States was prepared to spend the released billions on the urban environment.[8]

In our economic development programs overseas, we recognize that there is very little that can be done about underdeveloped countries until a large, stable, middle class has been established.

These countries that have been recipients of so much foreign aid are by and large characterized by a massive, undereducated, underskilled working or peasant class. Our own major cities are now taking on many of the population characteristics of the so-called underdeveloped countries. As the poor move into cities and the middle-class flees to the suburbs, the situation in the cities becomes increasingly unstable. Cities today are principally for the very rich and the very poor.

In New York City, traffic is at a standstill because we cannot bring ourselves to do the obvious: discourage private vehicles from entering Manhattan by imposing high tolls, and restrict the time when trucks can use the streets. A recent issue of *Newsweek* was devoted to the incredible difficulty that Americans experience getting around this country.[9] A city that is impossible to get out of without going through the added tension of traffic jams has a higher stress factor than one with decent, pleasant public transportation. There is an added element of the irrational here for, as Alsop says in the columns referred to above, we are willing to spend billions upon billions for freeways and expressways that pour automobiles into our cities, and virtually nothing for schools. Yet our schools represent one of the single most important features of our environment: people will make all kinds of sacrifices to move into an area where there are good schools, and almost nothing will hold them in an area where the schools are inferior.

When Europeans first settled North America, man was presented with an entire continent rich in resources. He had the tools, the know-how, and the energy to exploit it. No such situation has ever existed before, nor will it exist again on our planet. In the four generations since the Civil War, when this country was forming itself, we acquired some very bad habits which permitted every man to do as he pleased. Now we have suddenly run out of frontier, and we have produced an economy which, like a chain reaction, is self-sustaining. Our prosperity could ruin us, not because it is bad to be prosperous, but simply because we don't know how to plan for the added dwellings, automobiles, boats, and airplanes. Nor have we learned how to dispose of the resulting pollutants, or how to design the spaces for the masses of people that are moving in and out of our cities each day.

In the United States we allow individuals to do virtually anything: pollute the lakes, contaminate the atmosphere, build a high-rise next door that makes our own living space uninhabitable because it shuts off the view, create walled-in slums in public housing high-rise, transform a potential recreation area on a lake into a run-down industrial waste, plow up the countryside, bulldoze trees, and build thousands of identical prefabricated bungalows in open country. Peter Blake in his book, *God's Own Junkyard*, has documented this aspect of our anarchic and anomic approach to planning. I have discovered (to my sorrow) that in building a house, plumbers and electricians often make important decisions overruling the owner and the architect: they change walls with abandon, run pipes where they should never be, and arrange interior spaces at will. Similarly, important decisions on the national scene are often made by officials, both public and private, who have little or no knowledge of the consequences of their actions.

If our historical traditions have been no help to us in the face of our environmental crisis, the state of present day knowledge about man also leaves much to be desired. We need to learn much more about man's basic nature and his requirements as a biological organism. Also lacking is basic data on what constitutes optimum conditions for man's social and cultural development. In recent years I have been conducting research on one aspect of man's requirements: his spatial needs. In the course of my work on proxemics—man's perception and use of space—I've observed that man shares with lower life forms certain basic needs for territory. Each man has around him an invisible series of space bubbles that expand and contract, depending upon his emotional state, his culture, his activities, and his status in the social system. People of different ethnic origins need different kinds of spaces, for there are those who like to touch and those who do not. There are those who want to be auditorially involved with everybody else (like the Italians), and those who depend upon architecture to screen them from the rest of the world (like the Germans). A more detailed description of cross cultural differences in the perception and use of space can be found in my book on proxemics, *The Hidden Dimension*.

In addition to ethnic differences in spatial requirements there are differences in people's tolerance for change and mobility within their own culture. Studying the effects of urban renewal on slum dwellers, I've found evidence that indicates that very poor uneducated people have a much lower tolerance for being displaced than people of the middle class. Even a move across the street can be traumatic because it alters the pattern of social relationships. This is one of many reasons why the "Instant Rehab" experiments in New York are of great importance. These experiments involve a procedure for stripping the interior of an old building down to the brick or masonry wall, cutting a large hole in the roof and lowering a core of pre-assembled utility systems through the roof. Using this technique, trained crews of workmen have completely rehabilitated a small building in less than two days. For this short period, the building's occupants can be moved to a hotel and then moved back to their old home with no disruption of their relationships with friends and neighbors.

For several years I have been investigating the relationship of the working class urbanite to his environment. It is a widely known fact that high-rise public housing has not been popular with high-rise occupants, particularly those families who have recently come to the city from rural areas. My studies indicate that the high-rise not only structures relationships between the occupants in specific ways, but it removes many of the challenges and the reasons for neighborhood organizations that, in turn, perform important social functions. The high-rise has proved to be a new source of anomie in ghetto life.

To further complicate the problem of providing adequate public housing for our urban populations, Glazer and Moynihan have documented the long suspected fact that the United States is not the melting pot that we once believed it to be. Ethnicity is much more tenacious than had originally been supposed. Yet, nowhere do I find evidence that plans for public housing recognize the existence of different needs for different ethnic groups. Recent growing concern about air pollution and water pollution, sparked by newspaper and TV publicity, has helped alert the country to these dangers. Hopefully, we will soon have national pollution controls. Another grave danger, but one that is not widely understood, is the very real danger we face from overcrowding in our urban centers.

It seems obvious to say that our total environment must be protected and enhanced by the establishment of national and local planning authorities using the best available professional advisors. Two key disciplines needed for successful environmental planning are architecture and city planning. Unfortunately, neither discipline is presently prepared for this responsibility. The education of architects and planners is, with few exceptions, extraordinarily limited. Conspicuously absent from their curricula are the social sciences and humanities, to say nothing of ecology. Training in even rudimentary research procedures is rare. In the last seven years, I have addressed at least three thousand architects, published in the principal architectural journals, taught architecture students, and interviewed dozens of architects. In all this time I have failed to find a single instance of a systematic recording of feedback from users which could later be incorporated in the program or design phase of a new building. All over the United States, rooms have been getting steadily smaller, ceilings lower, walls more transparent to sound, views cut off, and what do we know about the consequences? What hard data is there? What feedback from users? Every year the Government spends millions for building, yet nowhere is there a requirement for impartial reporting on the degree to which these buildings serve the needs of their occupants. For example, FHA requirements for housing, promulgated with the best of intentions, bear little or no relation to man's sense of crowding and often place a straitjacket on all but the most pedestrian designers. Even the Pueblo Indians in New Mexico, if they are to qualify for FHA loans, must choose from among FHA designs (White man's designs). Pueblo designs do not meet FHA standards, yet they are vastly more suited to the needs of the Indians than any design produced by FHA.

The professions of architecture and city planning suffer from serious deficiencies which must be corrected if this nation is to plan intelligently to improve the total environment. I refer to: first, the widespread practice of architects and planners to pay close attention to a narrow reference group (other architects), awarding prizes on the basis of two-dimensional representations of structures often *before they are built!* Few designers see *people* in their projects, only prizes from other architects and planners. Second, there is a failure to get feedback on the consequences of their design decisions. Third, there are no plans for making available the results of studies that could be used in plans for future building: there is no clearinghouse for architectural programs or designs by geographic area, class, or ethnic group. The result is that even when architects and planners want such data they have virtually no way of finding it.

The extreme seriousness of our environmental crisis demands immediate and total response from this nation with the full participation of business, Government, and universities. By and large our universities have failed to become involved in environmental problems until very recently, and most of them are still only peripherally involved. It is no wonder that students all over the country are setting up their own underground colleges to meet today's problems. I would suggest that the university, as we know it, should be stood on its head. It is not enough to set up centers for "urban studies," which are usually only a sop to the urban crisis and a means to tap Government and foundation funds. Instead, the entire university should be *involved* in the urban process.

In recent years I have had the good fortune to work with design students. As a group they are the most responsive students I have ever taught. If they are properly trained, they question the basic design of virtually everything. They examine the processes at work in a given activity and they question assumptions endlessly. Because they are already trained to look for new ideas and new solutions, I have found that I can train these students in half the time required for liberal arts students. Tómas Maldonado has suggested that design education be integrated into the university curriculum on a level with the divisions of physical science, behavioral science, and the humanities. This idea should certainly be tried. I can think of nothing more important than teaching young people about environmental design, using data from such disciplines as ecology, psychology, and anthropology. Particular attention should be focused on research into man's spatial requirements. I am confident that such research and training would produce students who could discover better answers to man's needs than are currently being provided.

In addition to training and research programs, I would hope that some of our universities would begin to produce some working models of man's biotope. These would enable us to make accelerated studies of the total environment including our cities. At the moment we have no working model for the city.

In closing I would like to stress the importance of considering this small planet as an entire ecological system. This concept is basic to any planning for the improvement of our environment. We can regard our cities either as disaster areas beyond remedial action or as opportunities to learn more about man and his relationships to his environment. If we choose the latter course we will find that most of our urban problems merely reflect basic inadequacies in our total environment; inadequacies which will have to be remedied if man is going to persist on this planet.

References

[1]This process has been described in detail by John Christian (The Pathology of Overpopulation; *Military Medicine*, no. 7, pp. 571-603, July 1963) and V. C. Wynne-Edwards (Self-regulatory Systems in Populations of Animals; *Science*, vol. 147, pp. 1543-1548, March 1965: *Animal Dispersion in Relation to Social Behavior*, New York, 1962). Highly relevant here is the work of Wilhelm Schäfer, director of the Frankfort Natural History Museum. Schäfer's 1956 monograph, *Der Kritische Raum und die Kritische Situation in der Tierischen Sozietät* (*Critical Room and Critical Situations in Animal Societies*), deals with the added dimension of pollution and how it has been handled in the past on simpler organizational levels. Schäfer's point is that as population builds up, a critical situation is reached when a population contaminates its environment with its own waste products. If this crisis is not solved, the population dies rapidly and the process is irreversible. Each solution to a crisis has in it the seeds of new crises because solutions permit larger and larger concentrations of organisms, hence greater volume of pollutants which, in turn, demands more drastic solutions.

[2]In a paper presented at the 133d annual convention of the American Association for the Advancement of Science in Washington, D.C., on Dec. 27, 1966, A. S. Welch and B. L. Welch reported that small laboratory animals went into a stupor when crowded (overstimulated). The specific agent was an overabundance of three chemicals—norepinephrine, dopamine, and serotinin—which carry messages across the synapses separating nerve cells in the brain. See also: A. S. Welch and B. L. Welch, Differential Effect of Chronic Grouping and Isolation on the Metabolism of Brain Biogenic Amines, *The ASB Bulletin*, vol. 13, no. 2, p. 48 (April 1966); B. L. Welch, Psychophysical Responses to the Mean

Level of Environmental Stimulation: a Theory of Environmental Integration, Symposium on Medical Aspects of Stress in the Military Climate, Washington, D.C., April 1964 (sponsored by Walter Reed Army Institute of Research).

[3]Joseph Alsop, Matter of Fact, *The Washington Post*, Aug. 1, 3, and 5, 1966.

[4]Edmund K. Faltermayer, What it takes to make great cities, *Fortune*, vol. LXXV, pp. 118-123, 146-151, January 1967.

[5]Edward T. Hall, *The Hidden Dimension*, Garden City, N.Y., 1966. See, in particular, chap. XII, p. 155.

[6]This has been extensively reported on by: Charles Abrams, *The City is the Frontier*, New York, 1965; Constantinos A. Doxiadis, *Urban Renewal and the Future of the American City*, 1966; *Architecture in Transition*, New York, 1963; Marc Fried, Grieving for a lost home, *in* Leonard J. Duhl's *The Urban Condition*, New York, 1963; Herbert Gans, *The Urban Villagers*, Cambridge, Mass., 1960; Nathan Glazer and Daniel P. Moynihan, *Beyond the Melting Pot*, Cambridge, Mass., 1963; Victor Gruen, *The Heart of Our Cities*, New York, 1964; E. H. Gutkind, *The Twilight of Cities*, New York, 1962; Jane Jacobs, *The Death and Life of Great American Cities*, New York, 1961; Barbara Ward, The Menace of Urban Explosion, *The Listener*, vol. 70, no. 1807, pp. 785-787, November 14, 1963 (BBC, London).

[7]Marc Fried and Peggy Gleicher, Some Sources of Residential Satisfaction in an Urban Slum, *Journal of the American Institute of Planners*, vol. 27, 1961.

[8]James Reston, Washington: The State of the Union, *New York Times*, January 8, 1967.

[9]The Agony of Getting Anywhere, *Newsweek*, vol. 69, no. 2, pp. 43-48 (January 9, 1967).

Housing and Environment

MARVIN LIPMAN

Housing and Human Well-Being

In its broadest terms, the traditional theory of environmental determinism argues that by changing the environment, particularly the housing environment, it is possible to effect improvements in people's behavior, in their health, living habits and personal well-being. This assumption provided much of the impetus for early efforts to promote public housing and slum-clearance programs. It is still accepted by many to-day.

The hypothesis of a simple relationship between the housing environment and its social effects has given way to an increased understanding of the complexity of factors involved. Schorr, in his book *Slums and Social Insecurity*,[1] carefully documents the range of factors involved, while it is clear from the study *The Housing Environment and Family Life* that even in a carefully designed research study, it is difficult to show conclusively that a better housing environment brings improvement to any marked extent in specific areas of social functioning.[2]

In the Canadian context, a recent study by Kennedy and Smith of housing conditions in remote northern communities in the prairie provinces, brings out this inter-relationship of factors.[3] In their view, some of the poorest housing conditions in Canada

Source: Marvin Lipman, "Housing and Environment" is based on his chapter "Social Effects of the Housing Environment" in *The Right to Housing*, 1970. Montreal: Harvest House Limited Publishers. Reprinted by permission of the publisher and author.

exist in the communities included in this study and they suggest that improvement in the housing environment would lead to an advancement in other aspects of living. Nevertheless, the authors recognize that, without progress in employment and education opportunities, it is unrealistic to expect any major change simply as a result of improving the housing environment. A similar point is made in a report of the Conseil des Oeuvres de Montréal:

> While income, education and employment directly account for differences among people in standards of living, housing is both the product and expression of these differences. A country's housing is a general reflection of its standard of living and that of each social class in the society. Although an improvement in housing conditions does not necessarily imply an improvement in the standard of living of the people concerned, a better living environment creates a favourable climate for the pursuit of further education which in turn leads to better employment and the desire for better living conditions. Healthy and decent housing for all, and especially for the disadvantaged, constitutes an essential element of any strategy aimed at improving the living conditions of the population in question.[4] (Translation of French text.)

Social Implications of the Type of Housing

A drastic change has occurred in Canada in recent years in the type of housing being built; a trend full of social implications.

The proportion of single-family homes being built has fallen from two-thirds of all housing starts in 1962 to about one-third in 1968. It is even more marked in large urban areas. Recent figures from Toronto indicate that in the metropolitan area, four apartment units are being started for every single-family home under construction, while in the city proper, the ratio is sixty apartment units for every house.

Is this a change we have made by choice? It may be argued that low vacancy rates in apartments indicate many prefer this kind of accommodation and that recognition of this market has led to the change. On the other hand, choice suggests alternatives, and the possibility of single-family accommodation as an alternative for families with dependent children has been severely limited.

It is widely believed that the majority of Canadians still regard the single-family house as the most desirable form of living accommodation. Again, the reasons for this may be economic (the building of equity), but there are many social considerations involved. These include such factors as the pride of ownership, the desire for privacy, the control of property, and the fact that a house is a good place for families to bring up young children. In effect, the whole growth of suburbia has been geared to fulfilling this ideal.

In reality, nevertheless, it is land economics that are forcing a situation in which building at high densities is a necessity, particularly in the inner city. Row or town housing has resulted which, although it may not meet all the requirements of ownership and privacy, still allows for children to be close to ground level and better supervised. The major area of concern is the multi-storied apartment building, or "high-rise," particularly as it becomes an increasingly important source of accommodation for families in the central city, where land values are highest.

The objection here is that while high-rise living is satisfactory for certain groups (the swingers, the newly married, those with grown families), it is not a suitable housing environment for families with dependent children. For the first group, the proximity to employment, to services, to "where the action is," all help to create an environment in the central city which is considered desirable. For the latter group, the fact that children are far from the ground, cannot be easily supervised, do not always have the space deemed necessary for their development, all tend to argue against this form of housing for families.

It is not hard to find illustrations of this problem in both private and public housing. According to Elizabeth Wood "the basic evil of high rise apartments for families is the distance they place between the mother and her children when they are playing outside the dwelling."[5] A recent letter in a Toronto newspaper makes this point eloquently.

> I'm slowly going nutty with 3 children under five years in a high rise apartment. Believe me, an apartment is no place to raise children...They are all becoming little clinging vines because they really have never been anywhere without me. I'm afraid to let them outside the apartment door because the elevators are such a hazard...[6]

Studies have suggested that certain patterns of reaction result from apartment living. The husband, it is alleged, feels himself less of a man as a result of not being needed to do those things he would ordinarily be expected to do in a house. Young children are made more dependent by the need to be very closely supervised by the mother, who is unwilling to let them roam loose on the ground out of sight. Older children are removed from parental supervision and thus are allowed more independence than they may be able to handle.

If these two conditions (single-family housing and high-rise living) can be polarized to the extent suggested, how does one deal with the social effects of the housing types described? One way would be to make a social judgement that while high-rise living is desirable for certain groups, it is not desirable for growing families.

In effect, we would be saying that economic considerations are less important than social considerations in producing the kind of housing environment we want for families. Denmark, for example, appears to have made just this kind of judgement. There, the trend from high density and apartment living has been reversed. Statistics show that in 1959 over 50 per cent of all dwellings completed were multi-unit dwellings. This percentage has steadily diminished so that, although the number of dwelling units built has been rising, only 30 per cent were multi-unit dwellings in 1965.

In many ways, our current emphasis in housing and transportation policies are geared to the potential of increasing the supply of single-family housing. Land assembly, greater control of land speculation, satellite or new cities, and transportation corridors all tend to make more land available and to extend the range of reasonable housing choices for families. It is not difficult to develop ways of extending this range of choices to all income levels through such devices as rent subsidies, write-down of land costs, reduction of down payments and so on. If we feel some form of housing other than apartment living is best for families, even though it may cost us more money, it is within the realm of possibility.

However, because it will take time to increase the supply of available land required to expand the range of housing choices, we will continue to be forced by economic considerations to build family high-rise apartments for the time being. In the meantime we must try and create the best kind of housing environment possible out of this form of building. To date these buildings have not been designed for family use, except perhaps for the family with one small child or where children have reached adolescence.

There are many architectural and design solutions to the problems of providing play space within buildings, facilities geared to growing families, and work areas for fathers outside the apartment unit. New construction methods also promise a greater degree of flexibility to changing needs. The development of standards for space and amenity better related to family needs, and the possibility of finding mortgage financing to translate these standards into buildings, are more difficult problems to overcome. Perhaps the most important factor in creating the best kind of housing environment possible is a conviction on the part of governments that the present self-contained apartment unit is not sufficient for families, and something more suited to their needs requires encouraging. From this changes in standards, design and financing would tend to follow.

In urban areas, the form of housing has been standardized into the apartment, the row house, the semi-detached and the single family house. The promise of Habitat 67 as a stimulator of new forms of housing has not, as yet, been fulfilled, although thought is being given to new forms of housing arrangement to make better use of land and to reduce costs. New approaches to financing and different forms of tenure have been stimulated by the current housing shortage and rising costs. Condominium ownership is now seen as possible not only for high-income but for moderate-income groups as well. Other forms of ownership, co-operative and non-profit housing stimulated by churches, labor unions, and other groups all hold promise of increasing the supply of low—and moderate-income housing.

Tenure and type of housing assume particular significance in the rehousing of rural families and in the resettlement of people in urban "growth centres" as, for example, in the ARDA regional development program in north-east New Brunswick and the resettlement of communities from the outports of Newfoundland. These families bring with them a strong attachment to a particular type of housing—free standing and unencumbered by mortgages—in which standards of space, design and facilities may be of secondary importance. The minimal cost of housing in the budgets of these families can mean the difference between a modicum of economic independence and poverty. In these circumstances, efforts to improve housing conditions clearly have to be related to programs of economic development, while the housing programs themselves will need to take account of the social preference for ownership and the limited financial capacity to undertake it.

The question arises whether our standard for Canada is to be the three-bedroom suburban bungalow of our larger cities, or whether it might be more related to the minimum requirements of the N.H.A. Residential Standards. Does the house have to be completed or need it be only the frame, to be finished on the inside by the resident in his own time and with his own labor? Perhaps the basic question is whether the rural resident is not entitled to the same size, quality, and standard of housing as the urban resident. With increasing emphasis on regional development programs, these questions will require greater attention as well as specific policy decisions.

In northern and isolated communities, the problem of providing basic services such as water, heat, electricity, and sewage disposal, is a major one. This has led to the possibility of increasing densities along a service line, or building multi-storey units when building land is scarce. The socio-economic effects of scattered housing without the provision of basic services have been aptly demonstrated in the Kennedy-Smith report, and include high costs of transportation, servicing and maintenance, water pollution, poor sewage and garbage disposal, and an inadequate supply of drinking water.

Again, the question of an appropriate standard of housing is important. Whether the Indian residents will be satisfied with the "one room dwelling with a warm floor" proposed in the Kennedy-Smith report as a minimal but distinct improvement over their present housing, remains to be seen. On the other hand, low-cost housing in areas where climatic conditions are rigorous may be a poor investment in terms of the life of the housing. In any case, it will require all our ingenuity and considerable amounts of money to improve the often desperate housing situation in our northern communities.

Social Implications of the Location of Housing

(a) *Urban renewal programs* and the controversy they have given rise to, have helped to focus attention on the importance to people of the location of their housing. There are signs that the bulldozer approach may be giving way to a more careful concern to preserve and strengthen the social fabric of urban renewal areas. While there is little merit in an approach which leads to a "glorification of the slums," it is becoming apparent that there can be social advantages in living in low-income areas. The kinds of interaction (often thought to be missing in more middle-class communities), based on mutual support and help, are characteristics of urban life which are worth keeping at a time when primary group identification is supposedly decreasing. In Canada, we can point to the examples of Lower Town in Ottawa, Alexandra Park in Toronto and Hamilton North End, as attempts to renew a community rather than change its character.

(b) *Suburbia* lies at the other end of the spectrum posing equally controversial issues with regard to the social effects of location. If one is to believe the relevant literature, suburbs are the wasteland of our modern society, "strawberry boxes piled neatly row after row." Suburbs have been described as sterile, single-class communities, where fathers are never home and mothers are socially isolated. Yet they meet the needs of many who value the single-family home with its piece of ground, the chance for privacy if they so desire it, or social involvement if this is what they want. Gans in his "Levittowners" makes this point.[7] Most people who move to the suburbs find what they are looking for. It is not necessarily a sterile or a socially isolated life; in fact, people report more social involvement than in the central city.

In our efforts to create a range of housing choices, one preference will continue to be some suburban form of living. However, we have learned a great deal about ways of improving the quality of suburban life. Carver suggests the "Town Centre" concept as a way to do this; Gans specifies other factors requiring special consideration. While we may not be able to duplicate the diversity of the inner city in the suburbs, there is much that can be done to improve the quality of suburban living, for those who desire it, in the planning and timing of facilities and services, and the provision of meaningful activities for all age groups.

(c) *Declining communities* that have lost their economic base present as difficult choices for decision, only on a larger scale, as those posed by urban renewal areas. Some are in decline because of the move to the cities from the rural areas, the closing of single industries in resource towns, and the better transportation systems which have by-passed some of the older service towns in agricultural areas. The social effects of a declining housing environment may well be negative, particularly as in relation to money for services and improvements, unemployment and underemployment, and the young moving out to find opportunities elsewhere.

The handling of the declining community raises many issues. For instance, under urban renewal legislation, how much help should it be given? Indeed, is there any point in supporting the community at all when it may make more sense to phase it out or let it die a natural death?

Obviously there are many social and political implications to these questions. Perhaps the present regional approach as exemplified by the Fund for Rural Economic Development and the greater emphasis on regional development programs offer the best hope for the future of the residents of these communities.

(d) *New towns and satellite communities* involve a whole new concept of housing environment in which location, together with types of housing, site planning, transportation systems, provision of amenities and facilities, social organization, are all systematically related to each other to create a pleasant living environment.

More than in any other area, the provision of new communities has crystallized concerns about the kind of housing environment created, thus encouraging much discussion and research. The experience of the British New Towns has been examined in numerous research studies with a view to identifying the successful features in planning new communities as well as the problems. The total environmental approach as exemplified by Washington New Town in Britain and Reston in the United States are exciting both in conception and result.

In Canada, we appear to be on the threshold of developing new towns and satellite communities as a means of increasing our housing stock and the range of housing choices. The experience acquired in other countries has helped to define more clearly the important contribution to be made by the social planner in this process. Thus we are finding that such factors as social organization of the community, the development of communal facilities, the use of open space and the influence of the automobile on the environment, are receiving increased attention. The work of Nicholson on New Communities in Britain, although somewhat dated, focuses attention on the provision of adequate transportation, the relationship between housing and employment, the need for diversity in age groupings and house types, and the provision and timing of community facilities and social services.[8] In the American context, a study by Eichler and Kaplan of new communities, particularly in California, raises many issues with regard to financing, site planning, political and social organization, etc.[9] We are fortunate in Canada to have the experience and research of other countries available to us as we move into the building of these new communities.

Social Integration of Communities

Discussion of the preceding issues raises, in acute form, the question of the social integration of communities. Is it possible to build communities that are not just single-class communities but represent a range of income, of age, of ethnic groups? There is ample evidence to support the assumption that most people prefer to live among those who share a similar style of life. On the other hand, we are nowadays increasingly concerned about enlarging the range of opportunities for all of Canada's citizens and tend to view segregation whether along racial, ethnic or socio-economic lines as something to be deplored and something which it is possible to avoid through orderly development and planning of our communities and resources. Thus, the possibility of planning for greater social integration, if we desire to do so, seems greater at this time.

Perhaps "diversity" is better than the word "integration" with its implication of something much more positive than is either achievable or even desirable. For example, there are many who suggest that integration of public housing tenants in middle-class communities is a fallacious concept. Rather than integration, one author suggests that our goal should be based on planning for the community as a whole—"allowing diverse groups to live together peacefully and still have the social contacts and institutions each needs for a full life."

Two illustrations are offered to demonstrate some of the considerations involved in this;

(a) In its original conception, public housing, although tied to slum clearance, was often built in the suburbs. The theory was that if you took people from poor housing conditions and placed them beside higher status groups, the good example of middle-class standards of child care, respect for property, would "rub off" on the low-income groups. Unfortunately, rather than achieving integration, the result was often greater isolation. The choice of site for public housing was often on land considered uneconomic for private building. By its very nature, it isolated public housing tenants from the services and amenities of the community. At the same time, studies of relocation in urban renewal found that most people, including those desiring public housing, wanted to remain in the downtown area.

The possibilities of achieving a better population balance have been increased in some of our larger urban centers with the provision of larger numbers of public housing units in different parts of the city, and a correspondingly greater choice to the family in need of housing. Thus families are not necessarily forced to live in public housing in the suburbs if they choose to live downtown. A second, and perhaps more important reason, is that new housing developments are being planned to include both moderate and low-income (public) housing. In this way public housing avoids being cast in the role of something ancillary to the rest of the community, something forced onto it and thus resented. By including both types of housing from the outset it is hoped that this will result in less stigma and "marginality" being felt by the public housing resident. However, the success of this kind of "mixed" development will only be determined with the passage of time.

(b) A second example, which appears to negate the idea of integration, comes from Rosow's work on housing for the elderly. Rosow, after studying various forms of retirement housing, concludes that segregated housing, defined as a large concentration of housing units for the elderly, often with built-in facilities, appears to offer the best possibilities and benefits for the elderly. These units are not isolated from the larger community, nor are they scattered or integrated throughout the total community. Rosow suggests that in an age-graded society, integration can lead to social isolation. Inter-generational conflicts arise, and the younger age groups tend to have little understanding of the elderly. The benefits of segregated housing, as described by Rosow, include economy in building and in provision of services, the possibility of new group memberships for support and mutual aid, and the provision of role models for those making the transition into retirement.[10]

References

[1]Schorr, Alvin, *Slums and Social Insecurity*, United States Department of Health, Education and Welfare, Social Security Administration, Division of Research and Statistics, Report No. 1, 1963.

[2]Wilner, Daniel, *et al.*, *Housing Environment and Family Life*. Baltimore: Johns Hopkins Press, 1962.

[3]Kennedy Smith Associates, *Housing Study, Isolated Communities and Indian Reserves, Prairie Provinces*. Winnipeg, 1967.

[4]Conseil des Oeuvres de Montréal, *Opération: Rénovation Sociale*, Mai 1967, p. 173.

[5]Wood, Elizabeth, *Housing Design: A Social Theory*. Citizens' Housing and Planning Council of New York Inc., 1961.
[6]*Toronto Globe and Mail*, August 21, 1968, p. 9.
[7]Gans, Herbert J., *The Levittowners*. Toronto: Random House Ltd., 1967.
[8]Nicholson, J. M., *New Communities in Britain*. London: National Council of Social Service Inc., 1961.
[9]Eichler, Edward, and Kaplan, Marshall. *The Community Builders*. Berkeley: University of California Press, 1967.
[10]Rosow, Irving, *Social Integration of the Aged*, New York: Free Press, 1967.

The Importance of Privacy in Building Human Values into the Community

ABRAHAM HOFFER

Implicit in the theme "Building Human Values into the Community" is the belief that our environment, urban or rural, can be ordered, designed and constructed so that, as a logical consequence, positive human values are enhanced and negative human values minimized. Many may consider this a bold and perhaps impossible goal. In fact, it is bold, but whether it is attainable will never be known until someone tries.

Only within the past decade have planners, architects, psychologists and sociologists begun to talk to each other and to develop a new branch of science which might be called psychosocial planning. Perhaps we are at the beginning of the development of a new breed of community planners who might be said to practice the science of psychosocial community planning.

It may be asked, how can any planner build a community which enhances human values when human values cover areas of religion, economics, social, political, psychological, artistic, scientific, public health and many others. A community designed to enhance political values may not be very effective in furthering scientific values. A community designed by architects who ignore health values may be completely inappropriate.

Source: A. Hoffer, "Building Human Values Into the Community", *Review*, Vol. 19 (2), 1969. Reprinted by permission of the Community Planning Association of Canada and the author.

Does this mean that we must design a community for each kind of value system? This obviously is impossible and would merely create chaos. Or must we order our values in a hierarchy, using this hierarchy to establish priorities for those values which seem to be more important to the community while ignoring values which rank the lowest? I do not believe there is any way of doing this because it seems to be impossible to design one community which is going to account for all the human values. If it were possible, I would assume it would be a very rigid structure which would soon be out of phase with human evolution.

Development Laws

If we are going to create a science of community development, we must discover meaningful laws to be used as a guide. This is a problem which has faced every protoscience. For example, Galileo is properly honored as one of the first great scientists, not so much because he saw more stars than anyone else but because he showed how certain properties of matter can be abstracted and described by mathematical laws. He showed, for example, that it does not matter whether a ball is red or black, if one is interested in how fast that ball rolls down an inclined plane. What does matter is an abstract property called mass. In a similar way we can abstract from the total set of values simple rules or laws which can guide us.

Can we enunciate certain principles which, if obeyed, must necessarily lead to a community in which all human values are more easily attained? I am certain that this is fairly easy for technologically simple matters like sanitation where one could pass a law which stated simply, "Thou shalt not pollute the atmosphere or thou shalt not pollute the water". Once standards are set, these laws could be enforced if economic factors were not over-riding and would certainly control the problems of pollution.

If such laws can be found, not only will human values be enhanced but our communities will be able to grow and change in tune with cultural and social developments. Nature has general laws with which all life must conform but these leave enormous room for variation. Nature lays down strategy but allows much room for tactical variation. Since humans are animals and must live within the structure of their animal body, it seems self evident that these laws must be rooted in our biological nature, both physical and psychological.

For your consideration, I will propose one such hypothesis. It is this: "Achievement of human values is a function of voluntary privacy or its functional equivalent".

Need for Privacy

I do not think that many people will argue with the proposition that privacy is one of the major human needs. Sick people generally require much more privacy than do healthy people. But even for healthy people privacy is a very important fact of life and is an object of exchange which is bought and sold. It is bought and sold for example, in hospitals where people pay more for private rooms, in hotels, in transportation, in the theatre, in public restrooms where a quarter will purchase a few moments privacy.

Often privacy is a great luxury. For example, Phyllis McGinley writes, "The poor might have to huddle together in cities for sake of protection. But in each civilization, as it advanced, those who could afford it chose the luxury of a withdrawing place. Egyptians planned vinehung gardens, the Greeks had their porticos and seaside villas, the Romans put enclosures around their patios. . . . Privacy was considered as worth striving for as hallmarked silver or linen sheets for one's bed. In this same respect Goffman comments upon the lack of front and back region differentiation in contemporary lower class residences."

Invasion of Privacy

The ability to invade privacy is also reflective of status. Those for whom subjects are willing to lower their barriers of privacy are accorded high prestige. For example, a physician has a high social rank not only because of his training but because of his authority to ignore the barriers of privacy. Patients bare their bodies and souls to their physicians. This applies to the confessional, where penitents bare their actions and souls to the confessors who are accordingly given high prestige. This also applies to lawyers, who are able to obtain innermost secrets from their clients and cannot be forced to divulge them to anyone. People who are permitted to invade privacy have clear-cut obligations in the manner information is obtained and used. For example, there must be guarantees of confidentiality.

Invasion of privacy is generally considered a very serious matter and includes actions like breaking and entering, breaking into a home without a warrant, electronic snooping, eavesdropping, and peeping. One might even consider rape as the ultimate invasion of privacy. Surgery without the consent of a patient is an invasion of bodily privacy and, of course, murder is the ultimate invasion of privacy.

Thus it is clear that privacy is a vital need of man. It must be voluntary or else it loses its main effect. Involuntary privacy may be just as dehumanizing as involuntary lack of privacy and people will go to any extreme to overcome it. I think the best examples are the private cells or black holes of some of our prisons.

Functions of Privacy

1. *Group preserving function* Withdrawal into privacy often makes life bearable when living with a person with whom life is sporadically unbearable. If privacy were not available, the relationship might have to be terminated. One man I know finds his alcoholic wife's behavior unbearable but he still remains protective and kind toward her and fond of her only because he is able to be away from home several weeks at a time many times during the year. If he could not do so, I am certain that they would have been divorced a long time ago.

Entering and leaving others' privacy is built into our social and psychological structure. Before entering a home, one has to go through certain rituals, such as knocking on the door or ringing the bell; before leaving, there are certain rituals which occur in the hall. The same thing applies to members of one family where each member must respect the privacy of every other member.

2. *Status* It is quite obvious that the upper ranks or upper echelons of any institution or organization are given greater privacy than the lower ranks. In the armed forces, officers are given better quarters and have much more privacy than do privates. In civilian life, the president of a company has more privacy than the lowly clerk and this may be demonstrated by the size of his office, by the number of rugs on the floor, by the weight of the door which he uses to close himself in, and by the size of his desk.

3. *Deviation* All social groups apparently require some quotient of ignorance or deviation, for example, between child and father. It is quite obvious that if the father knew everything that the child did, or if the child knew everything that his father did, it might be very difficult for them to continue their fine relationship.

This also applies between husband and wife who are generally advised not to intrude too deeply upon each other's privacy. Over the years I have been amazed by the fact that so many schizophrenic men and women manifest the first indication of their illness when they begin to demand that their other partner share with them in detail many private matters which they had better not know.

4. *Secret consumption* It is quite obvious that there is some discrepancy between public attitudes and what is privately believed. This is especially true for sexual practices, but today there seems to be a closer approachment between what society believes and what society does. However, there still is a certain amount of secret consumption.

5. *Relaxation* Humans require relaxing attitudes which they cannot indulge in public. This is why in private many people are able to adopt positions and attitudes and do things that they could not possibly do in front of any public.

6. *Territoriality* The concept of territoriality has been widely examined by biologists in relationship to animals and human be-

havior. It may well be that the function of territoriality in humans is to insure privacy in the same way that the function of territoriality in birds is to insure proper reproduction of the species.

Sensory Privacy

Absolute privacy consists of space in which a person is unaware of the presence of any other person, where using all the known perceptual organs it is certain no one else is, in fact, present. If man had no perceptual apparatus, if he could not see, hear, touch, taste or smell he would never know whether his space is private or not. Every person is enveloped by a space whose dimensions vary with the perception used to sense it. We have a hierarchy of senses for detecting the presence of others and these range from sight, which samples up to infinity, to touch, which depends upon physical contact.

A decade ago there was a vogue for open living which became a form of togetherness. This was one result of theories of togetherness or of human interaction. As a result, some houses seemed to have only one large room in them which included kitchen, living room, etc. No one in the room would be visually unaware of anyone else in that room. I have often wondered what sort of effect this kind of involuntary living had upon children brought up in this environment which they had no free choice in developing. This might be an interesting psychological study. Walls are therefore visual barriers which help maintain one's privacy and they must be opaque. Large picture windows invite people to look in and thus invite intrusions upon one's privacy. Visual privacy may be the simplest to obtain.

Auditory privacy is harder to obtain for acoustic waves are not shut out as easily. It is also much more expensive and may involve not only the construction of special sound absorbing buildings and cities with special non-reflecting materials but may require either moving away from the noise pollution or moving the noise pollutants (for example, airports) away from cities. For some, acoustic privacy is even more important than is visual privacy. Some are very embarrassed when they flush the toilet in their bathroom if other people are present nearby. One of the complaints against apartment living is the lack of auditory privacy. Noise pollution is, after all, simply an intrusion upon our privacy and like all intrusions may be psychologically, socially, and physically harmful.

Olfactory space is much smaller in volume than either visual or auditory space and consequently should be easier to control. Air pollution is an invasion of our privacy but we have not yet learned how it should be controlled. We have, however, within the past decade become aware of its seriousness and at least there is general agreement that it should be controlled. Powerful perfumes or excessive body odor are considered an invasion of olfactory privacy by many. The solutions to olfactory intrusions are technologically simple even if they are not economically simple: it is to prevent air pollution and to improve ventilation in our homes.

Violation of taste privacy is very common and occurs when our food or water is polluted, poisoned or contaminated. This kind of intrusion of our privacy only operates when the pollutant has an undesirable taste. It then becomes an intolerable invasion of taste privacy, perhaps even more than is invasion of visual or auditory privacy.

The most intimate private space is that involving touch or contact. Intrusions against tactile privacy are often punished severely. Three of the most flagrant intrusions of touch privacy, although this also involves the other private spaces, are rape, assault, and murder. The penalty may be capital punishment, another form of retaliatory invasion of tactile private space.

Attaining Privacy

Privacy can be attained by careful design of space but since the concepts of privacy are rather novel, too little attention has been given to these problems. Visual privacy may be obtained by the use of walls, doors, opaque screens, vegetation, real or simulated, and by other opaque barriers using even darkness and shadows. In public places such as waiting rooms in airports, stations, doctors' offices, the functional equivalent of private visual space can be created by the proper use of seating arrangements, by visual barriers and by grouping of waiting spaces away from walking spaces. It can be provided by one-way glass which allows people to look out but prevents anyone from looking in. Auditory privacy can be obtained by sound barriers or baffles or by the creation of background or white noise. It may be attained by use of sound absorbing materials on floors, walls, etc., and on a community level by preventing sound pollution. It should not be difficult to design such spaces if planners and designers will recognize their need.

People seek a balance between their public and private world. About 15 years ago Drs. Osmond and Sommer began to investigate the way people related to each other in space. This type of study has been called proxemics by E. T. Hall. For example, they found that people tended to align themselves in particular ways depending upon the space in which they found themselves, upon their culture background, etc. If two people approached a square table they would, if given a free choice, more often sit at right angles to each other than side by side. In the right angle position people have a greater choice and can invade each other's privacy by looking or can look away.

A whole philosophical system of psychiatry was created because Freud could not tolerate having his patients look at him. As a result he developed the idea of having them lie on a couch while he sat behind them. This has the added advantage that it is possible for the analyst to catch a few naps while his patient displays his innermost thoughts.

Deprivation of Privacy

Another consequence of lack of privacy in mental hospitals is the interference with interaction with other people. Psychiatric patients often by their disease are alienated from their fellows. When they recover it is often a major problem to regain the social skills they had before they were struck by their illness. The lack of privacy in most mental hospitals inhibits human relations and so slows recovery.

Riots have plagued cities for centuries and perhaps they have their roots in the need for privacy. A recent study of riots in New Jersey found that the people who participated in riots were no poorer, or more unemployed than people living in the same area who did not participate in the riots. A factor which was not considered was the effect of lack of privacy and too much enforced privacy among certain members of the population. Ittelson defined privacy as a situation wherein a person had the widest range of personal choice. This seems to be an excellent definition. I suggest that among the important variables in racism and perhaps in riots is a deficiency in this kind of privacy. Blacks and other colored minority groups have not been given access to the same privacy as have the majority groups. Thus blacks have been kept out of certain areas of cities, out of certain institutions, out of some types of employment, etc.

I believe everyone wishes to have the right to participate in all areas of human activity whether or not he chooses to exercise that right. According to Ittelson, when privacy is forbidden on account of characteristics over which a person has no control such as height, weight, color of one's skin or hair, this is considered the most undesirable form of deprivation of privacy. Other reasons for privacy deprivation are economical. As I mentioned earlier, the rich can afford to purchase privacy not available to the poor. It has been suggested that people can purchase services by the use of money, or the use of time, or by the surrender of privacy. A motorist who drives into the centre of a large city must pay for his privacy in his car by the expenditure of money and of time since he may spend large chunks of time waiting to reach his destination. A poor man who has little money may have to pay for getting into the city by giving up huge chunks of privacy in buses or subways.

Human Values and Privacy

A. A. Berle, Jr., former assistant secretary of state, listed ten human values which he considered self-evident. These were:

1. People are better alive than dead.
2. People are better healthy than sick.
3. People are better off literate than illiterate.

4. People are better off adequately than inadequately housed.
5. People are better off in beautiful than in ugly cities and towns.
6. People are better off if they have opportunity for enjoyment —music, literature, drama, and the arts.
7. Education above the elementary level should be as nearly universal as possible; through secondary school and higher education as widely diffused as practicable.
8. Development of science and the arts should continue or possibly be expanded.
9. Minimum resources for living should be available to all.
10. Leisure and access to green country should be a human experience available to everyone.

In my opinion, these desirable human values and many more will be possible only when in the design of our communities and institutions, we take into account the aspects of human privacy which I have briefly tried to describe to you. Therefore, I believe that what little evidence we do have suggests that the hypothesis I have framed is more apt to be right than wrong, that is, achievement of human values is a function of privacy or its functional equivalent.

What is desperately needed is a massive effort to research this proposition. It is being examined on a small scale. We need to scale up this research a hundredfold and we must do so immediately.

Human Needs and Human Values for Environmental Resources

FRANCIS T. CHRISTY, JR.

I have been asked to consider resources as commodities and to examine the competing uses for these commodities in the light of human needs and environmental limits. There is, however, a major difficulty in tackling this assignment. And the difficulty is that we do not really know how to describe many of these resource commodities, nor do we know how to evaluate the importance of the uses. And in the absence of such knowledge, we find it hard to resolve conflicts.

Environmental commodities are best defined in terms of the uses to which they are put, or the services that they provide. And their uses and services are, in turn, best defined in terms of human needs or demands. This paper, therefore, focuses on some of the problems in the definition and description of human needs for environmental resources.

Our needs are great. We need redwoods for the construction of our buildings; we need rivers to carry our wastes; strip mines to provide our coal; and hydro-electric dams to generate our power. These very real needs, however, conflict with other needs that are more difficult to assess but no less real—the needs for clean water, clean air, a pleasurable environment, and enjoyable

---

Source: Francis T. Christy, Jr., "Human Needs and Human Values for Environmental Resources", from the Transactions of the 32nd North American Wildlife and Natural Resources Conference. Reprinted by permission of the Wildlife Management Institute.

---

outdoor recreation opportunities. To resolve such conflicts, someone has to determine which of these needs are greater.

If there were a market place where these needs could be satisfactorily expressed, the decisions would be relatively easy. But there is no adequate market place and the demand (or relative importance of the need) cannot be readily measured. Economists are searching for techniques that will provide better measures of people's willingness to pay for environmental commodities. These techniques will not provide the only basis for decisions, but they will be extremely helpful.

In the meantime, however, decisions are being made, and they require some *subjective* understanding of "needs" as well as whatever *objective* estimates of "demand" can be made. These words are not entirely appropriate. "Needs" implies exigency, and "demand" implies precise knowledge. Perhaps other words are more relevant, words such as human wants or desires. But whatever the word, it is important that we improve as best we can our understanding of what is desired and how valuable it is to our society.

By way of emphasizing the importance of improving our knowledge, I will suggest, first, certain categories of *human needs* and second, certain categories of *human values* that may be quite different than those needs and values that are generally assumed to be important.

Human Needs

The human needs of interest to us may be expressed in terms of pleasure. That is, in addition to our fundamental needs for food, clothing, and shelter, we have secondary needs or desires, for the pleasurable use of our leisure time and for pleasurable surroundings. These needs and desires are not necessarily oriented towards specific natural resources. Clothing, for example, can come from plants, animals, and even from petroleum. In large part, our concern is more with the texture, quality, and price of the material than it is with the source. There is, therefore, a wide range of substitutability among the resources that meet our clothing needs, so that if the price of wool rises (because of environmental limits), we can turn to cotton or synthetics.

The same can be said for the desire for a pleasurable use of our leisure time. Books, movies, hiking trails, skiing slopes, and television all compete for our leisure time and can, in general, substitute for each other. There are, however, certain individual preferences—just as there may be preferences for beef or pork, or for wool over synthetics. Consumption of the commodity is determined by the strength of the preference and the cost to the user, relative to the strengths and cost of alternatives. Since the costs of outdoor recreation are not generally borne directly by the consumer, it is important to evaluate the strength of the preferences or desires.

For this purpose, I suggest three categories of human needs for environmental commodities. These categories are made up of desires that are: (a) directed towards particular resources; (b) directed towards the image of the user; and (c) directed towards the enjoyable use of leisure time. Each recreation activity undoubtedly reflects a combination of these sets of desires. But the relative importance to users may be quite different, and the evaluation of these differences may be quite useful in reaching decisions about the supply and design of the commodities.

RESOURCE-DIRECTED DESIRES

The first category of demands are those that are explicitly directed toward kinds of resources or toward experiences that require specific kinds of resources. These would include desires to be warmed by the sun, to hear the sound of the surf, or be exhilarated by the beauty of nature. It would also include the more active desires of skiing, surfing, white-water canoeing—the development and testing of skills in the enjoyment of the natural environment. Fishing, not for trophies, but for enjoyment of a well-placed lure and the thrill of the strike, is another example of a resource-directed desire.

In addition, there may be demands in this category that do not require use of the resource. For many people, the knowledge that there is a wilderness may be important even though they never intend to make use of it.

IMAGE-DIRECTED DESIRES

The second category includes those desires not directed towards the resource but towards the fulfillment of an image. A recent article in the *New York Times* states that "recreational skiing is being sold to thousands of Americans who really would rather not be sold. They find themselves being pushed to the top of the hill by such pressures as the sport's image of youth, the thing-to-do motivation, their skiing children, or the chance to wear good-looking ski clothes and to drink the gluhwein around the fire afterwards."[1] Bil Gilbert reported on the same image-directed recreation in a *Sports Illustrated* article on skiing in the Southern Belt—the man-made snow, Swiss Chalet, warming hut with plastic deer antlers, the Austrian-accented ski instructor, a genuine ski-bum imported from Aspen, the whole bit.[2] And the developer of the ski area refers to himself as the "pioneer of super-market recreation." On the back cover of the same *Sports Illustrated* issue, there appeared a full-page, full-color cigarette advertisement of a handsome couple skiing gracefully in attractive ski clothes.

On the wall of my office, there is a stuffed, three-pound brook trout—a trophy reflecting the image of the fisherman. (And not a very reliable image at that, since the fish was caught by my wife.) The seekers of the sun-tan, rather than the sun; the guy in the "jams" with the surf board on the roof of his car; the color slides of the wilderness back-packing trip—all these are indications of the perfectly human need to provide oneself with a desirable image. Satisfaction depends not upon oneself, but upon others; and not upon the resource, but upon the way others view the resource.

LEISURE-DIRECTED DESIRES

In the third category, the desires are not so much for a specific resource nor for the enhancement of one's image as they are for finding a pleasurable way to use up leisure time. The aimless Sunday drive or the cross-country trip to a National Park are similar to watching television in that they provide relatively painless ways to pass the time. They are chosen because they are more pleasurable than doing nothing or than remaining in the familiar home environment.

EFFECTS ON SUPPLY

The three types of recreational desires—resource-, image-, and leisure-directed—are generally combined in the make-up of any particular recreational experience. The fisherman enjoys the fishing, gets pleasure in telling his friends about the lunker bass, and likes the escape from his 9 to 5 job. And the National Park visitor may be exhilarated by the beauty of the Park, put stickers on his bumper to show everyone where he has been, and find driving more pleasurable than mowing his suburban lawn.

But each of these sets of desires will receive different emphasis by different users. And it is the difference in relative importance that is significant for the provision and design of recreational supplies. By definition, the resource-directed desire requires supplies of particular kinds of recreational natural resources—sites for skiing, trails for hiking, white-water streams for canoeing, and others.

However, where the primary emphasis is image-directed, the use of leisure time does not necessarily require natural resources. Many indoor activities, such as arts and crafts, bowling, folk singing, can only serve to enhance one's image. To a large extent, this type of leisure time activity reflects the values of society rather than those of the individual. To the extent that this is true, there are three implications for the suppliers of recreation resources. The first is that changes may be induced by advertising campaigns or by the development of certain images by communications media. Perhaps one way to anticipate future demands on recreational resources is by study of magazine advertisements and television programs and commercials. The second implication is that there may be equally attractive substitutes that do not require large developments of public recreational land. Public support of the arts may help divert some of this image-directed demand away from the outdoors. And the third implication is for the design of recreation areas. Where the image is important, the design of the area should facilitate the fulfillment of the image. The approach of the "pioneer of supermarket recreation" is instructive. It is not enough to provide proper skiing trails and up-hill transportation. The design of the warming hut and other peripheral facilities is equally important.

In fishing, it may be desirable to plant trophy-size fish along with the smaller ones. And for surfing and water skiing, there may be some value in spectator congestion because of the opportunities it gives for demonstrating one's skill.

Where the emphasis is simply on an enjoyable use of leisure time, there are no explicit requirements for natural resource supplies. A psychiatrist has pointed out that "through the help of leisure time marketeers, the country has been led to believe that effective adaptation to free time is assured by providing more and more leisure time activities and facilities and developing and improving our external resources. People everywhere are overestimating and misconceiving the value of all these external resources and facilities."[3] This statement could well apply to the provision of many recreational resources and particularly for those, such as scenic roads and national parks, that involve major uses of leisure time. That is, the time consumed in getting to and from a national park may be more important than the park itself. In this case, Disneyland could be as satisfactory a target as Yosemite, or simply relaxing in the hammock may become as desirable as driving for pleasure. The points are that man-made resources and man's internal resources may be substitutes for natural resources and that we should explore these alternative ways of meeting man's needs for the pleasurable use of his leisure time.

NEEDS FOR A PLEASURABLE ENVIRONMENT

In addition to leisure needs, there are also human desires for a pleasurable environment, or, more specifically, for clean air, clean water, and pleasing natural and man-made surroundings. But here again, we do not really know how to define our demands or determine how much we are willing to pay for the commodities.

With regard to clean air and clean water, we want to remove stink, reduce unsightly smoke or sediment, and minimize the risk to our health. There are two problems in defining our needs. The first lies in finding out what elements in the air and water are damaging to health and how damaging they are. Much work on this is already underway and the results are satisfying, but a lot remains to be done. As an example, Dr. René Dubos recently questioned whether health is damaged more by the pollutants from automobile exhaust than by the pollutants injected into the air by the grinding of rubber tires on city streets.[4] And in addition to that, we don't know the degree of risk associated with different amounts of pollutants. If there is one part per million of a certain pollutant in the air or water, will this mean a chance of x deaths per 100,000, or 2x, 3x, or 10x deaths?

Obviously, in many areas we want a great deal more cleanliness than we're now getting—and we should have it. But the line has to be drawn somewhere. How much more cleanliness do we want and how much are we willing to pay for it? Answers to these questions will require a great deal more research on people's perceptions and desires.

Besides the displeasures of the environment, arising from polluted air and polluted waters, there appears to be some displeasure associated with the pollutants of the landscape—billboards, automobile junkyards, and litter. In this case, the measurement of human need or demand is even more difficult, because one man's ugly may be another man's beauty. It is probable that there is widespread agreement that a row of billboards between a highway and a scenic wonder is deplorable, but some wonders are more scenic than others and again, a line has to be drawn some place. Drawing a line at the borders of commercial zones may not be very helpful since some scenery beyond these zones may be relieved by a billboard or two and some scenery within commercial zones may be sufficiently beautiful to warrant protection. In addition to this, beauty controls open up the question of public aesthetics. Richard Babcock has pointed out that "when one embarks on a campaign to make aesthetics a public issue in a democracy the line between the conservationist and the philistine is narrow."[5] He fears that a democracy cannot distinguish between the ugly and the different and he points out how different zoning boards have attempted to deal with aesthetics. There are those that think harmony is important, and specify that each building should be similar in character to all other buildings in the neighborhood. There are those that hold an opposite point of view, who feel that too much similarity is dull and specify that each new building should be dissimilar from its neighbors. And there are even those who would have it both ways, such as Greenfield, Wisconsin, whose ordinance states that a new building should "not be...at variance with nor...similar to...the structures already constructed..."[6]

There is clearly merit in removing from the natural environment that which is universally considered as ugly. But how do we know what reactions are universal?

Human Values

The foregoing part of this paper has emphasized how little we know about "needs." The next few remarks deal with our knowledge about the human beings who have these needs. The use of the term, "human needs," seems to imply that humanity is homogeneous—at least that American humanity is. But the most that can be said with respect to environmental and recreational resources is that certain groups share certain values and certain ways of viewing and using the natural environment. And these values, viewpoints, and uses may be quite different.

One group may decry the values shared by another group, but this does not mean that one set of values is *necessarily* better than another. There are, of course, extreme values that are socially undesirable and harmful, and that should be changed. But, for the most part, the values are not undesirable; they are just different. Unfortunately, we sometimes forget this and assume that our way is the one way, and that everyone else must conform —and if he doesn't conform then he must be educated.

Gilbert White pointed out that "one striking fact is that a large number of environmental quality decisions are made by people who feel a strong professional identification. Their view of themselves as conservationists, economists, sanitary engineers, foresters, etc., may be expected to shape their perception of the environment and their competence to handle it. In these roles they not only inherit customary ways of defining significant parts of the environment but they are disposed to distort or ignore phenomena that they regard as beyond their professional responsibility or competence. (If you can't measure a diseconomy, sweep it under the rug.) Their perceptions and preferences become the implicit and usually unchallenged determinants of plans presented for public choice."[7]

This attitude sometimes leads to actions and programs that may do more damage than help to the cause of conservation. We try to convince by the use of exhortation, mysticism, and threat, unaware that the terms we use may be irrelevant, and the language foreign, to the ears of our audience. School books and filmstrips that ask slum kids not to start forest fires are like missionaries telling the natives to drive carefully.

I think that major efforts should be made to understand and appreciate the different values and viewpoints on the natural environment. The more we respect the values of others, the more likely they will be to respect ours—and this, in turn, should facilitate the process of mutual education. I have in mind an example suggested by Kevin Lynch and others in a report entitled *Open Space for Human Needs*.[8] Rather than deplore the mis-use of natural areas in city slums, they sought to undertand the reason for the mis-use. They suggested that low-income urban people might fear a wooded environment, because of its strangeness, just as some might fear a slum environment. And they proposed that such woods be opened up, that underbrush be removed, and wide straight trails be built into the woods. This would give the users a sense of confidence and encourage them to experiment in the use of a strange environment, and perhaps to begin to appreciate nature.

To make this kind of an approach successful, it is necessary to improve our understanding of the values that others hold toward the natural environment. It is obviously an oversimplification to think of a group as having sets of values that are clearly distinct and separate from those of other groups. There is undoubtedly a wide degree of overlap. But in demonstrating the importance of differences, it may be useful to characterize a few categories as if they were distinct.

One social observer and critic, Tom Wolfe, has suggested that there is a group of "ancient aesthetes," by which he means us, me included.[9] He feels that this group, which is closely identified with the natural environment, has little knowledge about a rapidly growing group that he refers to as the "prole generation" —a generation more closely identified with the automobile and associated paraphernalia and activities—the stock car races, demolition derbies, custom cars, the neon strips that form the gateways to our cities, and architecture as exemplified by the MacDonald hamburger arcs. J. B. Jackson, editor of *Landscape*, also speaks of the automobile identity and the neon strips, and suggests that large groups of people may actually prefer the artificial over the natural environment.[10] And think how artificial the environment has become—the Disneyland menagerie, a Niagara Falls that can be turned on or off like a cold water tap, man-made snow, fire-falls at Yosemite, and put-and-take trout fishing.

These observations indicate that there may be a large and growing number of people whose values are not strongly oriented towards the enjoyment and preservation of the natural environment—people who, by their votes at the polls and in the market place, may have a significant influence on natural resource decisions.

Another indication of possible change lies in the fact that about 50 percent of the people of the United States are 25 years old or less—and this is the generation of Berkeley and Bob Dylan and "pop" art and psychedelic drugs. Members of this generation can find beauty in a beer can (an empty one) and can take a "trip" with a drop of acid. Much of the protest associated with this group is directed against what they regard as the phony aspects of life and phony values. The precepts that have guided the behaviour of us "ancient aesthetes" are not taken as fundamental truths, and attempts to impose our precepts upon this group are likely to meet with failure. Will these members of the younger generation feel the call of the wild? Will they believe that nature is part of the moral order? Will they be concerned about irreversible changes in the environment? And, in addition to the possibility of holding different values, they may wish to allocate their leisure time in significantly different patterns—perhaps by placing relatively greater emphasis on social goals or on artistic and self-expressive forms of recreation, or perhaps by the development of internal resources, and of the ability to lead a more contemplative and relaxed life.

Most of us, I am sure, abhor artificiality, do not feel that we are identified with the automobile, and like nature the way God made it. But this does not mean that we should, or can afford to, reject the values of other groups, so long as they are not socially harmful. To return to Gilbert White's statement, we should examine our inheritance of the customary ways of defining the environment and we should avoid distorting or ignoring phenomena that we regard as beyond our responsibility or comprehension. We should make our preferences and perceptions explicit and open them to challenge from groups that may have different preferences and perceptions.

This, I think, is an essential first step. It will help remove our preconceptions about "human needs." The next step is to enlarge our understanding of the range, variety, and significance of demands on the natural environment. And finally, we should improve our understanding and appreciation of the different values of other people so that we can anticipate changes that might affect the demands on the environment. These steps should help us define environmental commodities with more precision and improve our decisions on competing uses of natural environment.

References

[1]William N. Wallace, "Swiss Bob Along on Ski Bobs," *The New York Times*, Jan. 26, 1967.

[2]Bil Gilbert, "A No-Snow Slope to Nonsport," *Sports Illustrated*, Feb. 21, 1966.

[3]Dr. Alexander R. Martin, as quoted in the *New York Times*, Nov. 8, 1965.

[4]Dr. René Dubos, "Destructive and Creative Consequences of Adaptation," paper given at the Smithsonian Conference on The Quality of Man's Environment, Feb. 18, 1967.

[5]Richard F. Babcock, "Billboards, Glass Houses and the Law," in School of Architecture, University of Texas, *Texas Conference on Our Environmental Crisis* (Austin, Texas: School of Architecture, 1966), p. 175.

[6]*Ibid.*, p. 180.

[7]Gilbert F. White, "Formation and Role of Public Attitudes," in Henry Jarrett (ed.), *Environmental Quality in a Growing Economy* (Baltimore: The Johns Hopkins Press for Resources for the Future, Inc., 1966).

[8]Kevin Lynch, Jerry Kline, and Carl Feiss, *Open Space for Human Needs* (unpublished report to the Open Space Branch of the HHFA, 1963).

[9]Tom Wolfe, *The Kandy-Kolored Tangerine Flake Streamline Baby* (New York: Pocket Books, 1966).

[10]J. B. Jackson, at a seminar at Resources for the Future, Inc. May 19, 1966.

People, Recreation, Wild Lands, and Wilderness

HOMER ASCHMANN

We are doing spectacular things to our environment without any recognizable intent or plan. Complaints arise when the aquatic life of Lake Erie is destroyed, or water foams from taps in Reno because of detergents dumped into Lake Tahoe, or the sweeping view of the Embarcadero is to be cut off by a freeway. But progress usually wins over such peripheral squawks. The real problem is that we as a society have not really decided what kind of environments we want to create or preserve. Our technological engine of inordinate power has not been put in gear except tentatively, but it is becoming ever more powerful. Until we know better what we want, I can only regard it as fortunate that the moon rather than places closer to home is receiving our attention. This paper is directed toward inducing some deliberate and relatively unrestricted thought about what the world, or the United States, or Southern California *should* be like a decade or a century from now.

My recent preoccupation with this question was provoked by being asked to review a recent polemic book published by the Sierra Club and entitled *Wildlands in our Civilization*.[1] The Sierra Club's attractive propaganda does not insult the intelligence nor jar one's sensibilities, and I tend to react positively toward it. As the book title suggests, one of the Club's concerns is to preserve

Source: Homer Aschmann, "People, Recreation, Wild Lands, and Wilderness", from the *Yearbook of the Association of Pacific Coast Geographers*, Vol. 28, 1966. Reprinted by permission of the publisher and author.

wilderness areas for society's benefit. It is their explicitly stated belief that such wilderness areas can afford more to man in their present state than if they were developed and put to use as sources of timber or water power or made more accessible for recreational purposes. Their premise is that a human being, to enjoy the fullness of his own life, must from time to time be able to isolate himself from other members of his species and sense other aspects of the community of nature. The dedicated enthusiasm of the proponents of the wilderness area is inspiring. The ultimate hopelessness of their cause and the inadequacy of their goals, even if by fortune and effort they should all be achieved, is depressing. One is reminded of Stephen Vincent Benét's nightmare which includes the lines

> *You will not be saved by General Motors or the prefabricated house;*
> *You will not be saved by dialectical materialism or the Lambeth Conference;*
> *. . . In fact you will not be saved.*

We might add a codicil,

> *"We will not be saved by the wilderness idea either."*

A more comprehensive approach appears in the California Public Outdoor Recreation Plan.[2] As is appropriate in an open society, the wants of essentially all interest groups—those who like to look at scenery from a car window or after a vigorous hike, those who hunt, and those who find a crowded beach attractive for reasons which are probably obvious—receive consideration. Real numbers and reasonable projections appear. Plans for implementation are not completely unreasonable, and if carried out vigorously the outdoor recreation opportunities in the State would not deteriorate too much by 1980. After that one can only hope that his own aging will dull his sensitivity to the loss. A further conclusion must come from perusal of the Plan. If the ordinary economics of politics are applied and the costs of preservation and development are divided by the number of effective users, it will go hard for the person who craves to view scenery in lonely isolation. Because of their willingness to spend money, hunters and fishermen can hope for some protection and support, and the hunter at least creates his own glacis. He who wishes merely to look at a landscape in which the works of man are not apparent will find it ever harder to satisfy his desire.

In an operational sense the problem arises subjectively, and at this point one who has lived some decades in Southern California may be especially sensitive. The theme of paradise lost is so easy to dote on that most of us seek to keep it out of our consciousness most of the time. The idea of walking to a wild or even a farmed landscape beyond the rows of houses is ridiculous for all but fringe dwellers and they know that their period of grace is limited. Reaching a wilderness in a one day automobile trip becomes progressively more difficult and above all is likely to dump the traveler into a mob scene peopled with others with similar unsatisfied desires.

The problem of crowding in the declining number of accessible wild areas has become worse. California's growth rate is slowing but is far from stopping; work weeks are shortening; living standards are rising; projections of future pressures on wilderness can only terrify. The chance to be alone with nature on occasion that was once the American's birthright, whether or not he ever sought to exercise it, may be lost within our lifetimes, and barring nuclear catastrophe it will never be reinstated.

The question is really, does mankind as a social organism need access to wilderness? If he does, even the notations sketched above demonstrate that tremendous efforts to preserve it are required immediately. Perhaps only a small fraction of the species has this requirement, and those who have the need will be bred out rapidly as the need cannot be satisfied. The evidence is less than conclusive. Clearly, some city-dwellers reach three-score and ten without leaving house and pavement. Rising tensions in central cities, however, cannot be overlooked, and some recent experiments with rodents, kept with abundant food and adequate sanitation but with ever higher population densities, are suggestive.[3] As you are all aware the experimental populations were afflicted with social malaise; fighting and infanticide finally reduced the population density. We, of course, are a different species, and we have culture. In fact one can develop a remarkably coherent theory that the most fundamental cultural creations had as their functional goal the preservation of privacy for the individual and for intimate groups within growing and economically interdependent societies. Properly diverse examples of such inventions are the universal incest taboos and housing. But are these inventions enough? Do we still need contact with other wild species and with land without artifact? Let me ask you to accept for consideration the proposition that we, or at least many of us, may have need for occasional access to a wild area in reasonable isolation. Crowded campgrounds, no matter how picturesque and sanitary, or scenic highway lookouts will not do.

Perhaps the most articulate advocate of the above proposition is the Sierra Club, and once their premises are accepted, their actions and positions shift from fanaticism and anti-popularism to the most enlightened altruism. The Club can only be criticized for excessive moderation. By their rather strict definition of wilderness—one which allows no permanent human habitation, exploitation of resources, or facilities for mechanical vehicles—some 2.2% of the contiguous United States remains in that condition. The possibility of making wilderness out of currently used land is recognized as hopeless. With literacy, photographic virtuosity, and effective exploitation of media of communication they attempt to block any desecration of extant wilderness. They and their associated organizations have become a force to be reckoned with and in many cases development has been blocked. But their war has many fronts. No victory is ever achieved, only a stalemate with recurring possibilities for new fighting and final loss.

A few recent or current actions may be listed: the San Jacinto Mountain tramway, a ski-lift and access road in the high heart of the San Bernardino Mountains, a better highway versus the redwood trees in Humboldt County, dams that would flood a little of the Grand Canyon National Monument, a reservoir in the California condor refuge. The list could be lengthened, but these points stand out. It is not only the greedy mining concern, grazer, or lumberman, Two-Gun Desmond vulnerable to attack by Bernard DeVoto, or even John Collier that assaults wilderness areas. It is also the Bureau of Reclamation with a scheme to make the desert bloom, industry flourish with low-cost public power, and the whole economy of a region expand. Or it is the recreationist seeking to enlarge with access roads the number of citizens who can and do experience our natural wonders. Before the ink was dry on the Wilderness Act of 1964, Congress set in motion studies for new dams to utilize more effectively the West's limited water resources. The greatest victory merely established a line for renewed fighting.

Perhaps you shared my shock when we read recently of the bureaucratic arrogance of the Internal Revenue Service's threat to the Sierra Club's tax exemption status because the Club is agitating against further dams on the Colorado. Distasteful as such action is, it is instructive. How can a special interest group claim tax privilege when it fights against progress and enhanced prosperity for the entire nation? The outcome of this contest is not so significant as the assurance that it will be renewed. Two-Gun Desmond is now the high-minded public servant seeking to promote national welfare and being obstructed by a few noisy wilderness fanatics.

The Sierra Club's battleground for the contest is terribly clearly defined: we will get no more wilderness. It is terribly fragile; erosion, degradation of vegetation, and extinction of animal species can come about from the most innocent access road. Once disturbed, the wilderness character of an area cannot be restored for generations, perhaps forever. Let us bend every effort to preserve, protect, and defend what we have.

In the struggle over wilderness that has raged for the past two decades, a few points have been clarified, and this presentation would be needlessly cynical if it did not note such developments as progress. Recreation planners and managers are now prepared to segregate users so that when wants conflict, it will not be the noisiest and most obnoxious or even the biggest spenders who always take over. As a corollary we may be prepared to recognize and perhaps even restrict the range of landscape-defiling, space-consuming machinery: power boats, trail bikes, et cetera. The hunter and shooter has fought well on the solid ground of game management. He may yet have to struggle to defend the space he requires. The absolute protection of tiny plots for scientific study, especially that of an ecological and ethological nature—of wild plants and animals in a diversity of habitats—seems to be established as a legitimate social goal.

Protection of a species from extinction has enough emotional appeal to justify uneconomic efforts within limits because of the absolute finality of failure to do so. Within these clarified frames of reference, the managers of publicly owned wild lands can probably improve their practices to everyone's benefit.

Certain inherent anomalies in the programs of the proponents of preserving wilderness remain. Most are individually familiar to everyone who has concerned himself with the problem. What may be new is a recognition that they make the maintenance of wilderness impossible in a free and democratic society.

Fire is a nice example. The conservationist and wilderness advocate abhors it and may have become involved in the first place because he saw the devastation resulting from man-caused fires. But not all fires are caused by man. In many climatic situations recurring fires are a part of nature and an essential element in the wild landscape. We need not confuse the bottom of Yosemite Valley with a wilderness, but there we can document the fact that the former lovely park landscape was maintained by repeated burning. Full fire protection has led to a far less appealing brush and forest tangle, though the parking lots and camp grounds are in another league for unsightliness. In less accessible areas, however, should there be access roads to make easier the limitation of naturally caused fires, or should such fires just burn themselves out?

The role of the American Indian has been deeply involved in the wilderness idea, both historically and currently. Most wilderness advocates seem to think that the territory of the United States was a wilderness as long as only Indians occupied it and ceased to be when Europeans appeared. It is true that the Indian had no bulldozers, but he did have an impact on the landscape, exploiting heavily certain plants and animals, occupying permanent or semi-permanent settlements, and creating trails, some of which can still be followed. Most importantly he used fire heavily to clear land, to drive game, and probably for recreation. No zoning limited his activities except that he could not remain long in areas so cold or dry that they afforded little food. The flora and fauna that the first European explorer of any part of the United States saw had been modified by at least 10,000 years of human use. The modern plan to zone out people is creating something that never existed before, as it is now clear that Pleistocene climatic patterns prevailed until after Indian arrival in this continent.

At present a very considerable portion of the remaining wilderness and primitive area in the country is on Indian Reservations. Reasons for this situation can afford little self-satisfaction to the American society, and the most important one is certainly that the Reservations contain much low grade land. Another is that paternalism of the Indian Service has not resulted in economic development on Reservations comparable to that enjoyed by the rest of the country. With incredible liberal self-righteousness, John Collier, the former Commissioner of Indian Affairs and now a wilderness advocate, can brag that he usually could persuade the various tribes to leave large fractions of their reservation lands roadless.[4] It is scarcely surprising that a fair portion of Americans believe that keeping Indians permanent wards of the Indian Service and specially protecting their lands from development is an unappealing form of segregation. Museums of live people, even if the inmates are well cared for out of public funds, require someone like John Collier, who confuses himself with God, for their justification.

The greatest contradiction, of course, arises from the fragility of true and strictly defined wilderness. In the first Biennial Wilderness Conference in 1949, sponsored by the Sierra Club, the dominant question was: Can a small body of enthusiasts educate enough individuals, especially youths who would be introduced to wild lands, to create mass support for the wilderness idea? Subsequent conferences show greater confidence as success in arousing enthusiasm outstripped expectations. Wilderness areas reasonably accessible to large population centers are already experiencing so much visitation that their wilderness character is threatened in both a subjective and an objective sense. They no longer evoke the sensation of isolation, and flora and fauna are perceptibly disturbed along heavily traveled trails. Projection of three parallel trends: population growth, increased leisure, and more effective education for wilderness appreciation permit only one conclusion.

The perceptive wilderness advocates are becoming concerned, but even moderately feasible adjustments are unpalatable. Building an obstacle course so that only athletes could enter a wild area is perhaps too ridiculous, and we are not likely to tear up extant access roads, though this may yet be the best solution for Yosemite. Some form of rationing may be necessary to assure each individual access to unspoiled wilderness. Should all of our society seek such access—and the announcement of scarcity by rationing is likely to stimulate demand—a week per person per year would be too much. Two weeks per decade is a reasonable but pretty thin diet.

The other prospect is de-education. Wouldn't you really rather go to Disneyland? The mosquitoes in the Sierra are terrible. My own predilection favors such an approach but the consequences are patent. Such mass support for preserving wilderness as it exists or might be generated is essentially precluded. And it must be reemphasized that the modern threat to wilderness comes not from easily maligned greedy private interests but from public servants dedicated to economic progress and increasing the nation's wealth and prosperity. Hetch-Hetchy serves a million thirsty people.

The picture could be painted blacker, but this should be enough. Let me state my own credo. I am glad the Sierra Club and similarly motivated organizations exist. I hope the Dutch Boy grows enough fingers to keep plugging holes in the dike, that obstruction to the erosion of progress continues to be effective, and that we retain wilderness areas into the distant future. Wild habitats for scientific study in as wide as possible a variety of environments can and must be preserved. But to be useful they must be restricted to a limited number of scientific investigators. On moral or religious grounds many of us will regret and seek to prevent the casual extinction of any living species. Even within a few decades, however, the lonely wilderness will not be available to all those who may seek it except on a rationed, once in a lifetime, basis. If man does have need for the good of his soul and the balance or humanness of his personality for direct contact with nature at reasonably frequent intervals, the wilderness area cannot provide it for him. Our world is already too crowded and it is becoming more so. Fortunately at least one other avenue toward solution of this fundamental human problem still exists.

As the human species, slowly at first but at an accelerating rate, extended its range and increased its numbers to become the biologically dominant large animal on earth, it necessarily modified ecological communities and landscapes. It had to, and there is no turning back. A wilderness world might support between one percent and one tenth of one percent of present human populations, and not especially comfortably. We can hope that the world's population growth curve will level off with no more than a doubling of the present total, though that is optimistic. These people need a modified, that is an agriculturally productive landscape on most of the earth's land surface, to support themselves. Their dwellings, mines, manufactories, and communication lines are similarly essential. Of such is the humanized world, and in it we must spend almost all if not all of our lives.

It need not, however, fail to provide us with rich contacts with the burgeoning diversity of nature. The cultivated agricultural landscape need be little if any less interesting than the wild one. If it be argued that the efficiencies of monocultures are greater than more diversified cultures, they also have their drawbacks and the real economic gains are remarkably small. What is essential is a recognition that the space of the earth is finite and must serve all of us. If I do not work the field, I have no entitlement to a share of its yield, but I do have a right, especially if I need, to look at it and be pleased thereby. At this point two sets of claims may be pressed against our wealthy society with its enormous, unused technological competence. Let us consider the larger and more general claim first. What should the humanized world that supports us look like and be like?

In a wonderfully perceptive essay, published in 1952 and entitled "Human, All Too Human Geography," J. B. Jackson postulated that man's goal in modifying the wild landscape is ultimately to create heaven on earth.[5] The house afforded privacy to the individual and intimate family group; the fields concentrated want-satisfying fruits; and the whole interrelated community structured its works to satisfy physical and social desires. If the arrangement was less than perfect, cultural evolution would move in the direction of the desired goals. If access to the observation of other forms of life was such a goal, it might readily be supplied. The Orient, tropical Latin America, and other less developed parts of the world suggest the preservation of some of this harmony. Perhaps the private intimacy of even the tiniest Japanese garden is a peculiarly successful achievement.

It is hard to view the humanized world of the Southern California coastal plain as a whole as anyone's concept of heaven, though many of its elements clearly have that attribute. I think of the separate suburban house with its yard and lawn. Somewhere in the agricultural and industrial revolutions the economic advantages of specialization and rationalization were allowed a dominance that we have failed to control. Because they occupy more space even than suburbs, our agricultural lands reflect the unbalance more seriously. The monoculture stretching for miles, interrupted only by roads on which produce is hauled out and supplies and gear needed for production are moved in. The factory in the field affords only its produce to the man who works it. There is esthetic gratification neither for him nor for the nonfarmer.

I would suggest that the workaday environments so needed to give us physical support can also provide infinitely more esthetic satisfaction and contact with nature than they now do. In fact they must; for there is now or shortly will be no other place to go. So great a problem can only be stated at this time, not solved. Making, by trial and error or by ingenious insight, our humanized world the closest approximation to paradise would seem a task capable of employing human creativity into the indefinite future. My only personal charge or dictum at this point would be that my paradise will certainly include diversity. I hope yours will too.

To move to a more operational level with potential immediate courses of action, almost all of you know the Coast Ranges from Santa Barbara to Monterey. This is the California landscape par excellence with rolling hills covered with grass and scattered oak trees. Range land is the common designation. It is no wilderness but privately owned, agriculturally moderately productive, tax-paying estates. Houses are rare though ubiquitous fences show the hand of man. An occasional bottom or gentle slope is cultivated, but such landscape modification involves no more than 5% of the total surface. I would submit that such a landscape can afford the same satisfactions to the visitor who passes through on foot as the ardently sought and protected wilderness of the High Sierra.

If you have ever tried, you know the answer. It is often impossible even to get off or slow down on the freeway. Adjacent to every country road there is an interminable barbed wire fence. Crossing it makes one liable to arrest for trespass, and pitching a tent or unrolling a sleeping bag is a jail offence. Why? Surely it is private property and I might scare the cows. I might also start a fire, but the fire-conscious National Forests accept my *bona fides* of reasonable discipline in season. Well, it would be a lot of bother to the owner if people wandered over his land.

Curiously, even as a foreigner I have these hiking and camping privileges in comparable terrain across the border in Baja California. The sorts of pressures on space that afflict our public lands can only increase to intolerable levels, but here we grant sanctuary to a small number of landowners whose land could add immeasurably to public welfare. That such lands often are held in low productivity at low tax rates as a tax haven for future subdivision makes the abuse a little more overt.

It does not seem necessary to play Zapata and cry for confiscation of these estates. We have in land taxes a potential but unused social tool. They are proving to be miserably unsuccessful as a prime source of revenue. Privacy is taxable too. We pay for it rather adequately on our suburban lots, and the owner of a 160 acre farm might well choose to exclude visitors at the cost of one or five dollars per year per acre. Would the owner of twenty square miles, not a large estate in California range country, choose the same exclusiveness? The privileges requested here are only those sought in a publicly owned wilderness. Cross-country jeeping and trail bikes that abuse the terrain make excessive demands. Hunters are probably willing to pay special fees, and since they drive out anyone else with sense they must be restricted to short seasons regardless of the state of the wild life; the random shooter, an overabundant sort of vermin, should be locked in a special and limited range.

This diatribe, Jeremiad perhaps, can only conclude with the plea that the subject is important. The quality of life for the next and all future generations is subject to serious threat. The present wilderness reserves are already inadequate. The modest palliatives here proposed probably are too, but serious consideration and creative discussion are called for.

References

[1]David Brower (editor), *Wildlands in our Civilization*, Sierra Club, San Francisco, 1964.

[2]Parts I and II, Sacramento, 1960.

[3]A remarkably provocative article by Edward S. Deevey, "The Hare and the Haruspex: A Cautionary Tale," *American Scientist*, Vol. 48 (1960), pp. 415-430, is well worth examining in this connection.

[4]*Wildlands in our Civilization*, pp. 116-118.

[5]*Landscape*, Vol. 2 (Autumn, 1952), pp. 2-7.

Not Every Prospect Pleases

DAVID LOWENTHAL

I begin with a digression. Why do people feel as they do about particular landscapes? My interest in this question was first aroused by a surfeit of sermons on the virtues of the wilderness. However, notions about wilderness serve me principally as points of departure for a broader inquiry: what is it that makes any landscape seem pleasant or repellent, fitting or unsuitable, to people of various backgrounds and inclinations?

The Wilderness Cult

Early man, according to some of his latter-day descendants, viewed his physical environment with awe and dread. To him, Nature was a tyrant; he survived only by strict obedience to her dictates. To us, it is not Nature but our own creations that are terrifying. Nature seldom threatens most urban Americans; indeed, she scarcely causes us discomfort.

Nevertheless, a new religion of nature is in the making. Worshipers of nature exhort us from the pulpits of countless conservation societies and Audubon clubs; the President's Advisory Commission on Outdoor Recreation transmutes their dogma into national policy; *Life* magazine gives it a four-color imprimatur. Nature is wonderful, they tell us; pay homage to it in

---

Source: David Lowenthal, "Not Every Prospect Pleases", from *Landscape*, Vol. 12, No. 2. Reprinted by permission of the publisher.

the Wilderness, and where there is no Wilderness, create Open Spaces.

The tone of Senator Wayne Morse's comment on the Wilderness Bill, in 1961, exemplifies the underlying rationale: "You cannot associate with the grandeur of this great heritage which God Almighty has given the American people and not come out of such a trip a better man or woman for having come that close to the spirit of the Creator." Americans are near a state of grace, runs this argument, thanks to their past and present intimacy with the wilderness. Our forefathers mastered a continent; today we celebrate the virtues of the vanquished foe: To love nature is regarded as uniquely American. "The outdoors lies deep in American tradition," chants *Outdoor Recreation for America*. "It has had immeasurable impact on the Nation's character and on those who made its history. This is a civilization painfully and only recently carved in conflict with the forces of nature . . . When an American looks for the meaning of his past, he seeks it not in ancient ruins, but more likely in mountains and forests, by a river, or at the edge of the sea."

But these are pious sentiments, not historical facts. Our civilization is mainly imported from Europe, and has had more to contend against in Main Street than in the forest and mountains; pioneer life was usually duller and safer than it is generally imagined; and Americans who seek the meaning of their past look for it in Europe, or in Bunker Hill, Gettysburg, Williamsburg, Freedomland, and the deserted mining towns of the Sierras, precisely because such places are humanized, not wild.

Converts to the wilderness cult, like conservationists generally, tend to feel that their preferences are not only more virtuous than those of others but also more enduring. "Conservation should preserve all the fine things in life. Our heritage must be preserved for those who come after us."—so runs a typical admonition. Long-term or eternal goals are considered ethically superior to immediate ones; and future generations are expected to accept present-day precepts about what is important. Yet our great-great-grandchildren may care little for our image of the wilderness. Moreover, a heritage cannot be preserved intact; if it were, it would have only antiquarian interest. Tomorrow's patrimony is bound to be different from today's. The wilderness was no "heritage" to folk who had to cope with it; it became one only when it no longer had to be lived in. The same is true of pastoral landscapes, rural villages, even of 19th Century industrial centers; and landscapes now despised will some day be prized as a precious heritage.

The wilderness is not, in fact, a type of landscape at all, but a congeries of feelings about man and nature of varying import to different epochs, cultures and individuals. For Elizabethans, the wilderness was barren, chaotic, frightful, "howling"; for contemporary Europeans, it is often associated with primitive and romantic tribes in distant lands; for many Americans, it is an entity distinct from the workaday world, an oasis where the laws of nature still apply.

The cult of wilderness—its origins and history, its philosophies and programs, its impact on landscapes and its implications for mankind—should receive thorough scrutiny. The way Americans feel about wild nature is intimately bound up, as has been suggested, with this country's special history. But the wilderness can hardly be understood except in the context of beliefs and assumptions concerning nature and landscape generally.

Elsewhere I have examined some causes and consequences of supposing nature to be good, wise, purposeful and balanced ("The American Image of Nature as Virtue," *Landscape*, Winter 1959-60). Let me discuss some assumptions about the *appearance* of landscape—assumptions concerning its origins or antiquity, its cultural context or function, and its esthetic congruity. For judgments about the way things ought to look are conditioned by how things are thought to have come into being, how old they are, what they are used for, and how well they fit into their surroundings.

The Genetic Vision

Comfortably ensconced in a Pullman car moving through Pennsylvania, the book critic J. Donald Adams saw something from the window "which revolted me, and . . . made me boil with anger. We had been passing through hilly, forested country, still lovely, even in its second growth," writes Adams in his weekly *New York Times* column, "when suddenly I saw a mountain stream so discolored, so noxious as almost to turn one's stomach. It was easy to imagine how it had once looked, sparkling and clear, before the mines somewhere beyond had polluted its waters and made it a thing of blasphemy."

What seems ugly to Adams he condemns as evil; but which of these judgments determined the other? He cannot be certain that the stream is polluted—he is no hydrologist. Suppose he learned the water was discolored not by mining but by a sulfur vent upstream, or simply by turbid spring floods; would he still find it "noxious"? If he knew nature were responsible for the color of the stream, would he "boil with anger"? Would he still conjure up an image of pristine purity? In short, Adams takes it for granted that landscapes he enjoys are natural, and that those he dislikes have been ruined by man. Nature beautifies; man deforms. To alter the natural order is inherently wicked and *hence* displeasing to the eye. The forest, like the stream, is judged by this dictum. "Still lovely, *even* in its second growth," the wooded hillside is more attractive than some denuded slope, but lacks the perfection of the primitive forest.

Where landscapes are not patently marred by man, it is all too easy to assume that they are primeval. To the city dweller, anything that is not geometrically arranged may seem in the realm of untouched nature. He seldom distinguishes the pastoral from the wild. Indeed, in a landscape seen for the first time every component—mountains, old houses, even billboards—is apt to strike the viewer as a durable fixture of the scene.

But no matter how natural or untouched they may look, most landscapes have been profoundly altered by man, directly or indirectly, over long periods of time. "A field of pasture grass looks as if it had been there forever," remarks Edwards Hyams, "and it is hard to absorb the fact that, like any urban square, it has been imposed on the wild." One intuitively feels that if man had interfered with the lovely vista it would bear obvious marks of manufacture, alteration or decay. "Surely a water-meadow, with its lush grass knee-high to the cows and its decoration of tall golden buttercups . . . is a gift of God, or nature." Not so; "we owe it all to the greed for gain of a speculating 17th Century nobleman and the engineering skill of some Dutch drainage expert." On the other hand, some aspects of nature seem artificial. Vegetation is apt to look more "natural" than barren rock, because we perceive analogies between geological and architectural structures—many tourists, asserts Joseph Wood Krutch, assume the Grand Canyon is at least partly man-made.

Misconceptions about man's role in landscape formation are universal and probably inevitable. Appearances lead people in all cultures and eras to assume that some things are "man-made," others natural, when the truth would reveal the opposite, or more likely an intermingling of agencies. What is unusual—and, to my mind, destructive—is to combine wrong notions of landscape genesis with the moral judgment that men generally act for mean motives and with effects offensive to the sight.

The contemporary tendency to find beauty and good in the "natural," ugliness or squalor in what man dominates is not only moralistic; it is an esthetic aberration in the history of landscape taste. The contrary view has usually prevailed. Thus to Daniel Defoe, Westmoreland was "the wildest, most barren and frightful" county in England; he liked nothing about it except "some pleasant manufacturing towns." In most canons of landscape beauty, man and his works occupy a prominent place. A century and a half ago, in a fairly representative view, Arthur Young described the clang and smoke and flames of the iron forges at Colebrook Dale as "altogether sublime." Russians today similarly admire Kochegarka mine, the "pride" of Gorlovka, with its magnificent slag heaps scattered over the steppe for miles around.

By and large, men find lived-in landscapes more attractive than wild ones. "We have in places made the Earth more beautiful than it was before we came," Sir Francis Younghusband maintained in his Royal Geographical Society address: "I can realize what the river-valleys of England must have been like before the arrival of man—beautiful, certainly; but not *so* beautiful as now. . . . Now the marshes are drained and turned into golden meadows. The woods are cleared in part and well-kept parks take their place. . . . And homes are built. . . which in the setting of trees and lawns and gardens add unquestionably to the natural beauty of the land."

Raw nature was condemned also by 19th Century Americans.

The Rockies and the Sierras displeased early tourists. "The dreariness of the desolate peak itself scarcely dissipates the dismal spell," one traveler wrote of Pike's Peak, "for you stand in a hopeless confusion of dull stones piled upon each other in odious ugliness." Americans preferred the picturesque—caverns evocative of cathedrals, pillars resembling ruined castles. If they could not have real ruins, they wanted make-believe ones; they had had a plethora of wilderness. To admire, much less love, wild nature, as Daniel Beard advocated, initially seemed ludicrous to almost everyone. Indeed, the first forest reserves were called "primitive areas" because, according to Earl Pomeroy, the government feared "the public might find the word 'wilderness' repulsive."

All that is changed; for contemporary Americans, it is civilization that is hard to endure. A "primitive area" is now a place, according to the Outdoor Recreation Resources Review Commission, in which one enjoys a "wilderness experience"—"a sense of being so far removed from the sights and sounds of civilization that he is alone with nature." The implications of this statement underlie most of the issues I have raised. Are the "sights and sounds" of civilization more difficult to live with than those of nature? Is being alone with nature the only, or even the best, alternative to civilization? What about being alone in rural or pastoral countrysides, or in landscapes full of historic ruins but void of present day activity? And how much do these distinctions matter if one is not aware of them? Consider an urbanite walking in woods where human enterprise is apparent to any Indian or woodsman, but invisible to him; does he not feel as alone with nature as he would in a truly primeval landscape? Alternatively, if J. Donald Adams suspected the green on leaves came from manufactured chlorophyll, would he not find the forest ugly? Oranges look unnatural only when we are told their color is artificial.

Few Americans, however, are devotees exclusively of the aboriginal; many are fond of the merely old. Landscapes that cannot qualify as pure wilderness may still be acceptable if they are sufficiently ancient, uncontaminated by contemporary life, or relics of an epoch when (it is assumed) man lived in harmony with his surroundings. Americans tout no particular era as an acme of esthetic virtue; all they ask is certified antiquity, preferably numerically precise. It is the anachronistic appearance that is all-important. Critics of Malraux's clean-up program for the *monuments historiques* of Paris protest that rejuvenation "has robbed them of their weight of reality, that the Concorde palaces now look like Hollywood movie sets of the Concorde palaces." And the Hotel Crillon rejected cleaning outright because, noted Genet in the *New Yorker*, "its clientele, especially the Americans, had faith in the dirt of the facade as a guarantee that they were living in a genuinely historic old place." Few people are really taken in by such a "guarantee." But this matters little; we are willing to be fooled even when we know we are being fooled.

At home, visual self-deception is unabashed. Dirt is all right on European facades; here, it is matter out of place. For every restored Williamsburg, there are countless generic prototypes like Old Sturbridge Village—sanitary facsimiles rather than actual places, which rely for verisimilitude on scholarly precision. Self-conscious and sentimental about the past, we fence it off in special landscapes of its own, as if history were a zoo. Repair jobs for Niagara Falls and other "natural" scenic wonders are deemed proper because they preserve or restore nature's creations; artifice is the means, not the end. But even where entirely new effects are produced, as with floodlights in caves or music piped out of scenery, the landscape passes for "natural" as long as the face of the earth is not grossly and visibly altered. In the classic phrase of a Long Island developer, "We don't tamper with nature . . . we improve upon it!"

The Functional Vision

What Americans see in landscapes, and how well they like them, depend also on how the landscapes are being used. Form is supposed to fit function; camouflage is arty and dishonest. We like to call a spade a spade: however ugly a factory, a city dump, a used-car lot may seem to the passerby, as long as it fulfills its function it is presumed to look all right. If the used-car dealer didn't like the way his lot looked, he'd do something about it—

not for his own visual pleasure, to be sure, but to attract customers. To enjoy a landscape or to commune with nature, we go to the wilderness. We do not prettify the rugged face of workaday America.

The landscape, in short, is worthy of its hire. Its ultimate critics are its residents, not its visitors, however unappreciative the former, however learned or perceptive the latter. This is the burden of a passage in William James's "On a Certain Sense of Blindness in Human Beings":

> Journeying in the mountains of North Carolina, I passed by a large number of "coves," . . . which had been newly cleared and planted. The impression on my mind was one of unmitigated squalor. The settler had in every case cut down the more manageable trees, and left their charred stumps standing. The larger trees he had girdled and killed . . . and had set up a tall zigzag rail fence around the scene of his havoc, to keep the pigs and cattle out. Finally, he had irregularly planted the intervals between the stumps and trees with Indian corn. . . . The forest had been destroyed; and what had "improved" it out of existence was hideous, a sort of ulcer, without a single element of artificial grace to make up for the loss of Nature's beauty. . . . Talk about going back to Nature! I said to myself, oppressed by the dreariness. . . . No modern person ought to be willing to live a day in such a state of rudimentariness and denudation.

Then a mountaineer told James, "Why, we ain't happy here, unless we are getting one of these coves under cultivation."

> I instantly felt that I had been losing the whole inward significance of the situation. . . . To me the clearings spoke of naught but denudation. . . . But, when *they* looked on the hideous stumps, what they thought of was personal victory. The chips, the girdled trees, and the vile split rails spoke of honest sweat, persistent toil and final reward. . . . In short, the clearing, which to me was a mere ugly picture on the retina, was to them a symbol redolent with moral memories and sang a very paean of duty, struggle and success.

And he points the moral: "The spectator's judgment is sure to miss the root of the matter, and to possess no truth."

James considers the mountaineers' impression truer and nobler than his own, not because they see better, but because they have a better right to judge. Beauty is in the eye of the beholder, to be sure; but which beholder is right? Why, the man who is usually on the spot—presumably the shepherd on the Downs, the sexton at St. Paul's, the elevator operator in the Eiffel Tower. He may have no time, training, or inclination for an esthetic appreciation of landscape; no matter, he acquires it by osmosis.

The Esthetic Definition

Preoccupation with purpose is in fact no aid, but a deterrent to landscape appreciation. The man who has to consider what things are used for is least likely to note their shapes, colors and patterns. To exalt his judgment is to promote a complacent inattention to appearance, an abnegation of esthetic response. The visitor's view is discounted, but the resident is too preoccupied to have a view.

There are a few who care, or pretend to care, about the way things look where they live. But many homeowners are satisfied by linguistic landscaping. Through emotive names—even by such geographical fantasies as Hilldale Heights, Valmont Gardens, and Glencrest Homes—"an idealized landscape is imposed on an existing one by verbal *force majeure*," as Arthur Minton points out in *Names*. Maybe only God can make a tree, but any real-estate developer can create a veritable forest in the mind's eyes of his clients.

Few people really look at the places they live in, work in, or travel through. Anesthetized against their surroundings, they spare themselves pain. "Start by looking at things, and then one becomes aware how hideous they really are," writes F.F.C. Curtis in the *Journal of the Royal Society of Arts*. "Some towns are hideous from one end to the other. I think it is because people do not open their eyes and do not recognize them as hideous."

The concept of scenic beauty, formerly tied to specific attributes, has since the 18th Century lost all precise meaning; it now promiscuously denotes anything that gives pleasure. "We talk about a 'sublime' or 'lovely' landscape," as Fenichel says, "because we feel sublime or lovely when seeing a landscape of this kind." No longer captives of the picturesque, we do not require that scenery look like a painting; and we can enjoy landscapes that point no meaning or moral.

Nonetheless, certain landscapes look right, others wrong or unhappily composed. They may seem incongruous because we have a pictorial bias against certain combinations of form and color, or a teleological outlook that condemns assemblages unless they look planned. Some of us find landscapes deformed unless the visual assemblage is familiar. Various objects, shapes or colors may seem out of place in certain settings. The totally strange and new may be less unsettling than a combination of known with unknown elements, or of forms belonging to two or more disparate cultural contexts. Those used to Western European or North American landscapes find something absurd and dissonant in lands where mules coexist with motorcars, and temperate zone flowers compete with tropical vegetation. The commingling of familiar and exotic, or of past and present, can be bizarre and disturbing.

Whatever the reason, most people expect a measure of visual harmony in landscapes. But the measure is personal as well as cultural: variety pleasing to one individual may pass unnoticed by a second and seem a shocking mélange to a third. Take litter. Most Americans pile junk in town dumps and automobile graveyards or throw it in rivers and down railway embankments. But streets and the countryside generally are free of cans and paper—otherwise, someone complains.

Other cultures treat litter differently. From an apartment in one tropical land I recently looked out at a garden, a stretch of grass that passed as lawn and pleasant buildings opposite. What made the scene seem so tawdry? Garden and lawn were strewn with paper and cans. Litter collected there, months on end, because *no one saw it*; to the residents, cans and paper did not seem out of place among grass and flowers. And to many folk, here as well as abroad, cans and paper are not litter at all, but valuable materials for construction and fuel.

The problem is made evident and vivid when litter is mistaken for something view-worthy. Disillusioned by mistaking a piece of blue paper on a hillside for a flower, A. M. Sayers asks in the *New Statesman*, "*Why* do we dislike litter? . . . Is the disgust rooted in fear of one's fellows as a whole? No. Ancient Roman or medieval 'litter' doesn't trouble us. . . . Is it to do with the Age of Paper? Why should amphorae be so much more respectable than old tin cans?" But some people see nothing disreputable in old tin cans. Everything depends on what is considered "out of place," on the rate of decay, on how rapidly artifacts cease to be junk and become part of the heritage. And these are matters of great complexity.

Consider the reactions of Reyner Banham on Tair Carn Isaf, in Wales. Fascinated by the spectral, other-worldly quality of the cairns, the rocks and the light, he stumbles against "a stumpy concrete obelisk"—an Ordnance Survey triangulation point.

> And it jarred. . . . The triangulation-point just seemed to dirty things up. It destroyed the landscape as surely as the sheep that were eating the grass cover off the peat-beds. . . . The thing was a mess in itself, rust-stained from its metal fitments. It was a mess functionally, weathered down to a drab grey-brown that made it invisible against the landscape, and thus useless as a sighting-point. . . . Failed on looks, failed on function, failed for cultural inertia, too, for what else could force the classical obelisk form, apt to stone and primitive technology, on a machine-age material whose nature enjoins no form in particular?

Man's other contributions to that landscape seemed to Banham quite inoffensive—the ancient castle across the valley, his own aluminum-stemmed pipe and butane-fueled lighter. These belonged, visually, because they were or had been functionally effective. "Success or failure by the norms of the time," Banham concludes, is "almost an absolute standard for evaluating buildings in the natural landscape. For the landscape . . . can never be anything but up to date. Against the ruthless standard of nature . . . only the most spit-hot artifacts can survive. The trivial pipe is competitive, so is the portentous castle, the dirty obelisk is not."

The principle Banham enunciates is debatable. But even if it is accepted, landscape judgments would differ from person to person. Lacking his special knowledge of technology and architecture, most observers would probably not be bothered at all by the triangulation marker. The main point, however, is that all the considerations Banham mentions are pertinent. They do not merely justify esthetic judgment; they help to form it. What makes one landscape appear harmonious, another incongruous, is the entire experience of the viewer.

Part Three

Toward a Quality Environment

Environmental Quality Control

DOUGLAS L. BROOKS

It wasn't too long ago, in terms of history, that Mark Twain was able to get an appreciative laugh by observing how everybody complains about the weather but nobody *does* anything about it. Nobody laughs anymore. Not because the joke has become a cliché; all successful jokes do. But now we are beginning to see that what's happening to our environment—the weather included—has turned out to be a joke on us. Absurd perhaps, but not funny.

Is it not absurd that in the midst of the greatest material development the world has ever seen—and in a very real sense, because of it—the American people have ever-increasing cause to complain? They complain not merely about the weather, but about virtually every aspect of their environment. And is it not utterly serious when scientists and government leaders are being flooded with exhortations from every quarter to *do* something about it and to do it *soon*?

Some would have us "preserve" the environment, implying that the thing we need do is arrest further change. Some would have us "restore" it out of a perhaps nostalgic belief in the existence of some hypothetical optimum "natural" state that prevailed before the noticeable impact of man. Others would "improve" it —by extending the coastline through massive engineering efforts, for example, to create artificial lagoons, estuaries, and

Source: Douglas L. Brooks, "Environmental Quality Control" from *BioScience*, Vol. 17, December 1967, pp. 873-877. Minor deletions to the original text have been made. Reprinted by permission of the publisher and author.

islands; or by converting Long Island Sound into a fresh water reservoir; or by modifying normal rainfall amounts and locations by cloud seeding.

Athelstan Spilhaus has named this kind of activity "geotechnology."[1] He defines it as "the emerging field through which we shall use our geophysical knowledge to intervene and change natural processes on a large scale, hopefully for the benefit of mankind." I wonder if you are struck, as I am, by the rather wistful use of the word "hopefully" in this quotation. Mark Twain would have appreciated its poignant literary possibilities and the opportunity for sharp-edged irony it might have afforded him.

Yet this is not a time for either irony or poignancy or cynicism or despair. On the contrary, a pattern of thinking that I regard as extremely hopeful is beginning to emerge in scientific and government circles. This thinking proceeds from the fundamental assumption that the phenomenon of environmental deterioration is not merely a transcendentally challenging subject for scientific study and understanding, although it certainly is this. More important and encouraging, this thinking accepts environmental deterioration as an urgent and challenging problem for systematic management and control.

Reflecting this emerging willingness of the scientific community to deal with urgent real-world problems, to which the solutions will always be less than ideal, but one hopes (not at all wistfully) livable, this paper is cast in a management framework, not a purely scientific one. I will, in other words, be talking about environmental management, not just environmental science. To me this means, first—and most exciting—the need for an unprecedented collaboration or partnership among many fields of science, the life sciences, the physical sciences and the social sciences. In a sense, we must all become social scientists. Further, it means that such cross-disciplinary studies must be done in an action framework, with prescription—not just description—as their goal.

Having set the stage with these general remarks, let me proceed quickly to the specific task—to help structure this still amorphous cross-disciplinary field of environment management by describing one of two related categories of phenomena into which environmental changes can usefully be divided for management purposes. The category that is my concern consists of those generally small or gradual changes whose individual and immediate effect on the environment is hardly noticeable, but whose cumulative and ultimately pervasive nature is eventually perceived as a drastic decline in environmental quality. The other category consists of more suddenly dramatic and immediately threatening changes in the environment.

A suitably pejorative term for describing the gradual changes is "environmental decay." The corresponding management problem is "environmental quality control." In addition to describing the phenomenon of environmental decay, I shall try to sketch the outlines of a promising approach to its control.

Environmental Decay

Views of what we mean by the complex term "environment" vary from person to person, group to group, and time to time, as do preferences regarding the meaning of quality control and methods for achieving it. A number of articulate and thoughtful spokesmen, however, have converged to a remarkable degree in books, reports, and articles that have appeared through the last dozen years on a description of the main features of environmental decay. The similarity of their viewpoints is sufficient to permit me to offer what now appears to be a culturally consistent and stable view of what is meant by this term.[2,3,4]

The various kinds of environmental decay that emerge from this apparent consensus can be described under five main headings.

First is the decay represented by the impoverishment of our resources. Two kinds of resources are involved here: essential resources such as food, minerals, water, and living space; and desirable resources such as wildlife, play space, walking space. (Parenthetically, I might add that I realize fully that one man's desirable resource is another man's essential one.) On a global scale, mass starvation as burgeoning populations overwhelm the already inadequate food supply is the most compelling problem resulting from resource inadequacy. But even within the food-surplus United States, our critical dependence on minerals and other natural resources from parts of the world where mounting food shortages threaten political and economic institutions makes their food problem ours. And, finally, our ability to utilize the impoverished and increasingly inaccessible raw materials needed by our industrial civilization is dependent on increasingly sophisticated extraction and processing technology. Destroy that, as nuclear war, for example, would inevitably do not only here but everywhere around the world and industrial society could probably never again get started.

A second kind of decay is represented by the increasing level of pollution, noise, and ugliness within which we are being immersed. The evidence here is too well known to need elaboration.

A third involves increasing crowding, congestion, and hence conflict over incompatible uses of the environment. Let me mention only one, the competition for space between men and their cars.

> Either one of these exploding phenomena can smother the continent. "Already," comments Edward C. Crafts of the Bureau of Outdoor Recreation, "automobiles occupy more space in America than do people. For the next decade the American scene that will experience a population growth of 58 million will shudder under a disproportionate avalanche of 50 million space-consuming cars. A four-lane highway consumes up to fifty acres of land per mile, preferably the most level and strategically located land." Underscoring this, Joseph J. Shomon in *Audubon Magazine* writes, "Everywhere the battle for open space is bitter, the competition mounting. The most profitable uses—however unsightly, ill-considered, or shortsighted—have been crowding out less lucrative but more aesthetic uses. A new highway, a new facility, a new development, each tends to go where resistance is weakest, and this is usually an existing park or some unspoiled open space. Atlanta has cannibalized more than 60 percent of its park land. Over cries of outrage the historic Morningside Park in Manhattan is giving way to a school."[5]

The fourth variety of environmental decay manifests itself in the increasing depersonalization or "thingification" of life, due to growth in size, complexity, and ubiquity of cities, traffic, and mass communications media.

Fifth, and finally, there is the environmental decay of potentially Wagnerian proportions, in which inadvertent and perhaps irreversible modification of the earth's weather and climate caused by man's activities could make all other kinds of decay of only academic concern. The production of carbon dioxide by world-wide burning of fossil fuels promises, according to some, to so increase the "greenhouse effect" of the heat absorbing constituents of the atmosphere that a world-wide climatic warming may take place, perhaps melting the Antarctic and Greenland icecaps and raising the sea level by a couple of hundred feet. Whether this will be in part counter-balanced or perhaps overbalanced by the solar radiation-reflecting effect of the increased cloudiness expected from air pollution is a moot question. So is the possible rainfall-inhibiting effect of pollution nuclei in producing clouds containing overly large numbers of abnormally small droplets which remain stably suspended in the air rather than coalescing to produce precipitation.[6] In any case, weather and climate changes of a possibly drastic nature appear to be in the making.

The Environment-Man System

One way to begin the job of environmental quality control is by identifying the properties common to all kinds of environmental decay. I am struck by six particularly. They are:

1. The changes, although accelerating, are slow and must be viewed over the perspective of the years and decades ahead for their full import to be seen.
2. The immediate causes of these changes are myriad.
3. Interactions among changes in the environment are numerous and complex; they involve nature as well as man, his instrumentalities, his artifacts.
4. More remote, let alone ultimate, causes of an environmental decay are unclear. As scientists, for example, are we to accept population growth and industrial productivity as the ultimate

causes of our troubles, or can these, in turn, be merely by-products of some more fundamental and perhaps unmanageable drive in mankind?

5. Our understanding of the overall problem is at best partial, and our knowledge is full of gaps.
6. There is no simple "magic bullet" solution, although there are many partial solutions being ardently advocated with only dim recognition of their interdependence.

Identification of these six properties common to all kinds of environmental decay sets us on the road to finding an answer to the question "What's to be done?" in that it at least shows us the dimensions of our ignorance. How do we diminish this ignorance even as we take the all-important first steps to *doing* something?

I think we can take this first step as well as subsequent ones with some assurance of eventual success if we look at man and his environment as *interacting components of a single closed system* of global proportions. Marston Bates has called this system the human ecosystem; and Kenneth Boulding has provided a vivid metaphor for it by referring to it as Spaceship Earth. It consists, on the one hand, of the subsystem "man" and some portion of his attitudes, habits, values, and the institutions by which he functions—the family, welfare and educational institutions, corporations, governments, and the like. And it consists, on the other hand, of the subsystem "environment"—the physical context in which man and society coexist. The physical environment itself is comprised of two interacting components: one is natural—geography, weather, climate, minerals, wildlife, etc; the other, the increasingly important one, is artificial—a man-made complex of cities, highways, traffic, and mass communications.

Basis for a Systems Analysis

To pursue this systems approach to managing the environment, we need to be able to do the following three things:

1. Specify the variables representing man's inputs to the environment (they will be related somehow to population and industrial productivity);

2. Specify the variables representing the environment's outputs of major concern to man (I have suggested five such, ranging from resource exhaustion to inadvertent weather modification);
3. Develop a quantitative model of the environment showing how the outputs are related to the inputs and to each other (even a first crude approximation would be a tremendous asset to thinking and planning as well as to research of more substantive kinds).

Then, turning to man in his limited and partial aspect as an environmental management subsystem, we need to begin with the environmental outputs and do the following:
1. Identify the problems they create for man in terms of his goals and objectives;
2. Identify alternative environments (or groupings of related and compatible environments) to be considered as potential solutions to these problems;
3. Develop a framework for comparing and criteria for ranking these alternative environments and environmental sets and for compromising conflicting goals and objectives;
4. Evaluate alternatives and present plans for pursuing them to decision-makers and to the public in a fashion that is understandable and useful.

Finally, decision-makers themselves need to acquire the tools needed to monitor environmental outputs and to activate the requisite corrective inputs in the light of the above.

Precedents and Prospects

Is there any hope that this approach can, in fact, be usefully adapted to environmental quality control—where the system to be managed is so complex and hard to understand, where the management goals are so ill-defined and contradictory, where experts already abound, each with his favorite and admittedly partial solution, and where the corrective control systems in any case are, at best, rudimentary if, in fact, they can be said to exist at all?

Perhaps not, but I believe there are some encouraging precedents. In 1940, for example, the field of military operations and systems management could have been described—and was—in these bleak discouraging terms. I am not saying that all the problems in the military systems management field have been resolved or that the systems approach hasn't been occasionally misapplied, but in just 25 years tremendous advances have been made in the art of rational, military decision-making for both planning and operations. The fact that no nuclear war has as yet broken out, in spite of the long-standing existence of the capability to wage it and provocations for doing so, is in part a product of such an advance. Industry, particularly big industry, is adopting it more and more in the form of management information systems and associated objective evaluation practices.

What, in scientific terms, have systems analysts done, whatever their institutional context? Methodologically, they have united the methods of the physical sciences with the viewpoint of the economist and applied the result to real-life problems of practical management, teaming up with specialists in relevant scientific fields as need be. Systems analysis emphasizes the importance of mathematical modeling, using techniques which originated with Bolzman and Gibbs and which reached their current culmination in the work of Norbert Wiener, and the cyberneticists. These techniques introduced statistics and uncertainty or probability into the description of phenomena, including physical phenomena, in a much more thorough-going way than had ever been done before. By doing so they enabled us to model "open systems with feed-back"—those systems that purposefully process information from the environment and communicate new orders to it; those systems that can at least locally and temporarily reverse the general tendency for the universe, itself a closed system, to tend gradually to greater and greater chaos and randomness, or in physical terms toward maximum entropy, or in environmental terms, "decay."

The computer is the most obvious example of such a system in the world of technology, but living organisms and societies can be understood, says Wiener,[7] in similar terms. In fact, he says that only in such terms can society be understood. For the objectives of environmental management, at least, I believe he is right.

Subjects for Early Consideration

If I were asked to nominate specific subjects for early investigation, I would, for example, begin with an effort aimed at developing a quantitative model of the environment. Or rather, I would try to get models of various distinguishable environments, for I suspect we need to define and consider many. Their definition would not only include such factors as geography, terrain, climate, and human habitation category, but—more important—would explore the perhaps unique set of mutually compatible human uses to which each environment could justifiably be put.

A tropical estuarine wilderness environment, for example, would imply a set of uses, perhaps centered about individual or small group nonmotorized recreation. But in any case it would be a set very different from that appropriate to a temperate inland rural environment, let alone a suburban or urban environment or what have you.

The point is to begin to classify environments in somewhat the way we now zone our cities and towns in terms of mutually compatible uses. Whether this would ever become the basis for regulation through "environmental zoning," it would at least permit us to inventory the mix of environments we now have and help us see what might happen to each under various projected conditions of use.

Other problem areas I would recommend for early analysis include:

1. Weather and climate modification—here we know inadvertent modification is already taking place and purposeful modification on a significant scale may be only a decade or two away. We need urgently to define our objectives. My thought would be to attempt to stabilize and make more reliable the climates we've already got, rather than try to improve some necessarily at the expense of others. Long-term investments in terms of residential and industrial location, gas and oil supplies, etc., are made on the basis of expected climatic conditions. Losses or disappointments occur when the climate deviates from expectations, even for a year or two. Climatic reliability, year in and year out, would be a tremendous

economic boon. If this could be combined with really high reliability forecasts of weather details a few days ahead, it would be hard to ask for more.

2. Pollution control—here the obvious long-term objective is total recycling of wastes.

3. Urban environment design or redesign—here especially the diversity of compatible uses to which a city can be put should be made as explicit as possible. A critical example for many is whether pedestrian or nonmotorized transportation is compatible with other forms of transportation. If taking a safe, pleasant walk is felt to be desirable in theory, to get it in practice you may need a commissioner of sidewalks to fight the now all-powerful commissioner of roads. And why should they be merely *side*walks?

4. This brings us to transportation and such general questions as, is safety one of our objectives and if so, how much?

5. Resources management, particularly space utilization, marine resource management, and food.

6. And finally, population, whose unprecedented growth is in a sense the cause of it all. Is it possible or wise to think in terms of population objectives, or at least, using theoretical models of the national and global environments, predict a little more certainly and meaningfully the kinds of human ecosystems we're headed for at various projected levels of population growth?

Summary

I can summarize very quickly. I believe the time has come to recognize environmental decay as an ubiquitous problem of unprecedented complexity and seriousness. We need to recognize environmental quality control as a vital social objective and take steps to establish the field of Environmental Management as a new cross-disciplinary applied science professional activity of extraordinary challenge and importance.

In doing so, we can and should take advantage of the analogy provided by such precedents as military operations research and systems analysis. Five features of these precedents are especially important when taken in combination. They are:

1. The methodological and philosophical advances in the physical and mathematical sciences, begun by Bolzman and Gibbs and culminating in the work of Wiener, Shannon, and the cyberneticists, which permit the modeling of complex systems with inherent randomness and uncertainty and, in particular, the purposeful "open systems" characterizing the human social half of the man-environment system.
2. The systems approach of operations research and system analysis with its emphasis on rational decision-making models and techniques.
3. The new technology, particularly the new information system technology, based on the computer, which has already permitted spectacular advances in modeling one highly complex component of the environment, the atmosphere and its weather, and the application of this technology to observational or environmental monitoring systems.
4. The establishment and linking together with the action agencies of government of three types of R&D institutions:
   (a) innovative, technology, or science-oriented laboratories, pushing the "state-of-the-art,"
   (b) advisory "think-tanks" of two sorts, one closely linked to the day-to-day or tactical decision problems of agencies, the other broadly chartered to study and advise on the long-term or strategic problems of Environmental Management.
5. The development and cultivation of an outlook which can best be described as ecological, or ecosystems oriented, an outlook which asks what stable and reciprocally-fit man/environment configurations are there and how are the consequences and side effects of actions and events at various levels, personal and social, industrial and governmental, likely to affect the prospects of achieving one or another of these configurations in the future?

I have tried to sketch very briefly some specific problems that I feel are ripe for attack by a program of environmental management studies, with some prospects of success. Such studies and the implementation of their results in the real world will take time, imagination, energy, and statesmanship—both scientific and political—of the highest order. Whether, in fact, success is achieved is, I believe, more a matter of a conscious decision to organize and fund the necessary effort than it is a matter of available competence.

References

[1]Spilhaus, Athelstan. 1966. Goals in geotechnology *Bull. Am. Meteorol. Soc.*, 47 (5).

[2]Report to Secretary, HEW, by Task Force on Environmental Health and Related Problems. 1967. A Strategy for a Livable Environment.

[3]Resources for the Future. 1966. Proceedings of a Seminar: *Environmental Quality in a Growing Economy*. Johns Hopkins Press, Baltimore, Md.

[4]Subcommittee on Science, Research, and Development of the House Committee on Science and Astronautics. 1966. Environmental Pollution, A Challenge to Science and Technology.

[5]Rienow, Robert and Leona. 1967. *Moment in the Sun*. Dial Press, New York.

[6]President's Science Advisory Committee Panel Report. 1965. Restoring the Quality of the Environment.

[7]Wiener, Norbert. 1954. *The Human Use of Human Beings, Cybernetics and Society*. Doubleday & Co., Garden City, New York.

A Framework for Dealing with the Urban Environment

HARVEY S. PERLOFF

The current interest in the quality of the urban environment is in large part a convergence of two other evolving public concerns. One is a concern with the quality of the natural environment—the quality of air, water, land, wilderness areas, and other resources. The other is a concern with the development of our urban communities—with all the matters coming under the rubric of more traditional city planning, but recently refocused to a special concern for the human beings in the city. The quality of life of all the people who are clustering into urban communities is clearly influenced by what happens to both the natural and the man-made environments in direct interrelationship with each other.

Our capacity to deal effectively with the enormously complex problems of the urban environment—problems that become more complex with each passing year—will certainly be much increased if we can sharpen our concepts, clarify the nature of the problems, improve our measurement tools (including the measurement of alternative proposed solutions), and be inventive about new institutional arrangements to cope with new situations. The present paper merely points, in an introductory vein, to some conceptual and measurement

Source: Harvey S. Perloff, "A Framework for Dealing with the Urban Environment" in Harvey S. Perloff (ed.), *The Quality of the Urban Environment*, Resources for the Future Inc., Washington, D.C., 1969, pp. 3-25. Reprinted by permission of the publisher.

issues that deserve attention within such a policy-oriented probing of the subject.

We know from experience that it is difficult to make much progress in the realm of public policy and co-ordinated public-private action unless there is fairly substantial common ground of understanding and agreement as to just what the public interest is and why group action is called for. This is true whether we are talking about cleaning up the rivers, improving mass transportation, or eliminating slums (or, for that matter, providing financial aid overseas). The importance of such common ground is particularly great where most proposed solutions involve governmental restraints on the use of private property and the making of profits, or the imposition of extra costs on private groups, or the expenditure of large sums of public money. In spite of the fact that some people see the United States as increasingly subject to creeping or galloping socialism, it takes quite a bit of doing to get the necessary public backing to enable a governmental agency to impose limitations on private activities.[1]

The rationale on which public action is based—and the breadth and depth of its acceptance—thus has a great deal to do with the ability of governments to carry out a coherent set of policies over a substantial period of time. This normally calls for rather broad social concepts which in their very essence point to the objectives involved, the nature of the problems or difficulties, and the kinds of solutions which would seem to follow logically. Concepts of this type are sometimes rather vague and at times might even have contradictory elements within them. They can also linger long after the situation has changed. But whatever the difficulties and dangers, such broad social concepts tend to play an important role in providing a foundation for public policy and action in given matters.[2]

In dealing with problems that are as numerous, diverse, and complex as those involved in the quality of the urban environment, there is a clear gain if we can have concepts that serve simultaneously a simplifying and unifying role, since they contribute to the development of a common ground of understanding.

I would like to suggest two concepts that can play such a simplifying and unifying role with regard to the quality of the urban environment. One is an extension of the meaning and scope of natural resources, to encompass what I have called "new resources in an urban age." The other is a view of the urban environment as a contained (but not closed), highly interrelated system (or subsystem) of natural and man-made elements in various mixes.

Extending the Concept of Resources

For a very long time—in fact, for many centuries—natural resources have been thought of essentially as the elements of the natural environment needed for the production of certain basic commodities (farm, forestry, fishing, water, and mineral *products*) and, to a much lesser extent, of certain services (especially recreation and water transportation). My colleagues and I have described elsewhere[3] the slowly changing meaning of natural resources ("the resources that matter") as the nation's economy has evolved from an agricultural to an industrial base and, more recently, as tertiary activities have grown in importance. The ever greater capacity for substitution among natural resource commodities (through developments in science and technology), the increasing elaboration of commodities so that the economic value of the "first stage" is a small part of the total value added, and the fabulous growth in the demand for services have all joined to reduce the relative importance of natural resources commodities. The extent of this reduction is suggested by the fact that contribution of the so-called natural resources industries to GNP has declined from a third of the total in 1870 to some 11 per cent roughly a hundred years later.[4]

In the process, the concept of natural resources has been broadened somewhat. Thus, in recent decades, the notion of "amenity resources"—particularly as it reflects a special juxtaposition of climate, topography, coast and seashore, etc., especially attractive for the location of economic activities and family living—has been incorporated into the resources concept. Similarly, there have been increasing references to "open space resources," i.e., open areas, particularly on the outskirts of cities, that offer breathing space and recreation possibilities for city residents.

The time has arrived, however, to rethink the basic concept of natural resources in a more general way so that it has the greatest possible relevance to our own day and to the foreseeable future.

At the core, the more traditional commodity resources *and* the newer environmental resources ultimately yield services to consumers; to use the jargon of economics, they enter the individual's utility function. However, the newer environmental resources are much more subject to externalities than are the commodity resources: the activities of all kinds of production and consumption units—whether family, business firm, or governmental—may generate either direct or indirect external effects on other units. This is the case when a firm emits wastes into the air or into streams, when one building cuts out the sunlight from other buildings, when planes roar over a residential section of the city, when a car adds to the congestion on a highway, or when a great new subdivision uses up a beautiful open area on the edge of town. In each case, costs or "illfare" are imposed on others. Analysis of the newer resources thus forces us to face up to a basic defect in classical economics: the assumption that the utility functions of individual human beings are independent of one another. Actually, resource economics has been concerned with this issue for some time, but now the questions of externalities and of collective goods must be brought front and center.

It has long been accepted that, in a socioeconomic sense, natural resources are those elements of the natural environment that have a use to man, and are therefore in demand, but whose supply falls short of the demand. Thus, as developments occur in science and technology, new resources (uranium, for instance) come continually into being; or existing resources greatly increase in value (for instance, with advances in construction, vertical transportation, and communication technology, airspace becomes more valuable), while others pass out of use. Where an element of the natural environment is in demand but supply is either plentiful for all or cannot readily be packaged for individual ownership and exchange, we have the case of a "free good" which is not considered a natural resource in the socioeconomic meaning of the term.[5] In almost all earlier economic texts, the classic case of a free good was fresh air. While in technical economic terms fresh air remains a free good, in a social accounting sense this is no longer the case in cities, where it entails large personal and group expenditures. If the meaning of natural resources is to be tied to the basic concept of features of the natural environment that are in relatively scarce supply, then it becomes necessary to invent a new category for those elements that, although they are in relatively scarce supply, still are not subject to individual ownership and exchange. This category would usefully serve to distinguish fresh air from, say, sunlight. The concept of free goods will clearly require rethinking.

Because natural resources have been associated with basic commodities important in national production for so long, there has been a lag in general appreciation of the extent to which the scarce elements of the natural environment today are of a non-commodity character. It takes quite a wrench in thinking to get away from the commodity view of natural resources and to be able to include in the resources category such elements as relatively pure air and water, three-dimensional space (including airway space, radio-spectrum space, city land, and underground space) and valued amenity features of the natural environment. Yet, in our crowded urban age, these are resources that count.

In trying to absorb the new resources elements into our conceptual scheme of things, and yet retain the major features of the more traditional interpretation of natural resources, there has been a tendency to associate these new elements almost exclusively with qualitative aspects of the environment and interpret this as essentially important for consumption rather than production. While the qualitative and consumption considerations certainly must loom large in any view of the newer resource elements, the quantitative and production aspects must also be seen as significant. A more complete view of the newer resource elements is provided most readily when we see them in terms of an extension of the basic natural resources concept—that is, when we accept an uninhibited interpretation of "needed elements of the natural environment that are in relatively short supply." This becomes particularly salient when we begin to grasp how different the whole production process is in the United States today compared to the past. Thus, less than 30 per cent of the labor force is engaged in commodity production and the proportion continues to decline.[6] The service industries loom increasingly large. The recreation and education industries, for example, will soon pass farming in importance in both labor force and GNP terms. Project these trends another generation and the picture of the economy has very little resemblance to the one that was pertinent when the early conservation movement in the United States first gathered momentum.

All this is familiar and yet we have a hard time getting away from the more traditional picture of the "productive plant" or the "economic base" as represented largely by the farms, the mines, and the factories. These are certainly still very important, but the productive plant must now be seen increasingly as a series of *interrelated networks* of training, research, communication (which is at the heart of an automated plant), transportation, water and air use, and many other processes, together with their capital embodiments, established mainly in an urban setting. Productivity changes are increasingly influenced by the efficiency of the urban "plant" or urban environment.

In the past, when agriculture was at the center of the economic stage, both the quantity and quality of the land and water resources in an intimate interrelationship (as well as the know-how and vigor applied in the production processes) were important to the results obtained. Similarly, when industrialization took hold, the quantity and quality of mineral as well as forest and farm resources were of central importance. Today, even if in a different setting, quantitative as well as qualitative factors are significant (always in an inextricable mix): e.g., the volume of water available for drinking, cooling, and waste disposal; the volume of air for waste disposal; the space available for the movement of planes or trucks; the land available for the construction of efficient industrial plants and for parking; the space available for radio-spectrum communications; and many other similar elements are a critical part of the production picture.

It is no trivial matter to establish the fact that the newer resource elements involve not only highly significant consumption and quality-of-living aspects but also equally significant production considerations. For example, if public annoyance with air and water pollution and traffic congestion should result in severe restrictions on industrial location, extremely heavy costs in industrial waste disposal, or severe limitation on the use of trucks, we may indeed pay a high price in rising costs of production. This is not to suggest, of course, that restrictions may not be appropriate under certain conditions; what is important is that the policy decisions should be made with a full appreciation of the production as well as the consumption factors. For in dealing with matters of the city, we are dealing with the very foundations of the nation's productive plant.

Once we begin to view features of urban land, air, and water, and space and amenity as significant natural resources, certain well-established principles, long associated with natural resources, come readily into play. These associations are not only significant intellectually (to the extent that meaningful classification is always important in the study of a subject), but also have important policy overtones. In the United States, the concept of natural resources carries certain strong connotations that influence the way in which we tend to approach an item that comes under the resources rubric. These connotations stem both from the impact made by the conservation movement, especially in the first third of this century, and from our experience with the use of our material (commodity) resources. They center on the well-established trinity of "conservation, development, and use of natural resources" and on at least some appreciation of the requirements and limitations posed by ecological considerations. Thus, the term natural resources sets up an image encompassing several principles:

1. Resources are part of the national heritage; they should not be used unthinkingly and selfishly by any one group at the expense of others or by any one generation at the expense of future generations.

2. The value that the nation can receive from its resources depends on its willingness to *invest* in the *development* of such resources, whether it is a matter of enriching the soil, harnessing river basins or harnessing the atom, or experimenting with the best means for desalinization of water.
3. To get the most value out of the nation's resources, development wherever possible and appropriate should seek to achieve *multiple uses*. The multiple-purpose development of river basins comes most readily to mind, but the same principle applies to the use of farm land at the outskirts of cities for open space and recreation as well as for agricultural output.
4. While man has demonstrated a remarkable capacity for manipulation of nature for his own ends, there are basic ecological principles he must understand and respect if he is to achieve his objectives over an extended period of time and without extremely high costs in real terms. Optimum returns can be obtained only through a knowledgeable and thoughtful mix of natural and man-made elements.

These principles can be described in other ways, but the core elements would be similar. The main point to be made here is that such principles have direct and important relevance to the "newer" non-commodity elements of the natural environment discussed here. Thus, by encompassing these "newer" elements into the natural resources rubric we achieve a unifying and simplifying end which, as suggested earlier, is extremely important in laying a foundation for coherent and consistent public policy and administration.

Thus, for example, under the first principle, the question can legitimately be raised as to whether certain resources—urban land, air, water, etc.—should be considered to be in the public domain[7] (or at least whether private holding and use should be extensively controlled) in order to protect the more general interest. Reference to established legal and traditional principles with regard to the "older" resources, while by no means binding, is instructive and helps to firm up the basis for public policy. Experience with law and policy touching on the more traditional resources, for example, can have important implications as we begin to make extensive use of air rights and underground or tunnel rights. Some legal scholars are beginning to make just this kind of extension; for example, with regard to air rights.[8]

In a similar light, the well-established principle of the desirability of *development* of natural resources to maximize social returns over time comes readily into play in thinking about the newer resources. Thus, for example, even in the face of a severe congestion problem in airways over and near cities, the existing approach is largely limited to the *regulation* of private commercial airlines, with limited investment in safety features and runways at the major airports. When airspace is viewed as a critically important natural resource, the desirability of addressing the problem through a developmental approach is immediately visible. The form and character of future city building should be examined in terms of achieving objectives with regard to the airways, as well as other objectives. For example, some airspace might well be set aside for the use of small airplanes only, to create what might be called air-commuting zones; this would clearly call for the development of a full ground-and-air approach to city building, in sharp contrast to the present two-dimensional approach.

The principle of multipurpose use of resources, which has evolved from, and has played such an important role in, river basin development, has great relevance for the urban-oriented resources. In fact, if sensibly applied, it is likely to achieve greater importance here than with regard to the more traditional resources. Communication and frequent interchanges are critical for most functions carried out in the city. The friction of space (transportation cost) not only produces the clustering of people and activities—that is, relatively high density—but in fact suggests that multiple-purpose use of space is at its essence a cost-saving device. Seen in this light, city building today tends to be highly inefficient. The present basically two-dimensional rather than three-dimensional city planning simultaneously promotes an outmoded single-purpose view of urban space (regulated by a simple set of zoning principles) and permits a wild jumble of incompatible uses, particularly on city streets.[9] Efficient and compatible multiple uses in a city require expert multiple-dimension planning. This is clearly a highly important area for additional thought and research. We urgently need principles that might guide decisions on when and how much multiple use is appropriate.

Finally, the importance of careful attention to ecological considerations in "conserving, developing, and using" urban-oriented resources should hardly need any special stress. It is evident that water and air can handle different amounts of pollution in different mixes under varying natural conditions; the capacity to make multiple use of these critically important resources is dependent in no small part on our knowledge of these natural conditions and the extent to which they can be modified. Builders who have constructed artificial lakes as space- and vista-providers often learn some quite interesting lessons about the ecology of still waters as algae emerge in abundance. The same is true of those who use or provide other amenity resources. A nice item along this line comes from Honolulu. It seems that Waikiki Beach may someday soon be scratched off the tourist's guide list because it is losing its sand. New shorefront hotels have been built where there are no beaches, so the hotel owners have created their own. These synthetic beaches have upset the normal action of the ocean tides and currents off Waikiki's shoreline so much that the ocean is reclaiming the sand. Beaches far from these hotels are also being denuded. (Incidently, sand costs about $6 a cubic yard in the islands.)

City people may find it a little harder than their country cousins to grasp the importance of ecological principles, but it will be a little easier to get the lessons across if they can first grasp the notion that natural resources are a significant part of their environment, not things way out there in the countryside. And once these lessons are learned, it might even be easier to talk publicly about externalities, and about costs imposed on others, and why new rules of the game may be needed if we are to achieve desirable urban environments.

The Urban Environment as a Subsystem

At an earlier point, I suggested that two concepts could play a useful simplifying and unifying role in creating a foundation for coherent and effective public policy with regard to the urban environment: in addition to the extension of the "natural resources" concept, there is need to see the urban environment as a contained highly interrelated system or subsystem. (Damage one part of it and other parts are immediately or soon affected; improve one part and other parts may be improved as a result.) In one sense, the "system" concept is an extension of the ecological considerations discussed above, but because of the importance of man-made features in the urban environment, the man-made as well as the natural elements must be seen as part of the relational system. Good and bad results are normally obtained as a result of the special *mix* of the two and therefore the two must be seen in all of their complex interrelationships.[10]

All urban units, whether city, metropolis, or megalopolis, are an integral and intimate part of the national scheme of things. None of them functions in isolated glory. It is not surprising, therefore, that all urban features, including the urban environment, comprise *open* systems. Roads, trains, and planes tie one city to others; messages go out and come in from everywhere; polluted water is carried from cities upstream to those downstream; polluted air is transported to distant areas; the size of the downtown of a given city will depend in no small part on how much of the nation's business is carried on there (thus, there is only one New York); urbanites vacation all over the country and the world; and so it goes. But the important consideration here is that the urban environment does comprise a meaningful and important system, signifying that, as with all systems, the internal elements—in this case, the main features that characterize the urban environment—have greater and more intimate relations among themselves than they do with units or features outside the identified system. Geographers, economists, human ecologists, and other students of the city generally define the urban unit itself in terms of its nodal characteristics; that is, in terms of the quantity and intensity of the interactions. For example, they may define it in terms of the movement of persons and goods (while there is a great deal of movement *between* urban units, it does not compare to the daily movement back and forth *within* such units), in terms of the volume and frequency of messages sent, in terms of the extent of the local labor market, and the like. The physical areas covered by such intensity-of-flow items do not coincide exactly, but while the edges may be fuzzy, the urban community emerges as an identifiable nodal-type unit.

The nodal characteristics, while physically presenting a seemingly chaotic picture in our metropolitan and megalopolitan regions, have a clear and understandable logic. This has been an important part of the field of study of urban economics. The importance of centrality of location of economic activities stems from a number of factors, key among which is the significant—and generally increasing—specialization of function in manufacturing and service industries. Such specialization calls for the shipping of goods to and from a large number of producers, each adding value through specialized activity and sending them on. Thus, clustering is an important cost-saving device. Most of the production activities, in turn, call for the assistance of many specialized services, including professional services. The services themselves are linked not only with manufacturing activities but among themselves, with forward and backward and lateral linkages of every imaginable type. Those who ship goods need ports, railheads, highways, and airports that are linked with other major centers, and these facilities are, of course, necessarily localized to achieve the economies of scale to which they are subject.

The highly sophisticated manufacturing and service industries that are characteristic of our day require a wide and varied set of worker skills, and call for large labor pools. These are to be found only in population centers. Members of the skilled work force—including the managers—who are in demand choose to work in areas that they find pleasant for family living, and industry adjusts to this preference. Since many such persons prefer to live in communities which provide a large number of services, facilities, and amenities, cities draw activities for this reason as well. Here, centrality is a factor, since the costlier services and facilities (for instance, a symphony hall) must draw on a large population, but with urban growth many of the services and facilities can be provided in subcenters. This, however, only means that although centrality is somewhat more complex than in an earlier day, the economies-of-scale factor still comes strongly into play.

Taken together, all this adds up to the creation and maintenance of an elaborate *system* of people, capital, and movement with an inherent logic.

Nodality is a physical as well as economic phenomenon. This is true of the key elements in the *urban environment.* Thus, we can usefully speak of an airshed and a watershed encompassing an urban community, each with a focal zone; we can demarcate the open spaces and amenity areas reachable within, say, a Sunday's drive (an open-space-recreation zone if you wish) on the basis of a "gravity model"; we can separate the city into characteristic areas such as the central business district (CBD), inner city residential areas, suburbs (including high-income enclaves), and exurbia; we can demarcate the major transportation movements in nodal terms; and we can characterize work environments—downtown, in industrial estates, and scattered.

Systemic elements of the urban environment are generated not only by interrelations of natural and man-made features, but by *trade-offs* between these features (as well as within them). For example, more airconditioning of homes and workplaces can serve as a substitute for more air pollution control (that is, controlling the micro- rather than the macroenvironment). Polluting plants can be moved to the edge of or beyond the local air- or watershed instead of providing waste removal features within these plants. More open space might be provided in town, or people may be encouraged (by good roads, etc.) to drive out to the natural open spaces at the edge of town.[11]

Urbanites are not accustomed to thinking of their environment as a contained, highly interrelated system. Thus, they will complain loudly about air pollution conditions and yet vote for a mayor who promises to bring new manufacturing plants into town and to build superhighways right into the heart of the city. They will complain about the rapid loss of open space and yet vote for severe restrictions on the height of apartment and office buildings, for large-lot zoning, and for building highways through parks in order to reduce their cost. They will decry the loss of amenity resources nearby and yet permit private building right up to the beach edge and the pollution of nearby lakes. Of course, all this is not simply a matter of overlooking an important concept or a lack of understanding of systems analysis. Diverse interests are involved (different people are affected differently by these seemingly contradictory policies) and there are profits to be made, costs to be avoided, and elections to be won. But the point still needs to be made that the creation of a common ground of understanding of what is involved in working towards a desirable urban environment is essential for the building of a foundation for sensible, coherent public policy concerned more with a broad range of interests than with powerful but limited special interests.

Elements within the Environmental System

If we are to develop an understanding of the urban-environment system, it will be necessary as a starting point to identify the key elements involved; that is, those elements whose relationships and interactions define and give special character to the system. This is a complex matter and can probably be done at various levels and in various frameworks. As a starting point and at a very general level, it is helpful, in order to sharpen the contrast between open and closed systems, to think of the key environmental elements involved in collective-living, high-density situations of an essentially *closed* character so as to identify similarities and differences with a more open situation of the type we are discussing.

At a very simple level, one thinks of the cavedweller situation (which evidently comprised the human environment for a certain group of early man over a very long period of time, possibly a million years). Key elements in such cave environments evidently were the maintenance of relatively pure air (smoke pollution must have been a serious problem); acquiring and storing drinkable water; provisions for warmth and general bodily comfort; and division of space between family living quarters, work activities, recreation, and other clan activities. (Development of different types of enclosures for various groups and activities was related to technology; for example, the use of animal skins as cave dividers.) Environmental aesthetics were evidently not neglected, as suggested by the numerous cave paintings which have been found.

Essentially the same elements are identifiable when we think of other relatively closed environmental systems, such as that of the present day submarine, bathysphere, and space capsule.[12] At the other extreme of complexity from the old cave environment, diving into the wild blue yonder, are the environmental elements involved in a space satellite of the far distant future. In *Beyond Tomorrow*,[13] D. M. Cole (a senior space scientist at General Electric's Space Technology Center) gives some attention to the environmental factors. His vision of "a new home among the stars" accommodates between 10,000 to one million people in a hollow asteroid, possibly 20 miles long, 10 miles in diameter. Such colonies, Cole suggests, could cruise space in their self-powered, closed cycle worlds by using new forms of macro-ecological relations and by developing flexible and extremely attractive interior environmental conditions. Here, too, air, water, weather conditioning, sunlight, space, and amenity features are pictured as key elements of the environment.

The closed-system view not only helps to highlight the basic elements that are essential for man's survival and comfort, but also suggests the many varieties of collective-living, high-density environments that are conceivable at different levels of technological development and different kinds of socioeconomic patterning. There is a strong tendency in our cities today to accept existing forms and relationships as given, merely because they are familiar. We simply do not think about these matters unless some problem emerges which makes us uncomfortable, such as excessive air pollution or noise. Actually, with vast opportunities for achieving varied and attractive urban environments, the key elements of the environment and the ways in which they are interrelated, or can be made to interrelate, should be subjects of continuing study and private as well as public concern. The existing uses made of urban and nearby land; of three-dimensional space; of air and water; of structures for living, working, and collective activities; of climatic elements; and of amenity features of the environment must be recorded in meaningful ways, so that the interrelationships and interactions can be highlighted as a base for decisions that will influence the environment in desired directions.

While discussing elements of the environment, it is well to note also that for the greatest part such elements do not interact only at the scale of the urban unit as a whole—say, the metropolis—but are found in different intensities and in special mixes at smaller scales. Thus, air and water quality (or degrees of pollution) are different in different parts of the metropolis (air pollution, for example, will be more intense at congested transportation points or in parts of the metropolis dominated by manufacturing industry). Similarly, availability (nearness) of open space is different for every section of the urban unit; the condition of structures and their spacing will be different in each neighborhood; and the condition of the water, sewerage, and waste disposal facilities will differ from section to section. A careful recording of these differences and of the total impact of the special mixes to be found in each identifiable section of the urban unit is critical for sound policy making. The issue is generally not how some hypothetical average individual is faring, but the quality of the environment within which different real groups are living, working, and moving about. Information on distribution of qualitative levels should not be overlooked. This can be summed up by saying that the reality of the slum, as well as of the magnificent high-income enclaves, must be recognized in any meaningful approach to the problems of the urban environment.

Differentiation must not only be provided in geographic terms, but also in terms of the various groups making up the urban society. Different groups react differently to various aspects of the environment and also make different contributions to the environment or detract from it. This is seen most readily when the question of crowding in the urban environment is considered. Edward T. Hall, a student of the subject, has pointed out:

> The degree to which peoples are sensorially involved with each other, and how they use time, determines not only at what point they are crowded but the methods for relieving crowding as well. Puerto Ricans and Negroes have a much higher involvement ratio than New Englanders and Americans of German or Scandinavian stock. Highly involved people apparently require higher densities than less involved people, and they may also require more protection or screening from outsiders. It is absolutely essential that we learn more about how to compute the maximum, minimum, and optimum density of the different cultural enclaves that make up our cities.[14]

Hall suggests that the various ways in which different groups handle time is reflected in their need for space. "Monochronic" and "polychronic" styles of time-use are characteristic of what he calls low-involvement and high-involvement groups and this in turn influences their relative degree of need to separate activities in space.

Beyond group characteristics, there are important individual differences that must also be taken into account.

The Urban Environment and the Environment of Urbanites

It has been noted that the urban environmental system is an open one. It is open in various ways. Thus, instead of ending discernibly at one line, the built-up relatively dense sector of a city or metropolitan region fades gradually out into the countryside. City and countryside intermingle in a rather wide belt. Villages, towns, and farms provide a somewhat different setting for living and working than does the more built-up portion: open space is hardly in scarce supply, travel distances tend to be longer, water and sewerage facilities are often not tied in to the core systems. Yet the people living in such zones are largely urbanites (or farmers much concerned with the question of the appropriate time to sell their land) and these zones are mainly areas for future building. Roads and utility lines built here, open space set aside, and other activities (or lack of them) will influence the future urban environment in important ways.

The system is also open, as suggested earlier, in its direct transportation and communication linkages with other urban centers. This deserves particular attention because of the tendency for "string" construction along highways in many parts of the country to provide a very special—and in many cases aesthetically horrendous—urban environment. Often such string developments are found in the outer zone mentioned above and are thus an integral part of the general exurban picture.

Finally, the system is open in the sense that urbanites living within the built-up, high-density areas—that is, within the core urban environment—spend greater or lesser periods of time away from that environment, largely for recreation purposes, and particularly for vacations. Some have vacation homes in recreation environments. In this regard, amenity resources achieve particular significance. The quality of these resources and their closeness to urban centers (which has a great deal to do with frequency of visits) thus is part of the "environment of urbanites" if not part of the urban environment itself. These resources, of course, also comprise part of the environment of rural populations, but for present purposes we are limiting attention to the urban population. The problems are clearly different for the rural population.

The value of recognizing these factors in any full-bodied treatment of environmental issues suggests that we have to be concerned not only with spatial elements—that is, the extent of the urban environment that is being described, analyzed, or controlled by public policy and action—but also with function, time, and intensity dimensions. We want to know how much time during the week, month, or year various groups in the population are "exposed" to the different kinds of environments and, if possible, the intensity of the exposure. These matters will be touched upon at a later point.

Policy Measures and a Decision Framework

It seems evident that the quality of the urban environment—as well as the environment for urbanites—will increasingly be a matter for public concern. The caliber of governmental policy and action with regard to environmental issues can be expected to be improved as our knowledge of the environment increases and as we develop better tools for decision making. It therefore seems appropriate to devote major attention to the question of reporting on the environment and on means for evaluating public action with regard to the environment.

Reporting on and evaluating the urban environment presents different problems from those presented by the more traditional commodity natural resources. While in the latter case there are usually some externalities to be considered and complex systemic interrelational elements to be dealt with, these features are so much greater in the case of the urban environment that it is a matter of kind more than of degree. The interrelationships among the elements of the environmental system and the externalities are so central in the scheme of things that we must come to grips with the question of how these can be highlighted meaningfully. This underlines the importance of a useful reporting and analytical framework. The problem of creating such a framework is hardly new. City planners have been struggling with the issue for over half a century. However, city planning has emphasized—almost to the exclusion of other considerations—past, present, and future *land uses*. Other urban natural resources (air and water, for example) have rarely received major attention; this is true also for systemic elements within the urban environment, such as the multiple relationships between land use and man-made structures.

We can probably go a substantial distance toward providing a useful reporting-and-evaluation framework through the use of what have come to be known as social indicators and social accounts. I have found particularly stimulating the proposal for an annual Social Report of the President, parallel to the Economic Report, but concerned with a different set of issues, including the quality-of-the-environment question. A system of reporting which would fulfill the requirements of such an annual report would have to characterize changes in environmental quality through the use of a few particularly pertinent measures, and to evaluate the results obtained through various public and private efforts to improve the environment. A national reporting scheme would necessarily have to be quite broad—and essentially limited—in scope. It should, logically, be supplemented by reporting on a local basis, that is, by state-of-the-region reports, which can provide a useful foundation for policy making and governmental action at the local and metropolitan scale. The problem of reporting at the national level would be much eased if the appropriate information was available for all the urban units within the nation.

What might such a system of reporting appropriately contain?[15]

First, it is necessary to decide just how much is to be included under the environmental rubric. It is evident, at one extreme, that it cannot be limited merely to physical (including natural) factors if the information is to provide a useful foundation for decision making. At the other extreme, it cannot usefully cover all matters that at one time or another are referred to as "environmental." The latter would bring in just about everything. The term environment is often used not only to cover the natural and man-made surroundings but also much of the social-political-economic ambience—i.e., frequent references are made to "a democratic environment," "a competitive environment," etc. These types of issues can be covered more appropriately under other headings in either a Social Report of the President or a state-of-the-region report at the local level, say, with regard to a discussion of "equality of opportunity" or under "political participation."

Any delimiting of a field, even for reporting purposes, involves all sorts of cultural (including language) and political considerations, particularly the explicit and implicit public objectives or goals that are currently dominant. For present purposes—mainly to introduce some ideas for discussion in a preliminary way—it may be appropriate to start with an attempt to look at the more important elements that directly influence *conditions of living and working of the urban population* and particularly where they influence *the health, comfort, safety, and aesthetic satisfaction of individuals.* This would suggest limiting coverage to those aspects that are necessary to *differentiate localized situations* of some importance to the lives of the people; for example, those aspects that are essential to describe either slum conditions in our cities or the relative purity of the air within given metropolitan regions, but not those features that are common for people everywhere, the host of essentially *national* economic, social, cultural, and political factors in the quality of American life.

The differentiation of localized situations would have to proceed at various levels to distinguish between significantly different *settings.* Thus, as already suggested, it would be necessary to distinguish between metropolitan and non-metropolitan (basically, small town) settings; between built-up and low-density zones, residential and nonresidential areas; and among the various characteristic types of communities, such as slum areas, middle-class areas, and the like.

Elements To Be Covered

It is proposed that the following items be included under the environmental rubric for metropolitan areas:[16]

THE NATURAL ENVIRONMENT

1. The airshed (to describe relative purity of air and air pollution);
2. The watershed (to cover water supply and water pollution);
3. The open space–recreation "shed" (to cover conditions within an area that can be reached on a one-day recreation trip);
4. Quiet-and-noise zones (to describe relative degree and time-span of noise exposure);
5. Olfactory zones (to describe relative degree and time-span of exposure to unpleasant smells);
6. "Micro-climate" zones (including uncomfortable heat, wind blockage, etc.)[17]
7. Sunlight exposure (relative condition of buildings with regard to good, bad, or indifferent sunlight exposure).

THE SPATIAL ENVIRONMENT

While basically part of the natural environment, it differs enough from the items under "The Natural Environment" to deserve special treatment. This category would attempt to characterize the use of underground space,[18] land, and overground space in terms of standards of efficient use (e.g., relative congestion and duration of what might be called low-quality conditions), changes in values of space, and degree of allocation of space in terms of relative values (thus, amount of subsidy would be highlighted).[19]

THE TRANSPORTATION-UTILITIES ENVIRONMENT

These have the characteristic of tying the metropolitan area into an integrated unit through a series of superimposed networks (or what might be called the skeletal features of the region). They tie directly into the natural environment through those utilities that provide water supply and provide for sewerage and solid waste disposal; also as they use underground, land, and overground resources. The latter is additionally significant in the case of electric and gas utilities, as well as telephone utilities. Aesthetic considerations with regard to such facilities have come increasingly to the fore.

The transportation network is particularly important for the urban environment. Accessibility, including relative accessibility to amenity resources, is a basic consideration in many aspects of the environment. The reporting should cover such items as availability of mass transit and other forms of transportation and the conditions surrounding movement in general, including considerations of trip-time, congestion, safety, and stress.

THE COMMUNITY-OR-NEIGHBORHOOD ENVIRONMENT

This item would cover the main environmental elements within markedly differentiated communities or neighborhoods—for example, slum areas, other central city areas, and suburban and exurban areas. The term community or neighborhood here is intended simply to imply the existence of distinguishable common characteristics of physical elements, together with important interactions between people and physical environment within a contiguous geographic area by the fact of juxtaposition and "mix." At the same time, in order to provide adequate coverage of public service and facility conditions, it would be desirable not to restrict the areas too narrowly in geographic terms. The services environment is necessarily variable (since different services extend over different zones) so that in defining areas some fuzziness at the edges might well be appropriate.

THE MICROENVIRONMENTS

The family or household shelter and the workplace are the settings for the individual's most intimate social relations as well as for his most direct and frequent contacts with the man-made physical environment.

The framework that is thus provided can be described as one of several environmental "envelopes" (although the term should not be taken too literally) through which the quality of the urban environment can be characterized: the large natural resources and space-use envelope, the community-neighborhood envelope, and the home and work microenvelope, all tied together in various ways and literally tied together through the transportation-utilities set of networks. Each of these is characterized by different underlying conditions, the first through the special role of urban-oriented natural resources, the second by the interrelations of group behavior patterns and these with the man-made physical environment, and the third—the microenvironment—by the primacy and intimacy of social relationships as well as by the special needs and characteristics of a limited group (the household in one case, and employees of specific workplaces in the other). The importance of the microenvironment is attested to by the fact that some 68 per cent of the total time of urban adults, on the average, is spent at home. The figure is 76 per cent for the total urban population.[20] Of the remaining time, almost two-thirds is spent at work.

Indicators, Accounts, and Policy Measures

A broad framework for what I would call a system of "policy measures for the environment" is suggested here (see Table 1). First, let me make some comments about the terms used. "Indicator" is normally used to describe the condition of a single element, factor, or the like, which is part of a complex interrelated system (employment, cost of living, production, etc., in the case of economic indicators). It is evident that in the case of the urban environment equally revealing indicators can be provided to describe existing conditions—say, with regard to air pollution, quality of housing, amount of open space available, etc.

"Accounts," on the other hand, refer to comprehensive systems of data characterized by a balance between inputs and outputs or inflows and outflows (such as national income accounts, input-output accounts, or flow-of-funds accounts) or providing the value of the total stock of various items in a total system, as in the case of wealth accounts. We have a long way to go before we are able to work out comprehensive social accounts for the environment. However, as noted at a number of points, it is important to provide a broad picture of the urban environment because it is essential to be able to highlight interrelationships and externalities. What seems possible at the present time is the provision of rather comprehensive "policy measures" or "decision measures" that, while not fully comprehensive or characterized by balanced two-way flows, could nevertheless serve a unifying purpose in reporting on the environment specifically as an aid to governmental policy decisions. These must include both stock and flow items and, because of the focus on public policy, emphasize outlays and investment and the returns on these.

Table 1 on pages 282-285 outlines the main elements of the data framework proposed.

The first task involved would be to work out meaningful "indicators of present condition" (column 1) for each of the items listed. These would reflect present goals and standards (both legislative and informal) with the data attempting to indicate where we stand with regard to these goals and standards. The establishment of standards is no mean task. It would require a good bit of research as well as a sensitive reading of the standards that have the broadest and most strongly-held acceptance. This clearly is an evolving task. In the first instance, the best standards at hand would be employed. At the same time, it would be useful to highlight the weaknesses of existing standards, particularly where too narrow an interpretation of objectives to be achieved could be misleading, and to explore the special characteristic of measures within the different categories.

As Joseph Fisher has pointed out (in his chapter in the "Preliminary Report on Environment" for the Panel on Social Indicators of the U.S. Department of Health, Education, and Welfare), the quality characteristics of the environment tend, to a considerable extent, to be subjective, with considerable variation in the views of different individuals. Further, air pollution and recreation opportunities, for example, affect different individuals quite differently, both physiologically and psychologically.

Table 1: Framework for Evaluating Policy Measures for

Elements in the environment
A. *The natural environment*
1. The airshed
2. The watershed
3. The open space–recreation "shed"
4. Quiet-and-noise zones
5. Olfactory zones
6. Micro-climate zones
7. Sunlight exposure
B. *The spatial environment*
1. Underground space
2. Uncovered land
3. Covered land
4. Radiospectrum space
5. Airways space
C. *Transportation-utilities environment*
1. Transportation: (a) commuting time; (b) alternative modes, including mass transit; (c) congestion; (d) safety; (e) stress; (f) aesthetics (e.g., billboards, landscaping)
2. Water supply facilities
3. Sewerage facilities
4. Solid waste disposal
5. Electricity facilities
6. Gas facilities
7. Telephone facilities
8. Other communication facilities

the Environment

Indicators of present condition	Costs of environmental maintenance at present levels		Costs (or other adverse consequences) of environmental abuses and shortfalls		Costs of achieving standards at various levels		Benefits of achieving standards at various levels	
	Private	Public	Private	Public	Private	Public	Private	Public
(1)	(2)		(3)		(4)		(5)	

(continued overleaf)

Table 1: Framework for Evaluating Policy Measures for

Elements in the environment
D. *Community-neighborhood environment* 1. Community characteristics: (a) mix (e.g., degree of segregation); (b) types and condition of structures and land uses; (c) community stresses; (d) design environment (densities, street lighting, billboards, interest points, landscaping, zoning, etc.) 2. Services environment (measures of quality and nearness): (a) educational-cultural environment; (b) personal safety and protection; (c) health facilities and services; (d) commercial facilities and services; (e) recreation facilities and services; (f) "caretaker" functions
E. *Household shelter* 1. Housing condition 2. Crowding 3. Rats, roaches, and other pests 4. Plumbing 5. Household equipment
F. *Workplaces* 1. Safety 2. Amenities (e.g., eating facilities, sanitation) 3. Work challenge indicators (assembly line, freedom of movement, etc.)

the Environment

Indicators of present condition	Costs of environmental maintenance at present levels		Costs (or other adverse consequences) of environmental abuses and shortfalls		Costs of achieving standards at various levels		Benefits of achieving standards at various levels	
	Private	Public	Private	Public	Private	Public	Private	Public
(1)	(2)		(3)		(4)		(5)	

Another point deserves attention: The various aspects of the natural environment are interrelated in numerous and sometimes confusing ways. One way of abating industrial air pollution is by filtering and washing smoke to prevent contaminants from going into the atmosphere, and instead sluicing them out into the water courses, thereby adding to water pollution. The interrelations extend beyond the realm of natural resources. For example, one way of reducing pollution from automobiles would be to discourage or prohibit certain uses, but this would greatly affect transportation and might also drastically alter the microenvironment in which people live and work. Just as the various kinds of environmental pollution tend to be interconnected, so also the measures for abating and controlling them tend to be interconnected. And one should be cautious about interpreting a favorable movement over time in an indicator of air pollution lest it is accompanied by an equal or greater movement in the opposite direction in an indicator of water pollution.

Concern for arriving at some overall indicator of environmental quality in which the various interrelations and trade-offs can be included leads one toward the concept of net social benefit—that is, total (or incremental) social benefit less social cost. This concept of net social benefit can be applied to a particular kind of environmental disturbance or it can be thought of in connection with a large range of environmental effects.

The social indicators alone can provide only a limited part of the story. If we are looking ultimately to policy, it would be essential to get a picture also of the costs of our shortfalls, as well as the costs and anticipated benefits of actually fulfilling existing goals and standards, or higher-level goals and standards. But this calls for more than indicators; here we would have to put policy measures to work. The key categories that might be employed are suggested in Table 1.

Thus, the reporting system proposed would set out, as a second item, "costs of environmental maintenance at present levels" (column 2), broken down by private and public costs wherever possible. In almost every instance, substantial sums are already being spent in order to maintain existing environmental conditions—no matter how unsatisfactory. This is true of the present expenditures involved in keeping down air and water pollution; it is also true of the costs involved in trying to create a relatively safe street environment and transportation environment. The setting down of current cost figures would provide a rough measure of the relative amount of effort directed at any one of the items of interest in the environment. It would raise issues about the priorities attached to the various subjects and it would also raise questions such as whether we are getting our money's worth. There is a tendency in most discussions of the environment to think only in terms of the additional expenditures necessary to achieve somewhat higher levels. This can be misleading, certainly as regards the relative emphasis to be given to different activities. As in the other major items to be covered, breakdowns in terms of the various sections of a metropolitan region (slums, suburbs, etc.), would provide a useful picture of the relative attention being given to the various parts of the region.

Column 3 in the proposed reporting system calls for estimates of the costs—or other adverse consequences—of environmental abuses and shortfalls. In this, an attempt would be made, not only to obtain rough estimates of such items as the costs resulting from air pollution, but also of inadequate public services. Such costs would be recorded in dollar terms wherever possible, even if some heroic assumptions have to be made. In cases where dollar costs are simply not to be had, sharply focused descriptions or indicators of a non-cost nature would be useful.[21]

Here, again, the specification of the standards to be achieved would be essential, particularly in measuring shortfalls. It is necessary to establish a wide variety of fairly narrow and specific standards—e.g., for housing quality—as well as broader, more aggregative goals, such as a satisfactory home and community environment. Not only must standards be quite specific in the case of the environment, but they are also inevitably rather variable, that is, they often have to cover a wide range. Thus, it is possible to set up standards for various degrees of "purity" in the case of air and water and to measure the cost of achieving such standards as well as the cost of falling short of their achievement. The same is true in the case of housing standards, standards of congestion, and many other features that might be included under the environmental rubric. To round out the picture, then, it would be necessary to provide estimates of costs ot achieving standards at various levels (column 4).

Thus, the whole system is built on a recognition of the fact that the quality of the environment is judged by the values of the society, that different levels of achievement are possible, that each of these has cost features attached—both in achieving the given levels and in falling short of achieving them—and that benefits are also to be derived from improvements in the environment. Unfortunately, these benefits are very much harder to define. In some cases they can be fairly firm, particularly when the benefit amounts to an avoidance of the cost of abuse or shortfall. But in other cases they are much more general. Over time, however, it might be increasingly possible to provide benefit estimates. Even short of such figures, it would be possible to describe in general terms the benefits of achieving specified standards and, thereby, to provide a better basis for public judgment.

At a later stage it might be possible to introduce additional types of indicators or other measures to round out the picture and provide a better basis for evaluating the present and alternative futures. One of these would be a "time budget" or measure of time expenditures, which would provide a picture of the time spent in major activities by various categories of individuals, and thus, in a general way, suggest the relative importance of different kinds of environments and the uses made of them.[22] Such a measure, together with direct measures of intensity of use of services and facilities as well as of homes, workplaces, and transportation, would provide the basis for measurement of relative "exposure" and the development of risk ratios. This, for example, would tend to show the tremendous importance of the street in poor neighborhoods, the extent to which some public facilities are overutilized and others underutilized, and the relative exposure of people to various areas of the city (thus emphasizing, for example, the relatively great importance of small intown open spaces—such as squares and school playgrounds—as compared to vast open spaces far beyond the reach of most people). An intensity index could be a very powerful tool for decision making in some of the environmental items.

Differentiation in the "policy measures" not only needs to be made with regard to various classes of communities within a metropolis but also with regard to various age groups, income groups, and racial and ethnic groups. Wherever pertinent, the indices or measures should be in terms of age, income, and race and ethnic categories as in the educational-cultural environment, in health, and in recreation.

The indicators of present conditions should, wherever possible, provide information on three kinds of items: (1) the *average* situation in the various communities for the key items, as well as group distribution around the average; (2) improvement or deterioration over time, and (3) extreme situations that deserve special attention. In general, treatment of extreme situations is necessary so that significant *special* problems are not overlooked: without such items any reporting scheme would tend to be much too bland. If the scheme is to serve policy and action purposes realistically, a description of community stresses when the situation is explosive or of pollution conditions when health is directly threatened should not be lost in a mere deluge of data on averages.

Final Note

The information framework proposed here is essentially a decision-making "model," highlighting the present state of affairs, what is deemed good and bad about it, the costs we suffer as a result of the shortcomings, and what is needed to bring the situation up to higher standards. The implementation of such a model would clearly require substantial effort but, when operational, it would provide an extremely valuable decision-making tool. It has the clear advantage of being close to policy and operations both in terms of its inputs and outputs; that is, on the one side, administrative or operating data could be used as the main sources of information while, on the other, it would provide a basis for policy decisions in a direct and meaningful framework. It is taken as an article of faith that governmental policy and action will be improved as knowledge about the urban environment increases and alternative possibilities can be reviewed in a broad and meaningful decision framework.

References

[1]A good example is the difficulty that state agencies have experienced in carrying out existing water pollution control legislation. The private interests in such a situation—the polluting industries—are specific and known (restrictions by a state pollution control agency can be very costly indeed for a specific firm), while the public interest is much more diffuse and vague. Not surprisingly, the energy that the state agency will normally exert will be more or less in direct proportion to the interest that the public, or representatives of the public, take in the matter. Matthew Holden, Jr., suggests, in an interesting monograph, that the whole matter of degree of application of state pollution legislation is the subject of *negotiation* between the agencies and the polluting industries. *Pollution Control as a Bargaining Process: An Essay on Regulatory Decision-Making* (Cornell University Water Resources Center Publication No. 9, October 1966).

[2]In an earlier period, for example, one thinks of the role of the concept centering on "the settlement of the West" encompassing notions of national stature, new opportunity, and the individual farmer as the backbone of democracy—all of which provided a base for governmental action "in the general interest" over a substantial period of time. In a more recent period, we have observed the role that the concept of full employment has played as a basis for public action in coping with problems of the business cycle and economic growth.

[3]Harvey S. Perloff and Lowdon Wingo, Jr., in Joseph J. Spengler (ed.), "Natural Resource Endowment and Regional Economic Growth," *Natural Resources and Economic Growth* (Resources for the Future, 1961), pp. 191-212; and Harvey S. Perloff, Edgar S. Dunn, Jr., Eric E. Lampard, and Richard F. Muth, *Regions, Resources, and Economic Growth* (The Johns Hopkins Press, 1960).

[4]Neal Potter and Francis T. Christy, Jr., *Trends in Natural Resource Commodities: Statistics of Prices, Output, Consumption, Foreign Trade, and Employment in the United States, 1870-1957* (The Johns Hopkins Press for Resources for the Future, 1962), as revised by Potter.

[5]A feature of free goods has been that they do not become property. Insofar as they have value, they are expected to be capitalized as a component of land value. "Land" is thus viewed as a *collection* of fixed-to-a-place natural environmental features, including not only the geographic territory and soil, but also the associated water, climate, sunlight, air quality, and other amenity features.

[6]Even this figure is too high in a realistic sense. A substantial part of what the census puts in the commodity (or product) category actually involves service activities, ranging from R&D activities to paper work and promotional activities.

[7]As Mason Gaffney has suggested for air.

[8]Michael M. Bernard, *Airspace in Urban Development, Emergent Concepts*, Technical Bulletin 46 (Urban Land Institute, July 1963).

[9]As Lawrence Halprin has put it: "It is too much to ask of a street that it serve, at the same time, for pedestrians and traffic and parking and shopping and children's play, and also provide amenity and quiet to the inhabitants along its way." *Cities* (Reinhold, 1963), p. 11.

[10]This is true, of course, of the rural environment as well, but the sheer volume of man-made items in the urban setting is so great that the question of mix has a special relevance.

[11]The trade-off notion is not always readily accepted. Thus, for example, a *Washington Evening Star* editorial (16 September, 1967) concerned with airplane noise, states: "The Los Angeles Department of Airports has come up with an unusual solution to the problem of noise from jet aircraft.... Officials are planning to award contracts soon for soundproofing a dozen homes around International Airport and measuring the before-and-after level of decibels. The project, which will cost some $200,000, seems designed to prepare the way for soundproofing of many dwellings with the help of local government subsidy. ... But one can't help wondering if this isn't exactly the kind of solution that the airlines would like best, since it involves no effort on their part. By the same reasoning, why not put a filter on every homeowner's faucets to cope with water pollution, or install universal air-conditioning to 'solve' the question of polluted atmosphere?"

Why not indeed? The editorial writer has overlooked the fact that most homes in the United States are individually heated while group heating is practiced in Sweden and elsewhere and that many other services have gone one way or the other over the years (including movie watching). The Los Angeles Department of Airports is indeed to be congratulated for carrying out a sensible experiment. I would hope that they are simultaneously looking into another alternative—that of location and relocation policy to cope with the noise problem—as well as into the question of the relative cost of building quieter planes.

[12]A lively and informative treatment of the problems and possibilities in the realm of closed ecological systems is provided in "2000+," the February 1967 issue of *Architectural Design*, John MacHale, Guest Editor.

[13]D. M. Cole, *Beyond Tomorrow* (Amherst Press, 1965).

[14]Edward T. Hall, *The Hidden Dimension* (Doubleday and Company, Inc., 1966).

[15]The materials presented here are based on a "Preliminary Report on Environment" which I prepared for the Panel on Social Indicators of the U.S. Department of Health, Education, and Welfare (May 1967) with the help of Joseph L. Fisher and Robert Gold. I want to acknowledge the many useful suggestions I have received on the earlier report from my colleagues, Irving Hoch, Lowdon Wingo, and Blair Bower, which I have incorporated in the present statement, as well as from Fisher and Gold.

[16]The metropolitan region is highlighted here because it calls for the most extensive coverage.

[17]Because of traditional usage, "micro" is used here, although on a different scale from that employed in the case of home and work environments, where the term is also employed.

[18]It is reported that in about a hundred cities in the U.S.S.R., 35 per cent or more of the investment in structures is in the portion that lies underground. American Public Works Association Research Foundation, *Better Utilization of Urban Space* (Chicago, June 1967), p. 7.

[19]Urban ground and near-ground spaces cover a remarkable (and fascinating) variety, including: streets of various kinds; alleys; freeways; minor and major

plazas; gardens; playgrounds; neighborhood, central, and regional parks; waterfronts; rooftops; open parking lots; etc., etc.

[20]Taken from a time budget study of forty-four U.S. cities. See Alexander Szalai, "Multinational Comparative Social Research," *American Behavioral Scientist*, Vol. 10, No. 4 (December 1966).

[21]A sense of how much information can be conveyed by focused description is provided by the statements in the Supreme Court 1954 school decision on the losses attendant on a "separate-but-equal" education system.

[22]See F. Stuart Chapin, Jr., and Thomas H. Logan, "Patterns of time and space use," in Harvey S. Perloff (ed.) *The Quality of the Urban Environment*, pp. 303-32.

Land, Water, and Ownership

J. H. DALES

I

Increasing public concern about the pollution of natural water systems in North America has confronted governments with a new problem in resource administration, and challenged economists to devise an artificial pricing system for water that will itself promote wise use of the resource, thereby greatly simplifying the lives of water administrators. The pricing problem turns out, not unexpectedly, to be a deliciously complex tangle of joint uses, externalities, and peak-load problems. The administrative problem of approximating optimum shadow prices by actual user charges promises to be a nightmare.

The economic and administrative complexity of water problems is commonly explained as being inherent in the nature of a fluid resource. Because of the self-mixing quality of a fluid, one use of water at a given point may affect other uses at the same point; and because water flows through space, use at one point may also affect uses at other points. Opportunity cost pricing is accordingly very complex because of the number of alternative opportunities that may be affected by any one use at any one point, not to mention the complications introduced by time of use, varying stream flow, different rates of self-regeneration of

Source: J. H. Dales, "Land, Water, and Ownership", from *Canadian Journal of Economics*, Vol. 1 (4), 1968, pp. 791-804. Reprinted by permission of the publisher and author.

different stretches of water, and the chemical interactions of different types of waste after they have been discharged into a natural water system.

Before we submit to this incubus of complexity, however, we might seek comfort in the reflection that the great virtue of a pricing system is that it solves, avoids, mediates, or somehow manages to dispel, all sorts of complexities, particularly those that arise from various interdependencies between uses and users of goods. Yet the existence of a natural pricing system depends crucially on the institution of ownership. What is not owned cannot be priced since prices are payments for property rights or rights to the use of an asset.[1] In the course of allocating property rights to assets among different owners, the price system in fact transforms most potential "technological externalities" into "pecuniary externalities," a synonym for prices. Thus we hear very little about externalities of land use, precisely because property rights to land use are well established and allocated by the price system. It is quite otherwise where water is concerned.

We can now re-formulate the water problem and blame its complexity not on nature and the laws of fluids, but on man and his failure to devise property rights to the use of natural water systems. Economists tend to assume implicitly that it is impossible to own water and therefore seek to devise artificial price systems that are identical to what prices "would be" if ownership were possible. The alternative strategy is to devise an ownership system and then let a price system develop. The purpose of this article is to suggest that there are very considerable advantages to attacking our water problems by means of a system of explicit ownership rather than by a system of shadow prices.

A geographical reflection is also in order. Despite the large numbers of people who live on the St. Lawrence, the Fraser, and the St. John, most Canadians live on lakes, or on rivers that flow into lakes, rather than into oceans, whereas most Americans, despite the large population around the southern rim of the Greak Lakes, live on river systems that discharge into salt water. Lakes are much less "mobile" and much less "self-mixing" than rivers. Most of the water in lakes *stays* there for prolonged periods, and recent research has shown that during much of the year the shallow, inshore waters of large lakes are effectively isolated from the very large volumes of water in their deep centres.[2] (Similar propositions apparently apply to oceans; otherwise the serious pollution problems of coastal cities such as San Francisco, New York, and Vancouver would not exist.)

People who live on river systems, as most Americans do, tend to pass on their pollution to the next downstream community, thereby creating vexing externality problems. American literature on pollution has been strongly influenced by the uni-directional flow of rivers, which makes it relatively easy to solve the identification problem of who pollutes whom. River pollution therefore lends itself to economic analysis in terms of externalities, and shadow-pricing schemes to offset them. People who live on lake systems (most Canadians) tend to pollute themselves; because inshore lake water, far from being uni-directional, tends to slosh up and down the shoreline, lake pollution tends to be a sort of Hobbesean war of all against all. It therefore requires economic analysis in terms of social decision-making and social welfare functions rather than in terms of the effects of autonomous upstream communities on autonomous downstream communities. The economics of Canadian water pollution is therefore quite different from the economics of American water pollution.

II

Rent theory has been the traditional vehicle for studying the economics of natural resources, and a review of some of the effects of the ownership-rental system as applied to land highlights the opposite effects induced by the absence of an ownership-rental system as applied to water. Following normal practice, we shall speak of the supply of land (or water) available to any society as fixed by nature. Though fixed in supply when measured in natural units (acres or gallons), the *quality* of land and water can be changed by human action. (Were we to measure the quantity of land in efficiency units of a given quality, its supply would be variable; we conduct the present argument, however, in terms of natural units, fixed supplies, and variable qualities.) Imagine a society where all land is being used and even the poorest of it commands a positive rent (this assumption allows us to avoid those not very illuminating discussions about no-rent land and the relationships between the extensive and intensive margins) and suppose that an initial state of equilibrium exists, and in particular that at existing land values and rents there is neither investment nor disinvestment in the quality of the soil. Population growth when superimposed on this initial state will lead to increases in land values and rents; these increases in turn will lead to economies in the use of soil by means of the substitution of manufactured fertilizers and other intensive farming practices against inputs of natural soil fertility. The process may be described as one of investing in soil fertility, and the equilibrium stock of soil fertility will accordingly rise (or its rate of decline will fall). In a general form, the conclusion is that *the level of rent determines the quality of the soil that it is economic to maintain*. It is also clear, as Ricardo showed, that when man-made inputs are substituted for natural inputs in the food-producing industry the real cost of food increases and the standard of living in terms of food falls. Rising rents, therefore, tend to slow down population growth and lessen the population pressure that produces them.

The working out of these processes in the historical development of the United States has been brilliantly described by Bunce.[3] In the early history of the country there was a high ratio of soil fertility to the human demands on it, and rent was accordingly low; "high farming" practices on the European model were therefore rejected, and economic use necessitated soil-depleting practices. In the course of time the man-soil fertility ratio rose, as a result both of population growth and of soil depletion; rents rose; more intensive farming practices became economic, and the rate of soil depletion was thereby reduced. A slowing down in the rate of population growth after 1900 further reduced pressure on the land; it is possible that in general soil depletion has now been brought to a halt in the United States and Canada, and that soil erosion and soil-depleting practices in some areas are balanced by soil-building investments in others.

The contrast between the history of land and of water use on this continent is eloquent. Property rights were established in land, with rent being the payment for the right to use the soil fertility; there were no water rents because property rights to water use were not established. Rising land rents led to more intensive land use and after 350 years there is no problem of population pressure on the land in North America. Water rents were zero; over-use of the water led to continuous reduction in water quality; and there is now a growing problem of population pressure on North American water resources. If we accept a simple dynamic extension of rent theory and assume a direct relationship between the level of rent and the development of improved technologies, the land-water comparison is again suggestive. Rising land rents have been associated with phenomenal improvements in land-use technology; zero rents for water have been associated with virtually zero improvement in water-use technology so far as quality-depleting uses are concerned.

The short-run function of land rent, of course, is to allocate parcels of land among different users and different uses. What is interesting is that potential externalities of land use, for example, the operation of a pig farm in the centre of a choice residential area, seldom materialize. Land being immobile, the ownership-rental system seems to work in such a way as to produce "natural zoning" in land use. Differential rents provide the mechanism for such zoning, and the result is that potential technological externalities are continuously transformed into pecuniary externalities, or prices. It should also be noted that a formal economic description of this process depends on a recognition of space, and particularly of the socially "insulating" quality of space. So long as space exists—and we must remember that in most economic analysis it does not—"zoning" solutions to externalities, or what Mishan has recently called "separate facilities" solutions,[4] are possibilities. Given space, there is no need for pig farmers and business executives to live as neighbours, and therefore no need to devise a system of bribes to compensate one or the other party for damages suffered.

The absence of an ownership-rental system for water has meant that water use has in fact been determined by such things as historical priority, gall, and force and fraud; it cannot be otherwise when property rights do not exist and when the price for the use of a valuable asset is zero. When no pricing process exists, there is no mechanism to transform technological externalities into pecuniary externalities. Accordingly we *do* observe striking examples of externalities in water use; stinking streams flow through choice residential areas, and anglers experience a mixture of rage and resignation as their favourite streams are polluted by industrial wastes. And then there are the externalities of all against all—householders help to destroy swimming beaches by their use of detergents (which promote algal growth), motorists pollute the air they breathe, and we all promote municipal and industrial pollution by insisting on cheap products and low taxes.

These considerations suggest the enormous social benefits that have resulted from applying an ownership-rental system to land, and, by contrast, the enormous social friction and economic waste that result from not applying an ownership-rental system to water. It has, of course, been relatively "easy" to apply property rights to land because land is both divisible and immobile. The awkward problem remains: is it *possible* to apply an ownership-rental system to the use of our water resources?

III

To speak of owning an asset is to use a convenient abbreviation for a complex interaction between a legal concept and an economic concept. An asset may be thought of as "a bundle of potential utility-yielding services that can be used in alternative ways." In the same vein, ownership consists of "a bundle of legally-defined user rights to an asset." As Coase has pointed out, it is rights, never objects, that are owned, and the rights themselves are always limited by law; "outright" ownership can never, by definition, extend to the use of an asset for illegal purposes.[5]

From the whole spectrum of possible ownership arrangements, we shall pick four major types for brief comment. What we shall call *common-property* ownership is, from an economic point of view, virtually non-ownership. A common-property asset is one that can be used by everyone, for almost any purpose, at zero cost. Examples are the mediaeval commons, the high seas, wild game, freeways, and (until recently in this country) air and water. Common-property ownership is justified economically *only* when the costs of enforcing a more restricted form of property-rights would be greater than the benefits of doing so. H. S. Gordon has shown that, neglecting enforcement costs, common-property ownership of an asset is economically inefficient in that the asset will be over-used by comparison with assets that are subject to more restrictive property rights.[6] Empirically it is clear that if the asset is depletable it will be continuously depleted on the grounds that "everybody's property is nobody's property": mediaeval commons were overstocked; modern freeways (but not toll-ways) quickly become congested; wild animals (but never domestic animals) become scarce or extinct; and the deteriorating quality of our air and water resources has become a matter of widespread concern. The concept of a free good has always been a contradiction in terms; it is time we appreciated its sardonic overtones, for anything that is treated as a free good is indeed likely to become a valueless thing.

In general common-property assets are nominally owned by some public body, usually a government, and the owner may restrict use of the property in a variety of ways. Some roads may be used by motorists but not by cyclists or pedestrians; some wild animals may be photographed, but not shot; on some lakes canoes and sailboats may be used, but not motor-boats. It seems reasonable to refer to such property as *restricted common-property*; though the type of use is restricted, it is still common-property in the sense that everyone can use it for designated purposes at zero cost. If uses that deplete the asset in a physical sense are banned, the quality of the asset can be maintained, though "congestion" problems may reduce its value to other users.

When the use of an asset is restricted by law to particular persons, or a particular person, we have what can conveniently be called *status-tenure* or *fixed-tenure* ownership. Such ownership guarantees exclusivity of use to the parties authorized to use the property, but these user rights are not transferable. Though secure right of access to an asset by a limited group of people is valuable, the absence of the right of transferability prevents an explicit price system from developing. Nevertheless implicit prices are likely to appear. If the right to send one's children to a particularly good school is limited to those who live in a particular area, the value of the rights are likely to become reflected in the value of real estate in the area concerned. The "regulatory" branches of modern governments create an enormous variety of valuable property rights that are imperfectly transferable, and that tend to be capitalized and monetized in ways that are usually unsuspected by their creators. The value of tariff protection, a quota to grow tobacco, a licence to transport milk or to operate a taxicab, are reflected in the values of tariff-protected businesses, tobacco farms, milk routes, and taxi fleets.[7] Though the indirect monetization of such rights is seldom illegal, contemporary populations choose to be as hypocritical about the process as mediaeval populations were about the evasions of prohibitions on the payment of interest; social inhibitions about a rational approach to property and prices have outlived social inhibitions about rational approaches to astronomy and sex.

From status-tenure to full *ownership*, in the usual contemporary sense of the term, is but a short step. Once the property right is separated from the person, it becomes transferable, and transfers of assets (rights) then take place at explicit prices. *Transferable* property rights stand in a one-to-one relationship to prices; everything that is owned is priced, and everything that is priced is owned—which is to say nothing about either the form of ownership (transferable property rights to assets may be owned by individuals, corporations, or governments) or about the precise functional relationship between ownership and prices. Ideological hang-ups on concepts of property rights and ownership are understandable because such concepts touch the very roots of society. We have not yet learned to discuss such matters unemotionally. Though we are inclined to take a condescending view of mediaeval man's distrust of full property rights to land, we tend to become quite agitated when valuable government-granted rights (licences to import, for example) are traded in the market place, or when suggestions to extend property rights to air and water are put forward for discussion. Property and prices still raise ancient fears that "the rich will eat out the poor."

IV

Since the right to use water is valuable, and since ownership consists of user rights, it should in principle be possible to devise an ownership-rental system for water. As is well known, however, certain characteristics of a natural water system create special problems in ownership.

The characteristics of an ownership system reflect in part the "divisibility" of the asset to which it is applied. Let us define an *asset-unit* as the smallest physical amount of the asset to which it is practicable to apply property rights, i.e., for which it is practicable to enforce exclusivity of use. In land, the asset-unit is very small, perhaps a few square yards; when the asset-unit is small compared to the quantity of the asset available, the asset can be held by a large number of individual owners. In such cases a "private property" form of ownership is likely to work well; decisions about the use of the asset will be decentralized among many owners, and a reasonably competitive market in asset-units will emerge.

In water, the asset-unit is very large. If water were completely "self-mixing," no one would pay anything to own Lake Ontario unless he could also own the whole Great Lakes drainage basin above the St. Lawrence river. As we have seen, however, water, especially in large lakes, mixes only slowly and imperfectly; because of this, and because of the self-purifying characteristic of water, the quality of water in the eastern end of Lake Ontario may be effectively independent of the uses made of the water at the western end of the lake. Even so, it is clear that the asset-unit is very large. It might be possible to divide the Great Lakes water system into, say, a dozen "regions" each of which would be self-contained for practical purposes, but it would certainly be impossible to divide them into a thousand such regions. In a democratic society it would be unacceptable to allow as few as a dozen, or even a score, of owners to control such an immense property as the Great Lakes drainage system. The only sensible alternative is the one actually adopted, namely, monopoly ownership by government. The reverse side of this coin is that the government must decide how its property is to be used and must enforce its decisions—assuming that it wishes to avoid the horrors of the common-property approach to resource management.

The decision about how water shall be used must be an arbitrary one from the standpoint of economics. Let me argue this point on the basis of a simple (but seemingly realistic) classification of water uses.

If we ignore such uses as navigation and the generation of hydroelectric power, which have insignificant effects on water quality, it seems reasonable to classify other uses into two categories: waste disposal, and "all other" uses, which we shall call amenity use. These two uses are competitive. Though it is not true that fisherman, swimmers, industries that use water for processing purposes, and municipal authorities responsible for residential water supplies all have the same quality demands, it is true that some of these users would be benefited, and none would be harmed, by an improvement in water quality. Waste disposers, on the other hand, would be harmed by such an improvement since it could only occur if less waste were discharged into the water. We thus reduce the many uses of water to two: amenity use and waste disposal. The social problem is then to decide on the division of water services between these two conflicting uses. In principle, the division should be made in such a way that the value of a marginal increment in the one good is equal to the value of a marginal decrement in the other. But since the value of a marginal change in amenity use cannot be measured, the optimum amount of waste disposal cannot be identified. In practice, the decision is made on a political rather than an economic calculus. Once there is a political demand for "pollution control," anti-pollution measures tend to be instituted incrementally until complaints about their cost outweigh complaints about pollution! That sort of solution, applied also to such things as education, road systems, and various social welfare schemes, seems to me to be eminently sensible, *faute de mieux*.

In water quality problems, however, it is important to keep in mind that, within limits, water can be "regionalized" for practical purposes, and that "zoning" solutions to quality problems are therefore possible in some cases. In practice it would probably be wise to provide for different ratios of amenity use to waste disposal use in different water "regions"; the socially insulating quality of space should be utilized wherever possible. People are mobile, and if they can consume the amenity services of water in the upper reaches of a river and the waste disposal services of the same river in its lower reaches, there is no need to force them to decide on the optimum division between amenity uses and waste disposal uses of the water in both the upper and lower parts of the river. But again, alas, economics has little to say about a feasible or desirable delimitation of water "regions"; a sensible "mapping" of water must be left to the good judgment of physical scientists and politicians.

The contention that there exists no economically optimum division between amenity and pollution uses of water will be resisted by exponents of damage-cost pricing.[8] In the classic example of an upstream community polluting a downstream community, an allegation of damage to the downstream user seems to rest on three assumptions: that the downstream community owns its water and in particular owns the right not to have its water polluted by others; that the downstream community gains no advantage from the upstream pollution, i.e., that its residents buy no goods from their upstream neighbours at prices that are lower than they would be if the upstream community were forced to reduce its pollution; and that the upstream residents suffer no disadvantages from the downstream pollution because they never visit the downstream area for fishing, swimming, or other recreational purposes. The property rights assumption has not generally been true in the past in North America, and even to-day it is far from clear that a downstream community has any more right to use the river water for swimming and drinking than the upstream community has to use it for waste disposal purposes. The other two assumptions about the inter-community immobility of goods and people are, in general, untenable. The "polluter-pollutee" view of the problem that underlies the recommendation of damage-cost pricing derives from the apparently easy identification of the two parties on a river. Once the mobility of goods and people up and down a river is taken into account, however, identification becomes much more difficult and the problem appears much like the "war of all against all" that is characteristic of lake and ocean pollution.

Even if everyone is at once a polluter and a pollutee, however, the optimum amount of pollution could be achieved if the value of a marginal dose of pollution could be measured. But it cannot be measured, because its value is the value of the amenity use forgone, which cannot be measured. Attempts have been made to measure the recreational value of particular land and water areas, but all such measurements are made on the partial equilibrium assumption that the recreational use of neighbouring areas is held constant. In general, however, a reduction in the amenity capacity of one river or lake will result in increased pressure on the amenity capacities of other rivers and lakes in the same general area. So far as I know, no one has been able to measure the amenity value of an acre-foot of water under general equilibrium assumptions. All we can be reasonably sure about is that the recreational value of water rises as population grows and the standard of living increases.

In brief, it seems to me that it is unrealistic to view water management as a problem in externalities, and that the question of how water should be used is purely a matter of collective decision-making. Economics cannot be of any significant help in making this decision. Even the principle that property rights should be set so as to maximize social product is of no use in the case of water because the values of amenity uses of water—recreation, and the simple aesthetic satisfaction that most of us gain from looking at, or even merely contemplating the existence of, clean water—cannot be measured, though such values are certainly part of any society's gross national welfare. Social welfare functions, community indifference curves, and benefit-cost analysis are ways of visualizing the social decision-making problem, but not of solving it.

What is special about the ownership of water, therefore, is that the owner must decide, without the benefit of economics, how his asset is to be divided among different uses. (When asset-units are small relative to the amount of the asset available, as in land, decentralized ownership is possible and the amount of the asset devoted to different uses is, for practical purposes, determined by market forces.) But this special quality of water (and air) ownership does not make it impossible to apply a rental system to water management.

V

If economics has nothing useful to say about the ownership decision of how water should be used, it has a great deal to say about how the decision, once made, should be implemented. What the government-owner of a natural water system must decide is how many equivalent tons of wastes may be discharged into the waters of each water region. The decision has at least three arbitrary components. Since in given circumstances a ton of one waste is likely to be more injurious than a ton of another, some equivalence must be established between different waste products, and since circumstances differ widely I assume that some average equivalence is chosen for each region in order to simplify the problem and reduce administrative difficulties. The other two sources of arbitrariness from the economic point of view, the mapping of regions and the choice of the amount of pollution in each region, have already been discussed. Let us now suppose that the owner has decided that during the next five years no more than x equivalent tons of waste per year are to be dumped into the waters of region A, and that x represents a 10 per cent reduction from the amount of waste that is currently being discharged into the region's waters. How can the government-owner enforce this decision?

The government can enforce its decision in one of six main ways. It can *regulate*: (1) a waste quota can be assigned to each waste discharger and set so that the sum of the quotas does not exceed x; or (2) an across-the-board regulation that each discharger must reduce his waste discharge by 10 per cent may be promulgated. It can *subsidize*: (3) dischargers can be subsidized to reduce their wastes, either individually or (4) on an across-the-board basis of so much per ton of waste discharge reduced. It can *charge*: (5) an effluent charge can be levied on dischargers, either individually, or (6) on an across-the-board basis of so much per ton of waste discharged.

I suggest that it is intuitively obvious that the *individual*, or point-by-point, procedures would involve staggering administrative costs. Yet it should be noted that politicians and civil servants seem to favour point-by-point *regulation*, and that economists who recommend damage-cost pricing favour point-by-point *charging* schemes. It seems intuitively obvious that in practice no point-by-point procedure could distribute the cost of reducing pollution among polluters in an economically optimal way, i.e., in a way that would minimize the total cost of reducing pollution by 10 per cent. To suppose that optimality in this sense is possible is to suppose that the administrative authority is able to solve a set of thousands of simultaneous equations, when the information required to write the equations in numerical form is not only not available, but also often unobtainable. It is also obvious that an across-the-board regulation to the effect that all dischargers must reduce their wastes by 10 per cent would result in a non-optimal distribution of the cost burden.[9]

Let us then examine the across-the-board schemes of subsidization and charging. Both possess the advantages of low administrative costs relative to the point-by-point schemes, and both would result in an optimum distribution of costs among dischargers; all dischargers would reduce their wastes up to the point where the marginal costs of doing so equalled the subsidy provided, or the charge levied. Both schemes have two disadvantages: a certain amount of experimentation would be necessary to establish the level of subsidy, or charge, that would produce a 10 per cent reduction in waste discharge; and the levels would have to be varied annually to take account of industrial and demographic growth (or decline) in the region in order to keep to the target of x equivalent tons of waste discharge. The subsidy scheme, however, has two disadvantages that the charging scheme does not have. First, if a subsidy of so much per ton of waste reduced is set, extra profits will accrue to those firms that can reduce their wastes at a cost per ton that is less than the subsidy provided, and no change in relative prices of goods is necessary. In the charging scheme excess profits will not be generated, and there will necessarily be a change in relative prices of goods, which in turn will result in a socially desirable adjustment of consumption patterns to reflect the differential costs of waste disposal as between different goods. Second, the subsidization scheme provides no incentive to choose production methods that reduce the amount of waste generated (and may indeed have the opposite effect!), whereas the charging scheme provides incentives both to reduce waste and improve the technology of treating waste before it is discharged. The across-the-board charging scheme is therefore clearly the best of the six possible ways of implementing the government's decision.

Its victory is made decisive by the fact that it lends itself easily to a market mechanism, whereas the subsidy scheme does not. The government's decision is, let us say, that for the next five years no more than *x* equivalent tons of waste per year are to be discharged into the waters of region *A*. Let it therefore issue *x* pollution rights and put them up for sale, simultaneously passing a law that everyone who discharges one equivalent ton of waste into the natural water system during a year must hold one pollution right throughout the year. Since *x* is less than the number of equivalent tons of waste being discharged at present, the rights will command a positive price—a price sufficient to result in a 10 per cent reduction in waste discharge. The market in rights would be continuous. Firms that found that their actual production was likely to be less than their initial estimate of production would have rights to sell, and those in the contrary situation would be in the market as buyers. Anyone should be able to buy rights; clean-water groups would be able to buy rights and not exercise them. A forward market in rights might be established. The rights should be for one year only, the price of one right for one year representing the annual rental value of the water for waste disposal purposes.[10] (There is no reason, though, why speculators should not gamble in one year on the price of rights in later years.) The virtues of the market mechanism are that no person, or agency, has to *set* the price—it is set by the competition among buyers and sellers of rights—and that the price in the market automatically "allows for" the regional growth (or decline) factor. If the region experiences demographic or industrial growth the price of rights will automatically rise and induce existing dischargers to reduce their wastes in order to make room for the newcomers. The government should make it clear that it reserves the right to alter the allowable level of pollution (the number of rights it issues) at stated time intervals (say, every five or ten years). All that is required to make the market work is the inflexible resolve of the government not to change the rights issue during the interval, no matter what the political pressures to do so may be, and to enforce rigidly the requirement that a ton-year of waste discharge *must* be paid for by the holding of one pollution right for one year. Pollution rights are fully transferable property rights, and any welching on the enforcement of the right would be a breach of trust.

The automaticity of the market mechanism reduces administrative costs by relieving administrators of the necessity of setting the charge for rights and changing it periodically to reflect economic growth or decline. The administrative costs of enforcement would remain, of course, but they would be no greater than the costs of enforcing any of the other implementation schemes that we have considered. Technological change in the form of automatic monitoring devices to measure the volume of effluents from discharge points promises to reduce the costs of policing for all anti-pollution schemes.

Compliance with any point-by-point regulatory or subsidization scheme of pollution control establishes a sort of *status-tenure* property right. The right inheres to the discharger that earns it, and is only transferable (at the capitalized value of its implicit price) when the property to which it applies is sold. The market mechanism of the across-the-board charging scheme separates the property right to water use from the other assets of the discharger, and thereby makes the property right *fully transferable*. Full transferability and explicit prices are, as has been noted, considered preferable to status tenure and implicit prices by contemporary populations in Western democratic societies.

VI

Having puffed the merits of the across-the-board *cum* market mechanism scheme of pollution control, I must now take note of its deficiencies. There are four arbitrary elements: the mapping of water regions; the setting of waste equivalents; the choice of the allowable amount of waste discharge; and the choice of time interval during which the number of pollution rights is fixed. By comparison with some ideal, Pareto-optimal scheme laid up in Heaven, each of these decisions is bound to introduce elements of non-optimality into the arrangements I have proposed. In each case, however, I suggest that the saving in administrative costs is likely to outweigh the loss in terms of resource misallocation, measured from some theoretical optimum that ignores administrative and other transactions costs

—notably the cost of acquiring enough information to administer an optimal pricing system.[11]

The question of the possible effects of pollution charges on the location of industries (and population) requires special comment. It is often suggested in the literature that waste discharged into a large, lightly populated river system does less damage than if it is discharged into a small, thickly populated river system, and that accordingly pollution charges for use of the former ought to be lower than for use of the latter. This reasoning assumes that the only costs of waste discharge are the objective, measurable, costs to residents in the area, or more generally—if people are allowed to live in one area and vacation in another—that the damage done to amenities by an extra ton of waste is everywhere the same. A system of charging that equalized marginal measurable costs as between water systems would then minimize the objective costs of disposing of a given tonnage of wastes over all the water systems in an area. But this argument does *not* hold if the goal is to minimize *total* costs of disposing of a given tonnage of wastes.

In general, as one river system (or one part of a lake) becomes more polluted, the amenity value of neighbouring unpolluted waters rises. Moreover, when pollution reaches a level that is inconsistent with all recreational uses, added waste discharge has no recreational cost, while added pollution (that destroys swimming even if not, say, boating) in a popular vacation area probably has a very high recreational cost. The demand for amenity uses of water is certainly not a continuous function of water quality. Not enough is known, or perhaps knowable, about the demand for amenity uses of water to devise a fully optimal use of water in an "*n*-region system." In general, though, when congestion problems arise—when people begin to realize the existence of a spatially generalized pollution problem—it is clear that as pollution levels in one area rise the amenity value of relatively clean water in neighbouring areas rises; thus the opportunity cost of using such waters for waste disposal purposes also rises. This consideration by itself, therefore, suggests that pollution charges should be *higher* in areas where pollution is currently at low levels than in areas where it is at high levels—the reverse of the pricing system usually recommended. The system of low pollution charges for a low pollution level tends to spread pollution evenly over the countryside. I prefer the opposite system of high pollution charges for a low pollution level; it tends to create the separate facilities recommended by Mishan.

In any event, in the present state of knowledge about amenity values of water, it is obvious that the spatial pattern of pollution, or the price differentials between regions for pollution rights, will reflect an arbitrary decision by government. In the scheme outlined in this paper initial differentials in the prices of pollution rights will probably not be large if waste disposal were to be reduced by 10 per cent in each region. As time goes on, however, price differentials will tend to change as other forces lead to the centralization or decentralization of industries and populations. These tendencies can be offset, or encouraged, by the government's decision about the absolute and relative numbers of rights made available for sale in different regions. Thus the government-owner of a water (or air) system must decide not only the over-all quality of his asset, but also the quality of the asset in each region.

It should be noted, finally, that the market in pollution rights is not a "true" or "natural" market. In natural markets price creates two-way communication between sources of supply and demand and affects amounts supplied as well as amounts demanded. (Where supply is fixed in natural units, as in the land market, price affects the equilibrium quality of the asset, and mediates between the users of land on the one hand and the users of the products of land on the other.) My market provides only for one-way communication. It transmits the government-owner's decisions about the use of water to the users of the asset, but there is no feedback from the users to the owner. A rise in the price of a pollution right signals that the waste disposal use of water is becoming more valuable; but this does *not* mean that the supply of allowable waste disposal capacity should be increased, for the value of the competing amenity use of water is also likely to be increasing under the impact of the same growth forces that make the waste disposal use more valuable. The price signals that the government gets from the market are "false," in the sense that they are largely echoes of its own arbitrary decision about the supply of rights. The market proposed in this paper is therefore nothing more than an administrative tool. But administrative tools that have some *prima facie* claim to efficiency should not be ignored in an increasingly administered society.

References

[1]One never owns physical assets, but only the rights to use physical assets. Professor Ronald Coase writes that a factor of production "is usually thought of as a physical entity which the businessman acquires and uses (an acre of land, a ton of fertilizer) instead of as a right to perform certain (physical) actions. We may speak of a person owning land and using it as a factor of production but what the land-owner in fact possesses is the right to carry out a circumscribed list of actions. The rights of a land-owner are not unlimited." See his "The Problem of Social Cost," *Journal of Law and Economics*, Oct. 1960, 1-44, reprinted in W. Breit and H. M. Hochman, eds., *Readings in Micro-Economics*, (New York, 1968), 423-56; the quotation is from p. 456.

[2]See G.K. Rodgers and D.V. Anderson, "The Thermal Structure of Lake Ontario," *Proceedings Sixth Conference Great Lakes Research*, 1963, University of Michigan publication 10, 59-69; P. F. Hamblin and G. K. Rodgers, *The Currents in the Toronto Region of Lake Ontario*, publication (PR 29) of the Great Lakes Institute of the University of Toronto, 1967; and G. K. Rodgers, "Thermal Regime and Circulation in the Great Lakes," in Claude E. Dolman, ed., *Water Resources of Canada*, Royal Society of Canada, studia varia 11, (Toronto, 1967), 87-95.

[3]A. C. Bunce, *The Economics of Soil Conservation* (Ames, Iowa, 1945).

[4]E. J. Mishan, *The Costs of Economic Growth* (New York, 1967), chap. 8.

[5]See Coase, "The Problem of Social Cost."

[6]H. S. Gordon, "The Economic Theory of a Common-Property Resource: The Fishery," *Journal of Political Economy*, April 1954, 124-42.

[7]On this general question, see Charles A. Reich, "The New Property," *Yale Law Journal*, 73, no. 5 (April 1964), 733-87.

[8]A good exposition of damage-cost pricing is to be found in Allen V. Kneese, *The Economics of Regional Water Quality Management* (Baltimore, 1964).

[9]Paul A. Bradley, "Producers' Decisions and Water Quality Control" (Background Paper D 29-3 in *Pollution and Our Environment*, papers presented at a conference held in Montreal, Oct. 31 to Nov. 4, 1966, by the Canadian Council of Resource Ministers) discusses various possible reactions of individual firms to the regulation of effluent standards and to a system of effluent charges. Standards, charges, and subsidies are discussed extensively in Kneese, *Economics of Regional Water Quality Management*, chaps. 4 and 8.

[10]Professor Neufeld has suggested that it would be desirable to issue rights of different durations; more complicated schemes than the one outlined in the text could easily be arranged.

[11]A referee for this paper wrote that my scheme requires "that the questions of how much pollution, where pollution is to be allowed, how it is to be measured . . . etc., are all answered beforehand. But *these* are the really big questions." I agree. I don't think that economic analysis can answer these questions; it can, however, point to the best means of implementing the given answers.

Reviving the Great Lakes

JOHN R. SHEAFFER

The death of Lake Erie has been announced. Premature aging, brought on by excessive intake of powerful stimulants, is given as the cause. And it is said that the whole Great Lakes system is rapidly being brought to the end of its life by the same malady.

This calamitous news should not be accepted as the final word. The Great Lakes have been grievously abused, but the effects are not irreversible. Technology competent to restore a fondly remembered past is available. All we lack is the will to use it.

The revival could be started by one simple official order: "No direct discharge of any wastes into any watercourse."

There are those who will say that such a directive would be meaningless for practical purposes because alternate means of waste disposal either are not available or are far too expensive to contemplate. But the Federal Water Quality Administration of the U.S. Department of the Interior is gambling the biggest single project grant in its history on the conviction that a workable substitute for indiscriminate dumping into the lakes is at hand. FWQA is committed to spend $2 million on the opening phase of a research project intended to demonstrate that sewage and factory effluent presently being poured into Lake Michigan can be diverted to fertilize barren land in Michigan. If all projections for the scheme prove out, this new waste disposal system

Source: John R. Sheaffer, "Reviving the Great Lakes", from the *Saturday Review*, November 7, 1970. Reprinted by permission of the publisher and author.

will pay for itself and net a profit, perhaps even stimulate the economy of Michigan by building up an agro-industrial complex of respectable size.

Michigan's Muskegon County, fronting on the eastern shore of the lake directly opposite Milwaukee, is the scene of this precedent-setting experiment, which is built around acceptance of the principle that nature is a closed ecological system and that wastes, when properly cycled back into the system, are valuable resources. Wastes become liabilities only when they lose their rightful place in the cycle. Human and animal excrement, emptied into watercourses, stimulates aquatic plant growth and turns lakes into bogs. When spread upon the land, however, the same chemical constituents of waste give nutriment to food grains and vegetables.

Historically, the closed-system principle, though recognized by professional ecologists, has been ignored in practice in this country. We have dumped our wastes into rivers and lakes for generations. As long as the human population remained a statistically insignificant factor in the system, oxygen and bacteria in the water decomposed the waste and redistributed the chemicals in the purifying process. A certain amount of acceleration occurred in the rate of eutrophication (a geological process through which lakes gradually fill up and become first marshes and then dry land) but not enough to be distressing.

However, as cities and towns multiplied and grew and as household conveniences such as detergents were added to the burden of sewage, the amount of waste rose to flood proportions. Phosphorus, potassium, and nitrogen released into the water encouraged proliferation of colonies of plants to choke streams and lake beds, exhaust the oxygen supply, and overwhelm the restorative microorganisms. Idyllic watercourses deteriorated into stagnant, stinking pools.

Eight years ago, public-spirited members of the faculty of Pennsylvania State University reminded us of the intelligent way out of this dilemma. Long before then, the university had built a sewage disposal plant to serve the school together with the borough of State College, which existed chiefly as a dormitory community. The plant was designed in two stages: the first a sedimentation basin in which solid waste particles were separated out by gravity, the second a biological trap in which microorganisms digested organic matter in the wastes. The chlorinated effluent from the plant emptied into nearby Duck Pond and thence into Spring Creek, a tributary of the Juniata River, which flowed into the Susquehanna and on to Chesapeake Bay.

As the town and the school expanded, the amount of effluent added to the water rose from a million gallons a day to 3.5 million gallons a day, and the university faculty anticipated the time when the volume might reach six million gallons a day. Ultimately, if matters continued in that direction, Spring Creek would no longer be a body of water carrying away the liquid residue of human waste but a torrent of human waste carrying unrecognizable water through the beautiful Nittany Valley.

The geological structure of the valley was underlaid with limestone, which formed aquifers for storage of water underground all the way from Bellefonte to Scotia Mine. The water level in these subterranean reservoirs had been falling at the rate of 75 feet a year for a period of years. Being followers of the land grant college tradition, the Penn State faculty members were well aware of the remarkable filtering properties of the soil. They decided to test whether it would be possible to divert the sewage effluent from Duck Pond and spread it instead on adjacent crop land, open fields, and woods owned by the university. A network of irrigation pipes was spread out from the pond (thus avoiding Spring Creek) to the test plots, and the sewage effluent was driven through these pipes and sprinkled onto the soil summer and winter for a period of six years.

At the end of the test period, it was found that the water level in the underground aquifers had dropped only a few feet each year in contrast to the precipitous annual decline previously experienced. Corn and hay grown on the irrigated land yielded three times the harvest of fields not involved in the experiment. Wheat planted in the test plots retained the same yield as before, but the protein content of the wheat rose. Northern pine trees grew as rapidly as southern pines usually do. The bird and animal population of the test area thrived on the new regime.

One of the inspirations for this experiment was work that had been done at Seabrook Farms in New Jersey by the late Professor

Warren Thornthwaite, who was associated with the geography department at the University of Chicago while I was a graduate student there. I remember listening to his descriptions of the Seabrook project and wondering why he did not propose its application on a grand scale. Consequently, when I began to receive personal reports of the Penn State project from one of its prime movers, Dr. R. R. Parizek, I pondered more deeply than ever the implications of the idea's application to widespread urban areas.

Parizek, a young geologist who had taken his Ph.D. at the University of Illinois before going to Penn State, had been a college roommate of Dr. Arthur J. Zeizel, my assistant during my tenure as resource planning officer at the Northeast Illinois Planning Commission. Parizek visited Zeizel periodically and would tell us about what he was doing in Pennsylvania. The information he conveyed went into momentary storage at the back of my head through the three years during which I was occupied —first at the Northeast Illinois Planning Commission and then as research associate at the Center for Urban Studies of the University of Chicago—with problems of flood plain management. But in the spring of 1968, the subject moved to the front of my mind in response to a plea from Roderick Dittmer, director of planning for Muskegon County.

Dittmer dropped in at the Center for Urban Studies one day and said he would welcome some guidance in drawing up a policy to govern Muskegon County's planning for the future use of the county's water resources. Muskegon County was party to a four-state (Wisconsin, Michigan, Illinois, and Indiana) pact calling for an 80 per cent reduction in phosphates discharged into Lake Michigan by the end of the year 1972. It was Dittmer's responsibility to recommend how this cleanup could best be done in his county. My research associates and I agreed to help him in return for what the experience could teach us about managing urban environments. Muskegon County had about every modern problem we could imagine—racial, economic, educational, environmental—yet it encompassed an area small enough to study in everyday operation. A population of 170,000 is contained within 512 square miles.

Our initial investigations identified an interrelationship between two major causes of Muskegon County's economic woes.

The county had never developed an agricultural economy to balance its industrial strength, nor had it capitalized on the recreational resource potential represented by Muskegon, Mona, and White Lakes. Popular use of the lakes was inhibited by pollution of the water, while the poor agricultural yield was caused by low fertility of the soil. Obviously, a wastewater irrigation system similar in its fundamentals to the one demonstrated at Penn State could fertilize the barren land with chemicals recovered from sewage diverted from the lakes.

Why had such an eminently sensible concept not been pushed to a stage that would give it national prominence? Was it because no set of elected officials had ever laid down a sufficiently demanding policy to suggest the notion to public appointees responsible for municipal water and sewage works? Acting on that probability, we wrote for Dittmer a statement of policy that could be effectuated only by banning discharge of pesticides, insecticides, phosphates, and other pollutants into the rivers and lakes. Dittmer courageously endorsed the statement and presented it to the Muskegon County Planning Commission. The commission, rallying behind its fighting chairman, Michael Kobza, added its approval. And then we encountered trouble.

The Michigan State Water Resources Commission did not like our point of view. What we proposed would meet any situation anyone could think of up to the year 2000. Why go to all that expense? It was costly enough to try to think in terms of 1980.

If the United States Supreme Court had not delivered its famous legislative reapportionment decision—the "one man, one vote" edict—we very probably would have lost our case right there. The old forty-man board of Muskegon County commissioners almost certainly would have bogged down in endless rounds of precinct politics. Fortunately, a reapportioned board of only fifteen members took office on January 1, 1969. With a remarkable disregard for partisan considerations, the nine Democrats and six Republicans (with F. Charles Raap sitting as chairman) voted in February to support the County Planning Commission in the face of the state Water Resources Commission's displeasure. We were thus authorized to come up with a plan to carry out the policy we had enunciated.

In earlier efforts to break through the conventional restraints that have kept politics so far behind technology in the handling of waste disposal, I had formed a professional liaison with William J. Bauer, founder of the Bauer Engineering Company of Chicago. I now proposed that Muskegon County hire Bauer to draw up engineering specifications for a comprehensive sewage disposal system that would leave no environmental after-effects for future generations to worry about. A contract with Bauer was underwritten jointly by the county and the U.S. Department of Housing and Urban Development.

Bauer worked out a system far more sophisticated than Penn State's experimental project. He proposed coupling of the sewage outlets of twelve cities and townships into one great outlet pipe that swung away from Lake Michigan, Muskegon Lake, Mona Lake, and White Lake—traditional sinks for the wastes in these communities—and fifteen miles inland to virtually uninhabited sandy barrens of the eastern part of the county. There the pipe would empty into three aerated lagoons, each covering eight acres. These manmade basins, agitated continually by streams of air from mechanical mixers to minimize odor while bacterial colonies in the waste matter decomposed their host, would be big enough to hold the waste flow up to three days. This would enable accommodation of sudden surges of water such as occur after storms. And, because of the volume of water contained at one time, toxic industrial spills could kill the restorative bacteria and yet remain under treatment long enough for a new bacterial colony to grow and do its necessary work.

The enormous advantage represented by the latter circumstance may not be widely appreciated because most people do not realize that the conventional sewage treatment system in use in most American communities suffers regular spells during which the helpful bacteria are dead and the sewage simply passes through the system in an almost raw state. These spells last anywhere from seven to ten days. If six of them happen each year (one Midwestern state suggests that as an average), almost raw sewage is dumped into watercourses about one day in every week.

The system Bauer designed for Muskegon County called for two storage lagoons to hold the waste after it had passed through the aerating lagoons. Each of these storage receptacles would occupy 900 acres. Their purpose would be to hold the waste during the winter months when the ground would be too hardened by cold to absorb the effluent. After being withheld until the return of milder weather, the waste might be used as fertilizer during the remainder of the year.

Bauer's system finally called for the effluent to be piped from the storage lagoons to rotary irrigation rigs, which would spray the liquid with its suspended solids over almost 6,000 acres of now unproductive but potentially valuable sandy soil.

One appendix to the plan estimated a profit of $740,000 a year from sale of corn that could be grown on the irrigated fields, a quadrupling of the value of the land because of the irrigation, opening of at least 1,200 new jobs, recreational development of shorelines now useless because of uglification caused by water pollution, and construction of a 200-boat marina. Another appendix described a new industrial complex that might be built around the corn crop. Among its suggested products were feed for cattle, oil for the human diet, charcoal for use in Muskegon's existing paper mill, starch for the paper mill and for a foundry, carbon dioxide gas for a carbonate mill, calcium hydroxide for use on the irrigated land, and furfuryl alcohol for the finishing of office furniture.

Apart from its dollars and cents aspect, the Bauer system offered an intangible human bonus of inestimable value. This arises from a growing suspicion among public health physicians that many rapidly spreading diseases in this country are transmitted by viruses. How do the viruses travel? Their presence is not sought by any water quality tests now in use. Studies have been made of viruses in sewage, however, and thirteen different viruses have been found in raw sewage, in effluent from primary (one-step) sewage treatment plants, and in effluent from secondary (two-step) treatment plants as well. A month-long sequestration of the effluent in oxidation ponds kills 70 per cent of the viruses. But only after the effluent is filtered through soil do the viruses disappear altogether. Researchers have discovered that soil particles possess an electrical affinity for viruses, which allows the viruses to be grabbed by the soil and held long enough to be dismembered into innocuous protein.

Students of irrigation had one serious question about the Muskegon plan. It had to do with the established fact that elsewhere, in the past, prolonged irrigation saturated the land and created within it a mound of water that in time destroyed the enterprise. Because the thick layer of glacial debris—sands and gravel—underlying Muskegon County is incapable of holding water for long, the danger here was not great. Nevertheless, the Bauer system eliminated it by providing a network of drainage wells through which any threatening accumulation of excess water could be pumped back into the county's rivers and lakes.

The very farsightedness of the plan frightened some people away from it. They just could not believe it would perform as promised. The cities of Muskegon and Muskegon Heights already had drafted plans for systems that would continue dumping treated sewage into the water. From a shortrange perspective, these systems looked cheaper than ours. Consequently, they seemed more desirable to the local politicians, who not unnaturally followed the advice of sanitation consultants they had known and trusted for years: men who were still working with technologies no longer competent to anticipate the needs of an exploding population.

The continuing absence of approval from the Michigan Water Resources Commission encouraged this local opposition. To counter it, we invited Parizek to come out from Penn State and show a short documentary movie of the Penn State project in operation. Dittmer, Kobza, Raap, and Muskegon County Administrator Ray Wells responded by rounding up their colleagues and chartering an airliner to take them to Penn State to inspect that experiment personally.

The political struggle surged back and forth, with the outcome unpredictable, until N. J. Lardieri, corporate director of air and water pollution for the S. D. Warren Paper Company, a division of Scott Paper—one of the three dominant industries in Muskegon County (Ott Chemical, a division of Corn Products, and Continental Motors, a division of Teledyne, are the other two)—asked to be shown the facts on which our policy decisions had been based. Although we figured his company would have to pay more than half the operating costs of the disposal system Bauer had planned (because charges for the system would be allocated according to the flow rate, and effluent from the S. D. Warren factory would make up 55 per cent of the total discharge into the system), Lardieri saw that our concept had the advantage of solving the water pollution problem once for all; the costs could be amortized with business-like predictability. When the other Muskegon industries followed S. D. Warren, our opposition began to crumble. But we still lacked the approval of the state of Michigan.

Michigan Congressman Guy Vander Jagt is the ranking Republican member of the Conservation and Natural Resources Subcommittee of the Government Operations Committee of the U.S. House of Representatives. On one of his frequent trips home to consult with his constituents, he heard of the furor we had raised. After meeting with us at dinner, he said: "It appears that our present efforts [in handling sewage disposal] are headed in the wrong direction." Later he added, "I will predict that the Muskegon County facility will be the focal point for the nation's battle to solve water pollution problems." He returned to Washington to make this prediction come true.

From David Dominick, head of the Federal Water Quality Administration, the Congressman went to Russell Train, chairman of the White House Council on Environmental Quality, and from Train to President Nixon's assistant for domestic affairs, John Ehrlichman, and Ehrlichman's environment specialist John Whittaker. The President must have heard about this round of visits, for he wrote me a letter expressing interest in the development of Muskegon's "new and promising approach to sewage disposal." Train voiced his enthusiasm to Dominick, who wrote glowingly to Congressman Vander Jagt. The Congressman personally carried Dominick's letter to Michigan Governor William Milliken. The Governor thereafter announced that he would make an environment tour of Michigan, with Muskegon as one of the stops. After his return to the capitol in Lansing at the end of this tour, the approval we had awaited from the Michigan Water Resources Commission came through.

In mid-September U.S. Interior Secretary Walter J. Hickel announced that FWQA, which operates within his Cabinet jurisdiction, had awarded a $1,083,750 research and demonstration grant and an additional $981,650 construction grant to the Muskegon project. These sums cover only the first year of a seven-year commitment. Secretary Hickel fixed the total cost at approximately $30 million. Of this, the federal government will pay 55 per cent, the state of Michigan 25 per cent, and Muskegon County the balance. Design specifications are now being prepared for bids. Construction will be awarded about January 1, 1971, and the system ought to be in operation in 1972.

"If this project is completely successful, there will be many more opportunities to utilize similar systems in the Great Lakes region," Secretary Hickel said in his September announcement. This is unquestionably true. The Great Lakes basin is made up of glacial outwash plains. Large stretches of well-drained soil suitable for irrigation lie within reach of urban centers but beyond commuting zones and thus are susceptible to purchase at unexploited farmland prices. If we take the Muskegon irrigation tract as a model, simple mathematics tells us that a billion gallons of waste water per day (that is the flow rate of Chicago's sewage disposal system, the largest in the country) can be disposed of on 260,000 acres of land. A preliminary survey of the major metropolitan areas in the United States suggests that all of them could be served in this manner by using marginal lands equivalent to no more than 2 per cent of the acreage on which fifty-nine principal crops were harvested in 1968.

Canadian Law and Aircraft Noise Disturbance

LOWELL S. FINK

The considerable attention given to legal aspects of aviation noise in Great Britain and the United States has not been duplicated in Canada.[1] This survey will illustrate a common law approach to the problems of aviation noise disturbance, which will be useful not only to common law practitioners, but to Quebec attorneys as well. The British and American approaches will be compared as a prelude to an examination of the law of Canada and of Quebec law in particular. It will be considered whether the Civil Code of Quebec effectively resolves conflicts centering about aviation noise disturbance.

Aviation noise may arise from the operation of several classes of aircraft. For present purposes domestic civil aircraft, foreign civil aircraft, and domestic military aircraft are considered of primary importance. Note further that the emergence of supersonic aircraft compels a determination of whether "sonic boom" is part of the overall noise problem or requires separate analysis. This question can best be answered after an evaluation of the analytical tools which presently exist. Therefore, examination of the sonic boom question will follow comparison of American, British and Canadian law. That comparison will consider *all aircraft noise disturbance, including sonic boom*, to be subject to uniform analysis.

Source: Lowell S. Fink, "Canadian Law and Aircraft Noise Disturbance", from *Chitty's Law Journal*, Vol. 17, No. 5, May 1969. Minor deletions to the original text have been made. Reprinted by permission of the publisher and author.

The American Experience

Recent American case law evolved from litigation involving military aircraft. Since that litigation took place prior to the enactment of the *Federal Tort Claims Act*,[2] ordinary tort doctrines were not available to the plaintiff. Instead, the plaintiff in *Causby v. United States*[4] argued that the government had effected a partial taking of his land by continuous overflights which unreasonably interfered with the use and enjoyment of his land. Plaintiff alleged violation of the fifth amendment of the United States Constitution[3] and sued under the *Tucker Act*, which renders the government liable for its contracts, both express and implied.

Despite the fact that the offending overflights had complied with pertinent federal regulations, the Court found an unreasonable interference with use and enjoyment, and awarded compensation for the diminution in value of the plaintiff's property. In 1958 a county airport authority was held liable under the *Causby doctrine*. In that case the Supreme Court conclusively indicated that compliance with federal regulations does not insulate a defendant from liability to landowners.

Of paramount significance is the fact that these cases employ language peculiar to traditional nuisance analysis in order to grant recovery. This has led to serious conceptual difficulties. In 1962, *Batten v. United States*, a decision of the 10th Circuit Court of Appeals, held that there could be no recovery for taking by unreasonable noise in the absence of a direct overflight (ground testing of engines) of a plaintiff's land. Stated otherwise, without overflight, disturbance however severe is non-compensable "consequential damage" from authorized aviation activities. It is submitted that this decision misconstrued the evolution of the doctrine of eminent domain in American law. Furthermore, the Supreme Court in its 1963 decision, *Dugan v. Rank*, clearly indicated physical entry was not indispensable to a finding of a "taking". It did so, in fact, upon the same authority that *Batten* had relied on for its contrary decision.

Another currently unresolved issue in American law is the extent to which a municipality may regulate aircraft noise. It has been held that a municipality may not pass ordinances directly conflicting with federal flight rules. However, where the local ordinance deals with noise, per se, which is not expressly regulated by federal statute, it is uncertain that local regulation is precluded. This question is currently being litigated in the case of *American Air Lines et al v. Town of Hampstead.* The outcome of this case is critical not only to the landowner–air transport conflict, but also to the evolution of the federal-state power scheme in American constitutional law.

The following principles emerge from the American treatment of aviation noise:

1. The rights of landowners have been considered in terms of use and enjoyment of land.
2. Recovery has been predicated upon the degree of interference, with no controlling significance attributed to the presence of material damage.
3. The doctrine of trespass has been rejected in resolving aircraft disturbance cases.
4. No federal legislation directly treats aircraft noise disturbance liability.
5. Compliance with federally promulgated flight regulations does not obviate the aircraft operator's potential liability to the landowner. The effect of existing regulation upon the right of a municipality to regulate aircraft disturbance is undetermined.
6. Although the status of nuisance doctrine as a basis of liability is uncertain, its use as a method of analysis is accepted.

For present purposes no distinction need be made between liability attaching to domestic civil aircraft and to foreign civil aircraft in American law. As to domestic military aircraft, *Causby* illustrates the constitutional attack. Perhaps the enactment of the Federal Tort Claims Act has provided additional approaches, but detailed examination of that act is beyond the scope of the present study.

The British Experience

As early as 1920, Great Britain had legislated trespass and nuisance out of existence as regards aircraft noise.[4] In 1949 additional legislation legitimized noise and vibration created by aircraft on aerodromes.[5] The protection of these enactments is conditional upon compliance with pertinent flight regulations.

In contrast, however, British legislation imposes absolute liability where material damage occurs.[6]

> Where material loss or damage is caused to any person or property . . . by, or by a person in, or an article falling from, an aircraft while in flight, taking off or landing, . . . damages shall be recoverable without proof of negligence or intention or other cause of action, as if the loss or damage had been caused by the wilful act, neglect, or default of the owner of the aircraft.

The meaning of "material loss or damage" in this provision has never been considered judicially, nor have the other noise provisions of the British act. Notwithstanding, there is no reason to suppose that material loss or damage may not be occasioned by aircraft noise.

The provision pertaining to noise on aerodromes applies to both civil and military aircraft. The provisions precluding nuisance and trespass and imposing strict liability for material damage do not apply to military aircraft. Regarding the latter, the *Crown Proceedings Act* of 1947 raises the question of whether any liability whatever may attach to such aircraft. As will be seen later, the Canadian *Crown Liability Act* contains similar language.

No distinction need be drawn in British law between foreign and domestic civil aircraft. Of significance, however, is the British choice of material loss or damage as the essential element of landowner's recovery. From that point the following comparisons may be made:

1. Compliance with air-traffic regulations does not afford the American aircraft operator the protection enjoyed by his British counterpart.
2. Where the American landowner has recovered for disturbance unaccompanied by material damage, the British landowner is denied a cause of action.
3. Recovery for material loss or damage must be sought under

traditional theories in America, while in Britain strict liability is imposed.

4. America has entrusted aircraft disturbance to common law analysis and judicial resolution, whereas Britain has rejected common law entirely in cases of aircraft disturbance.

Some Preliminary Questions

In light of the almost polar approaches seen above, several questions should be posed:

1. Is the interest of the aviation group so superior as to preclude its liability entirely?
2. If not, should the existence of material loss or damage be indispensable to recovery?
3. Has the application of common law analysis satisfactorily resolved conflicts of interest in America?
4. If not, is the failure due to inherent inadequacies in common law analysis, or rather, because the American constitutional framework has demanded an unnatural application of common law techniques?

These questions serve as guides in considering the present state of the law in Canada and in suggesting modifications which may seem desirable. In Canada, treatment of the problem of aircraft noise disturbance is unhampered by factors which have shaped American law. In addition, Canadian lawyers are afforded a direct comparison between common law and civil law techniques. Considering for purposes of discussion that traditional nuisance doctrines apply in common law provinces in the absence of specific Dominion or provincial legislation, comparison may be drawn with the Civil Code of Quebec.

The Law of Canada and the Quebec Civil Law

As mentioned above, noise disturbance may arise from three basic classes of aircraft. Canadian law will be examined as it may apply to each of these classes. *This study will concern itself only with operations conducted in compliance with ap-*

plicable flight regulations, thereby posing directly the problem of damage from authorized activity.

DISTURBANCE CAUSED BY DOMESTIC CIVIL AVIATION OPERATIONS:

The Canadian Aeronautics Act,[7] unlike the British Act, does not deal with aircraft noise, so provincial law must provide applicable principles. Likewise, no Dominion case law directly treating noise disturbance exists. Nonetheless, two cases should be noted. The first is *Nova Mink Farms v. Trans Canada Airlines*, a decision of the Nova Scotia Supreme Court. There, the court held in dictum that compliance with pertinent flight regulations does not lessen the common law duties of the aircraft operator to parties on the surface. Even so, that court took a dim view of recovery for mere noise in the absence of unusual circumstances known to the defendant.

A second case is *Lacroix v. R.* in which the Exchequer Court denied plaintiff recovery for the alleged taking of an easement over his property. In so holding, the court expressly rejected the claim that section 414 of the Quebec Civil Code entitles the owner of land to ownership of superadjacent airspace. Though it could have ended at that point, the court went on gratuitously to underscore the landowner's right to full enjoyment of his land. Despite this, the court stated that aircraft operations which comply with regulations would not give rise to liability. Two things must be kept in mind about *Lacroix*. First, its force goes only to ownership of airspace since the other issues treated were beyond the scope of the plaintiff's claim. Secondly, the expression in dictum of the court's opinion disregarded the Civil Code of Quebec, looking even to the United States for authority. Since it is provincial law which is to be applied under the Exchequer Court Act, the propriety of this is questionable. Nonetheless, the dictum in *Lacroix* indicates the direction the Exchequer Court may take in deciding potential disturbance cases to which the Crown is a party and which arises in a common law province.

Whether the defendant in a disturbance case involving civil aviation operations is the Dominion or a private party, the law of the province where the offending conduct took place applies. Therefore, the Civil Code of Quebec should be examined as a means of resolving landowner–air transport disputes. Attention is directed to sections 1053 and 1054 dealing with extra-contractual responsibility. Article 1053 states that

> Every person capable of discerning right from wrong is responsible for the damage caused by his fault to another, whether by positive act, imprudence, neglect or want of skill.

Not only is the person responsible for his own fault, but his responsibility extends "also for the damage caused . . . by things he has under his care," under article 1054.

Recovery under 1053 turns upon plaintiff's proving fault. Note that the right to conduct aviation operations is specifically regulated. It is the manner in which that right is exercised, not the harm suffered by landowners that is central to determination of fault questions under 1053. Thus, so long as aviation operations comply with pertinent regulations, a finding of fault is unlikely in the absence of malice.

The possibility remains of claiming under 1054, which raises a rebuttable presumption of fault. In order to recover under that article a plaintiff must prove two things: (1) that an autonomous act of the thing caused the damage and (2) that defendant had the "garde juridique" of that thing. The first requirement might be answered by arguing that aircraft noise disturbance emanates not from the fault of the operator, but rather from the nature of the aircraft itself. Thus, the autonomous act requirement is met. The other requirement, "garde juridique", is met since the defendant is exercising control over the aircraft for his own benefit.

Even if this argument were acceptable, the exculpatory clause of paragraph six of article 1054 would likely protect the defendant:

> The responsibility attaches in the above cases only when the person subject to it fails to establish that he

was unable (by reasonable means) to prevent the act which has caused the damage.

In the overwhelming majority of cases, airlines can show that they have taken all reasonable steps to prevent unreasonable noise disturbance.

These inadequacies of the Civil Code are relevant not only to domestic civil aviation operations in Quebec, but to certain foreign operations as well.

FOREIGN CIVIL AVIATION OPERATIONS

In the absence of specific Dominion legislation, provincial law applies to the conduct of foreign air carriers within provincial territory. However, specific legislation does apply to carriers of states which are party to the 1952 Rome Convention. Enacted in Canada in 1955, that convention imposes absolute, but limited liability on foreign civil aircraft causing damage to third parties on the surface.[8]

Here, as in the case of the British Civil Aviation Act, the meaning of "damage" is unclear. Noise disturbance from types of aircraft known in 1952 was not intended to be included within the coverage of the convention. However, the subsequent development of large jet aircraft has made real the threat of damage due to noise. It is therefore argued that the Rome Convention extends to cases of material damage caused by aircraft noise.

Employing this interpretation of the Rome Convention, aircraft of non-member states would presumably be governed by provincial law. Since only fourteen states are parties to the Rome Convention, provincial law is predominant, and several difficulties emerge. If provincial law affords no recovery for damage caused by aircraft operated in compliance with flight regulations, non-member states' carriers would be subject to no liability, whereas those of member states would be subject to absolute but limited liability in cases of material damage. Contrarily, in provinces whose law affords recovery, non-member states' carriers would be subject to unlimited liability for material damage, whereas member states' carriers would be subject to "Rome Convention liability".

This diversity of laws could be rectified by making the provisions of the Rome Convention applicable to all foreign aircraft entering Canadian airspace. Such action might be strongly objected to, notably by the United States, which opposes strict liability. Nonetheless, this action is within the sovereign rights of Canada over her airspace.

Notwithstanding this suggestion, the present state of the law of Quebec would apply the law of that province to cases of aviation disturbance arising therein which did not involve material damage. Where material damage occurs, Quebec law would apply to non-member states' carriers, and the Rome Convention would apply to carrier of member states.

CANADIAN MILITARY AVIATION OPERATIONS

As mentioned above, certain aspects of the law of governmental liability in tort are common to Canada and Great Britain. Notably, the Canadian Aeronautics Act does not appear to apply to military aircraft. Rather, they are under the control of the Minister of Defence. In addition, the *Crown Liability Act*, article 3 section 6, "... does not make(s) the Crown liable in respect of anything done or omitted in the exercise of any power or authority exercisable by the Crown, whether in time of peace or war, for the purpose of the defence of Canada or of training, or maintaining the efficiency of, any of the naval, army or air forces of Canada."

There has been no judicial construction of the above provision, so its effect upon liability of military aviation operations is uncertain. However, actions have been taken successfully against the Crown for acts of its military personnel.

In any case, the law of the province in which the conduct complained of arises controls any liability the Crown may have. However, it is the provincial law as it existed in 1947, the date of the enactment of the Crown Liability Act. It is anomalous that the Crown, with its tremendous power to inflict harm through governmental activities, should be judged by law not subject to change. Aviation activities are but one example of technological evolution demanding contemporary legal treatment. The development of necessary concepts is rendered impossible by the present construction of the Crown Liability Act.

Towards a Canadian Policy

Reviewing briefly, provincial law will apply in nearly all cases of aviation noise whether caused by military or civil aircraft. The exception is where material damage is caused by aircraft having the nationality of a state party to the 1952 Rome Convention. Further, the Civil Code of Quebec appears to consider only the defendant's conduct, not the quantum of harm which flows therefrom. The seeming inadequacies of the law of Quebec make necessary a consideration of the preliminary questions posed earlier in this study. Those questions raise alternate means of resolving the conflict between groups interested in air transport and landowner groups. Note that the landowner as a member of the public shares an interest in aviation, thereby assuming a dual role.

In answer to the first preliminary question, it is urged that there are circumstances in which aviation operations, though conducted in compliance with flight regulations, should be actionable. Secondly, material damage should not be a prerequisite to recovery. In extreme circumstances frequent noise and vibration unaccompanied by material damage are not dismissable as mere neighborhood inconvenience.

Management of the air transport–landowner conflict centers, then, about two inquiries. First, what is the extent of the landowner's burden as a member of the public interested in aviation? At what point or points along the scale of conduct should liability attach? Secondly, of what elements should that liability consist?

The landowner's role as a member of the public does not warrant that he suffer material damage to his property. Rather, strict liability should be imposed on mere proof of causation.

In contrast, mere aircraft noise becomes unreasonable only in extreme circumstances. The question is one of degree, unlike the certainty that material damage has occurred. The choice is one of recovery *vel non*. If recovery is to be granted in the absence of material damage a judicially manageable means of identifying actionable circumstances is required. This raises the third and fourth preliminary questions, which deal with the result of common law analysis of aviation noise disturbance in

America. The American treatment has not been entirely satisfactory, but this is due to the requirements of American constitutional law coupled with the pre-1946 governmental tort immunity. The existence of these factors in American constitutional law has made necessary the employment of the "taking" doctrine, whereas pure nuisance concepts are available in Canada.

An added problem in American law is that a respectable body of authority insists that where the public suffers a nuisance, an individual can recover on his own account only if he has suffered damage differing in *kind* from that suffered by the public at large. Plaintiffs seeking recovery for material damage could overcome this argument, but those suffering mere disturbance would be denied recovery under the abovementioned view. However, this view does not prevail in Canadian common law provinces. An individual must show that he has suffered harm "above and beyond that suffered by the public" in order to recover on his own account in a public nuisance situation. Pure nuisance theory seems, therefore, both appropriate and available to the resolution of aircraft noise disputes in Canada's common law provinces.

One final alternative must be considered, that of promulgating an empirical test couched in terms of maximum allowable noise levels. Although such a test would afford certainty, it could only be a compromise. As such, it could leave certain plaintiffs without recourse in unusual circumstances. Thus, an ad hoc approach employing nuisance analysis is preferable.

In light of the above, the following twofold scheme is submitted as a satisfactory resolution of aviation-landowner conflicts:

1. Physical damage to property is not to be tolerated by landowners as part of their role as members of the public. If causation of material damage is considered indispensable to development of air transport, the resultant costs should be borne by aviation enterprises and connected groups.
2. In the absence of material damages there are, nonetheless, certain extreme circumstances which will give rise to liability. Identification of such circumstances is to be on an ad hoc basis.

Adoption of "1" above makes uniform the treatment of material damage cases, regardless of whether the defendant is a domestic or foreign carrier. Adoption of "2" raises two questions. First, are the carriers of Rome Convention states amenable to provincial law treatment of mere disturbance since the convention did not intend to cover mere noise? Secondly, note that the law of Quebec seems to offer no recovery to landowners, no matter how severe the harm from air transport operations conducted in compliance with pertinent regulations. Ostensibly, the Rome Convention serves only to impose responsibility for damage, not to provide immunity from liability for conduct not covered by the convention. Thus, the first question may be answered affirmatively. The second problem illustrates patently the need to assess the propriety of the Quebec law in light of existing technology. Discussion thus far has assumed that sonic boom requires no departure from the proffered scheme of analysis. A brief examination of the nature of sonic boom justifies that assumption.

Sonic Boom

Sonic boom may be described as a cone of high pressure air consisting of closely grouped sound waves accompanied by a loud cracking noise. Its intensity is a function of the size, weight, altitude, geometry, and flight attitude of the aircraft. In addition, atmospheric conditions exert considerable influence on sonic boom intensity. The destructive potential of these supersonic overpressures is conjectural, but present purposes are served by noting that sonic booms have accounted for damage ranging from minor glass breakage to the 1959 incident at Uplands Air Force Base near Ottawa, in which a low supersonic overflight caused structural damage in excess of $500,000 to the newly erected terminal building. If man deems it indispensable to travel at supersonic speeds, the resultant material damage is presumably no more the burden of the subjacent landowner than is damage caused by a falling aircraft.

A more difficult question is presented by sonic booms which cause no material damage. Their noise is sudden; trailing the path of the aircraft, they could affect wide portions of the populace unfamiliar with aircraft disturbance. Furthermore, the frequency of sonic boom over a given area may be dependent on a multiplicity of factors, some of which are uncontrollable. Nonetheless, in final analysis, sonic boom is merely noise. As such, it becomes unreasonable under extreme circumstances. Ad hoc recognition of such situations renders sonic boom amenable to the suggested scheme even though actionable facts may differ from those where subsonic operations are in question.

Conclusions

A legislative approach thus appears to be the most equitable solution to aviation noise problems. These issues should be treated with a view to the just distribution of the burden of air transport operations between the industry, its consumers, the public, and finally, the landowner group. This can best be accomplished by preventing legal formalism from eclipsing the interests of the groups involved, as it has done to a large extent in the United States.

Several policy factors may be noted in conclusion. First, it is arguable that the air transport interests are better able to bear the cost of offending operations than is the landowner group. Further, these costs may be passed on to users of aviation services and products. Secondly, as regards material damage, it is not anticipated that prolific litigation would flow from adoption of the suggested scheme due to the high cost of litigation and the involvement of insurance companies which tend to settle out of court wherever possible.

References

[1]However, the Canadian Bar Association has considered the problem at several annual meetings.

[2]Federal Tort Claims Act, 60 Stat. 842, 28 U.S.C. 1346 (1946). See generally *Aviation Noise Under the Federal Tort Claims Act*, 24 Fed. Bar. J. 165 (1964).

[3]U.S. CONST. amend V, "...nor shall private property be taken for public use without just compensation."

[4]*The Air Navigation Act*, 1920; (10 & 11 Geo. V, c. 30) s. 9 Now *Civil Aviation Act*, 1949; (12, 13 & 14 Geo. VI, c. 67) s. 40(1) which reads, "No action shall lie in respect of trespass or nuisance, by reason only of the flight of an aircraft over any property at a height above the ground, which, having regard to wind, weather, and all the circumstances of the case is reasonable, or the ordinary incidents of such flight so long as the provisions of part II and this part of the Act and any Order in Council or order made under Part II or this Part of this Act are duly complied with."

[5]See for general background Richards and Kaplan, *The Control of Aircraft Noise Perceived at Ground Level*, 68 Jo. Royal Aer. So. 45 (1964).

[6]*Civil Aviation Act*, 1949, supra note 19, s. 40(2).

[7]R. S. C. 1952, Vol. 1, c. 2.

[8]*Foreign Aircraft Third Party Damage Act*, 3-4 Eliz. II, c. 15 (1955). c. 1, art. 1: "Any person who suffers damage on the surface shall upon proof only that the damage was caused by an aircraft in flight or by any person or thing falling therefrom, be entitled to compensation as provided by this Convention. Nevertheless, there shall be no right to compensation if the damage is not a direct consequence of the incident giving rise thereto, or if the damage results from the mere fact of passage of the aircraft through the airspace in conformity with the existing air traffic regulations." See R. S. C. 1952, Vol. 1 c. 2, Part II, s. 18.

Pollution Probe: fighting the polluters with their own weapons

D. A. CHANT

Most Canadians are now convinced that the quality of our environment is deteriorating at an exponential rate because of population pressures and expanding technology. The day of pollution horror stories is passing rapidly as most of our society is becoming knowledgeable about the ecological crises we are facing. What must be devised now for the guidance of all who share concern about the quality of our environment, are effective action programs.

One kind of action still in its infancy is by uncommitted citizen groups that owe no allegiance to vested interests other than that of optimal living. Action from this source is needed to encourage and guide progressive governments and industries in environmental quality control, to pressure inert governments and industries into awareness and progress, and to counter lobbying and other counter-pressures from polluters who have selfish, short-term economic interests without environmental conscience.

A number of citizen anti-pollution groups are springing up across Canada. One of the most successful is Pollution Probe at the University of Toronto. Its formation and methods of

Source: D. A. Chant, "Pollution Probe: fighting the polluters with their own weapons", *Science Forum* 14, April 1970, pp. 19-22. Reprinted by permission of the author and of *Science Forum: A Canadian Journal of Science and Technology*.

operation suggest principles of action that may be useful to other groups with similar aims and to the informed reader who wonders: "What can *I* do?"

Pollution Probe came into being at the University of Toronto spontaneously in February 1969. Many students and staff had been alarmed for some years over the rate at which our environment is deteriorating. They had watched the CBC-TV program "Air of Death" by Larry Gosnell and Stanley Burke and approved of its message and the impact it had on concerned Canadians. Some of these students were dismayed, therefore, to learn that the Canadian Radio-Television Commission (CRTC) planned to investigate the program. They decided to band together to protest this investigation, both on the grounds of journalistic freedom and because the program was considered accurate and well balanced. They studied air pollution intensively, including, of course, the fluoride pollution from the Electric Reduction Company (ERCO) at Port Maitland and the biased and inaccurate Hall Commission Report (Report of the Committee Appointed to Inquire into and Report upon the Pollution of Air, Soil, and Water, September 1968). They invited Larry Gosnell to screen "Air of Death" at the University of Toronto and to answer questions afterwards, and the meeting had an overflow attendance. Finally, these students, still without a formal organization, wrote briefs to the CRTC protesting the inquiry and supporting the CBC. Many of them attended the three-day hearing in its entirety, and were appalled, in their innocence, at the tactics of the opposition, particularly the ERCO legal and public relations staff. They decided on the spot that there were ills in a society that permitted such moral outrages that called far more urgently for condemnation than the Vietnam war or the lack of decision-making rights of university students. And they decided to do something about these ills.

That "something" was to organize a university-based group that would, on the one hand, fight pollution and the polluters with their own weapons of publicity and government pressure, and in the courts; and on the other, seek out the basic roots of our environmental crises and change them if possible by education and even by advocating new kinds of institutional frameworks for our society as a whole.

Accordingly, in March 1969 Pollution Probe came into being as a visible entity with a name, an executive, a constitution, and most important, members from everywhere in the university—fine arts, engineering, the social and natural sciences, the humanities, administration, both staff and students. Later membership was opened to any concerned citizen for $2.00 a year, and now Pollution Probe is about 1,000 strong.

Much thought was given in those early days to aims and the most appropriate executive structure for achieving them. Probe's objectives as finally defined are broadly to seek the redress of environmental ills by activities ranging on one extreme from public education (Probe members have spoken to dozens of citizens' groups and to more than 15,000 primary and secondary students in the last six months) through information gathering and the stimulation of similar organizations at universities across Canada, to militant action programs of parades and demonstrations, and finally to the other extreme of legal action against polluters and inert government agencies.

Probe has no conventional executive. There is a board of advisers nominated by the membership, which guides but does not run the organization; it is there when wanted or needed, but otherwise does not intrude in the organization's daily affairs. It is composed of prominent dedicated people such as Marshall McLuhan, Stanley Burke, John Dales, Richard Judy, and others. In addition, Probe is organized into work teams responsible for its major activities—education, newsletter, office management, publicity, research, fund-raising, phosphate detergent pollution, SO_2 and other air pollution, legal affairs, and so on. Leaders of each team emerge not by edict or appointment but rather on the basis of dedication and interest, and most important of all in the increasingly complex and busy university milieu, availability of time. Those with keen interest and some available time evolve as team leaders. This loosely knit, sometimes rather ephemeral group of team leaders actually functions as a sort of quasi-executive. Probe's successes to date can be credited largely to this group of 15 or 20 young people who have given its affairs their concern and much of their attention; supported, of course, in a very substantial way by the membership as a whole, who turn out by the hundreds to regular monthly meetings.

To be successful a group such as Probe must be businesslike.

It must follow through effectively on administration and all its other activities, and in fact have a recognized, stable, physical presence. To ensure this, Probe became an official project of the University of Toronto, with an account administered through (but not by) the department of zoology, and an office in the Ramsay Wright Building. There is a full-time secretary and an office manager, and the office and adjoining work and study area are the centre of all Probe activities. The key workers, mostly undergraduate and graduate students and recent graduates, work from there and it is there that they meet to plan activities and make decisions.

Adequate finances also are essential to success. Probe has yet to mount a major fund-raising campaign but has done reasonably well with membership fees, a few individual gifts, a grant from President Bissell, and substantial subsidization from the department of zoology. It has also enjoyed truly gratifying contributions in advertising art work and layout from one firm, and free publication of educational and promotional material from the Toronto *Telegram*. More than anything else, these last two have enabled Probe to bring issues to public attention and to gain public recognition. Probe, however, is becoming a modestly expensive affair and cannot for long continue its hand-to-mouth existence. Substantial and continuing financial support must be found.

There are other characteristics of Probe to understand before discussing its accomplishments. The first is the strength it gains from the breadth of professional competence represented in its membership. There is scarcely an aspect of pollution, whether it be pesticides, urban congestion, noise, air, or water, on which one or more members are not acknowledged experts, either through personal research experience or by study and exposure. This means Probe can address itself to almost any pollution problem with confidence and authority, sure of its facts and without the vagueness that so often characterizes anti-pollution groups.

The second is the close and productive relationships that Probe has established with the communications media. The results have been so successful and important that some members of Probe have been accused of being publicity-hungry. This is unfair. Probe simply recognized the necessity of bringing pollution problems to public attention, and what more effective way is there of doing this than by using the modern, efficient methods of mass communication? The willingness, almost the eagerness, of the newspapers, radio, and TV to co-operate probably stems partly from the fact that pollution has excellent news value, but partly, I am convinced, from the fact that news reporters are not only professional communicators but also citizens. They have wives and families themselves, and they share the common concern and fear over our deteriorating environment.

Probe recognized early that effective anti-pollution action inevitably would lead to legal actions: actions to seek injunctions preventing polluting activities, and perhaps even suits to seek redress from intransigent polluters. It was fortunate in forming an association with an effective Toronto lawyer, James Karfilis, who has a well-developed environmental conscience and is willing to handle Probe's legal affairs for a retainer of one dollar per year.

Finally Probe believes that when seeking decisive action on environmental problems one should approach the real centres of power: Cabinet members, provincial or federal, and other political leaders. It is only at this level that one can rise above the inertia or outright helplessness of some arms of the civil service to bring pressure to bear, explain data and views, and seek new laws or changes in policy that will result in a cleaner environment. Probe has been fortunate in that the present Ontario and federal governments are becoming sophisticated and knowledgeable about pollution and moving in the direction of effective environmental control. Members of these governments, with few exceptions, have received Probe freely, listened to its cases and in most instances, been convinced.

In its short life Probe has embarked on several major projects. The first was a program to have DDT and other persistent organochlorine pesticides banned in Ontario. We were advised that this would take two years and even then we might not succeed. Probe's interest in DDT was activated by the author, whose personal research for 20 years has been on the principles of pest control and who is convinced that DDT and its relatives are one of the most serious long-term environmental threats now facing the world ecosystem. Initial contacts with the provincial government almost immediately resulted in a total ban on aldrin, dieldrin, and heptachlor, announced on 4 June 1969. But any restriction of DDT was refused, and this accelerated Probe's campaign. Speeches were given, meetings were held with cabinet ministers, a new minister of health and a new minister of energy and resources management were appointed and Probe compiled an up-to-date world compendium of scientific data on the physical chemistry of DDT and its effects on food chains, on avian and fish reproductive physiology, and on learning and behaviour. The Environmental Defence Fund and the Senate in the United States provided newly released information on the carcinogenic properties of DDT in laboratory animals, and the University of Florida sent manuscripts linking high DDT residues with liver cancer and other disorders in humans. This material was incorporated into a massive brief to the premier of Ontario requesting a ban, but it was never used; in September the minister of health announced restrictions on DDT that would reduce its use in Ontario by 90%. Probe, flushed with the feeling that it had played an important role in this "ban," decided to transfer its attention to Ottawa to seek a national ban.

Accordingly in October the petition was readdressed to Prime Minister Trudeau and copies were sent to every federal minister, to every premier, to all leaders of the opposition, to every major radio and TV station, newspaper and magazine across Canada, to every university, and to all major conservation groups. Support was massive and irresistible. In November Mr. Trudeau announced nation-wide restrictions that will reduce DDT use by 90-95%.

Other action programs that achieved their aims were on the misuse of a pesticide on Toronto Islands and the sewage pollution of Highland Creek in suburban Scarborough, both of which led to actions to obtain injunctions against government agencies. Both suits were withdrawn when effective anti-pollution steps were taken. Probe has also co-operated with legal actions initiated locally by conservation groups in Peterborough and Sudbury.

Probe has carried out successful programs of public education regarding litter and the gross pollution of the Don River in Metro Toronto. Moreover it is lending strong support to groups attempting to preserve the Quetico Park area as a wilderness sanctuary and to prevent the further construction of the Spadina Expressway in Toronto.

There are two current major programs. The first is aimed at Ontario Hydro, generally acknowledged to be the most serious air polluter in the Metro Toronto area. This has involved meetings with cabinet ministers and the chairman of Hydro and his advisers, climaxing in a three-day public hearing at which expert testimony was presented by all interested parties, and all sides of the question were examined by a panel of five "commissioners." The ultimate objective is to encourage Hydro to reduce or eliminate sulphur pollution by installing effective air washing devices or by changing from high to low sulphur content fuel.

The second current program is on water pollution caused by phosphate detergents. Probe has analyzed all major detergents and water conditioners sold in the Toronto area and is mounting a major campaign with two objectives: to persuade housewives to buy only low-phosphate detergents and thereby pressure the manufacturers in the marketplace; and to work with and encourage the provincial government in its inclination to ban phosphate detergents by 1972.

What principles of effective anti-pollution action have been established by Probe to date? They seem to be as follows:

1. Individuals acting alone are virtually powerless to prevent further degradation of our environment. They must band together for effective action and they must decide what particular sorts of action suit them best. Is is education, discussion, study, political pressure, demonstrations, or legal action? Or can they tolerate and support all of these and more in a single organization, such as Pollution Probe?

2. They must be shrewd tacticians. There is little point or hope of success simply to attack total environmental degradation as a vague, all-embracing concept from the beginning. They must start on a limited basis with clearly identified, highly visible local issues with which the public can readily identify before moving on to larger issues of more far-reaching importance.

3. They must be sure of their facts, and this means they must have professionally competent people within the membership—engineers, biologists, chemists, economists, political scientists, sociologists, lawyers.

4. They must work effectively with the communications media, not only by appearing in headlines and on TV but by providing background and leads and by willingly giving advice and information without regard for public credit through personal publicity.
5. They must develop educational programs by public lectures to groups of citizens, no matter how small and obscure, and to classes of students at all levels from primary schools through university. Without public awareness and broad support, environmental control will be impossible.
6. Within the limits of their collective conscience, groups must be responsible. Nothing erodes credibility more quickly than irresponsible statements or actions that cannot be supported by facts. This does not mean that dramatization has no role, perhaps even over-dramatization to overcome strong negative resistance; but there is a fine line between this and irresponsibility.
7. The group must have a physical presence in the sense of an office, a listed telephone number, and a permanent office staff. Without this, effective communication and action follow-up is impossible.
8. Finally, groups will learn quickly that the pressure they generate must be applied at the top—at the level of cabinet ministers, heads of agencies, and company presidents. It is futile and ineffective to approach anything less than the ultimate centres of decision making.

What have we learned from Probe's activities to date? Perhaps the most striking thing is the ruthlessness and vigour with which the vested interests will fight back. This sort of backlash is seen in counter-publicity, in direct personal abuse, and in subtle innuendo among our colleagues and others in the Canadian scientific community. It is not quite proper, some suggest, for scientists and academics to get involved with public action groups, with communications media, with politicians, and with legal action. Somehow, it would seem, we are betraying our more inert brethren who would prefer to live quietly in their ivory towers behind massive walls of pseudo-objectivity, scientific "detachment", and perhaps plain fright. They "Don't want to get involved." The increase in this counter-activity, we believe, is a measure of our success to date.

Is there any justification for the view that scientists should not become involved in public controversy with timely issues such as pollution, which threaten our survival and cast serious doubts on the viability of our traditional institutional framework and social organization? I can accept the possibility that scientists in government and industry must at times be reticent and defer to official policy set by their superiors, as long as they continue to work effectively behind the scenes. But I cannot accept the same thing for scientists in universities.

Scientists in universities are independent of both government and special interest groups and are in the most advantageous position to exercise their social conscience and relate to controversial problems of the real world. I am not suggesting that a university as a whole should take a policy position on environmental problems—far from it, although the University of Toronto has given open, substantial support to Pollution Probe. Rather it is the professionals in universities who either have special competence through their research or, simply as educated citizens, have a sophisticated concern about environmental quality, who must take leadership in public action programs. To be blunt, not only do I consider this appropriate and desirable, I consider it absolutely essential. It is a major responsibility whose abdication can be read only as a lack of interest in the world around us and callous disregard for the welfare of our society as a whole.

It is necessary, however, to make a firm distinction between an individual's professional side and his active involvement in environmental issues. The principles of one can all too easily be compromised in the emotional commitment of the other. Probably it is because of this that many in the scientific community frown on those who participate in public action. Science should be rigorous and above all objective; nothing is established as truth until it has withstood the rigours of experimental analysis and repeatability. Pollution action programs, however, often depend on data obtained by inference, extrapolation, and perhaps even intuition. Usually they cannot wait for time-consuming, rigorous scientific study and analysis. Environmental problems beset us from every side and they are right-now problems; they are crises, and action right now is required for their easement.

For example, studies in a number of major cities have shown that SO_2 air pollution is harmful to plants and animals and aggravates respiratory disorders in humans. An SO_2 concentration of 0.25 parts per million for periods longer than one hour is hazardous, and 0.40 parts per million is downright dangerous. Similar studies have not been done in Toronto, to my knowledge, yet when the SO_2 concentration reaches 0.37 parts per million, as it did on Thursday 22 January 1970 we *know* that action must be taken immediately to eliminate the major sources of sulphur pollution. We do not need a local scientific study to prove this.

Moreover, our commitment to the solution of environmental problems often is emotional. It is based on knowledge of sorts, often with extrapolations into the future, but nonetheless emotional. I personally am outraged at the abuse of our environment by industries and some government agencies; but I am outraged in the part of me that is *informed citizen*, not the part that is *trained scientist*. I may say and do things that are uncomfortable to my professional standards as a scientist but are fully in keeping with my determination as an ordinary citizen to protect my environment. All of this is not easy, and some of it may well be facile rationalization. But it helps, I think, to explain how some scientists are able to get involved and it may encourage others to do so.

Scientists who can make this distinction between their various parts should adopt Pollution Probe's motto: "Do it!" Now.

Our Total Environment

F. KENNETH HARE

We live in such revolutionary times that it is no longer reserved to grandparents to say that "times aren't what they used to be". It barely takes five years for us to outlive our tastes, preoccupations, familiarities; and for the world outside us to propel itself headlong into a state we can hardly comprehend, and barely endure with patience. This is the accidental century, to quote Michael Harrington, in which events seem to propel themselves, and change takes on the role of a juggernaut.

And so I often wonder whether the current excitement about environment will last very long. In a short time the word has become as fashionable as motherhood was in Victorian times. It could become unfashionable in no time at all. I have been talking about it for over thirty years, ever since, while still a student, I worked in the slums of London, and came to the conclusion that man's inhumanity to man took the form of a hell that he had built for himself. I thought then, and still think, that the vital element in the human environment is the other men around us and their works, not the physical world. We are certainly busy despoiling the air, water, soil and living world on which we depend. I'm not decrying the effort to beat pollution, to restore environmental quality. Thank God, in fact, for Donald Chant and Pollution Probe. I *am* saying, that the quality of life depends primarily on other things, that surround us just as pervasively, just as perniciously and just as avoidably as do smog and deter-

---

Source: F. Kenneth Hare, "Our Total Environment", from a speech made before the Men's Canadian Club of Toronto on January 26, 1970. Reproduced by permission of the author.

gent foam. And, moreover, that the phenomenon of pollution is itself a social problem, reflecting our attitudes and prejudices as regards technology, which we misuse.

Will the new concern for environment last? How deep does it really go? On the face of it, very deep. It has penetrated the Republican White House of Mr. Nixon. Quite recently his consultant on urban affairs, Mr. Daniel Moynihan, a Harvard professor in real life, told the North Atlantic Assembly in Brussels that a study of the environment should become the alliance's "third dimension", coming after defence and political consultation. To ram home his point he added blandly that we are facing an ecological crisis using the words "we may well have even less than a 50–50 chance of living until 1980". I am quoting from the London *Times* story by Peter Strafford, which was printed on page 5 of their October 22 issue. This shows that the editor didn't really believe that bit about the 50–50 chance—if he had, he would have printed it on page 2.

No, *they* didn't believe it, *you* don't believe it, and frankly *I* didn't believe it. I am much more afraid of nuclear war, of civil uprisings in North American cities, of the anguish in Africa and south-east Asia, than I am of pollution; and so, I suspect, are most other Canadians. Some of the polemicists for the environment are overplaying their hand, egged on by the headline writers. And to be cynical for a moment, it is convenient for central governments to have an issue that doesn't really divide the electors, that doesn't antagonize the campuses, and that so often doesn't involve any concrete action. It's a lot less easy for provincial and state governments, and very hard for city governments, to take this line, because *their* electorates can see the smoke belching, and know who's making it. If the time comes for government to dump the environmental lobby, it will be very easy for a shrewd politician to play on the latent resentment of a public that feels that these stories are exaggerated. So I have a message for the conservationists and environmental watchdogs: just tell us the facts, and make sure they *are* facts. They are quite bad enough without amplification.

It would be a pity if we let this suspicion that the case is being overstated cloud our judgment, because we *are* at a cross-roads, we *do* need to act, we *can* ensure the future—but we are close to the date when we can no longer say these things. So let me propose a few things we should and should not do, to prove Mr. Moynihan wrong.

First a few should nots. I don't like to talk about this problem as if it were just pollution control—setting a thief to catch a thief. Some very distinguished people talk like this—Sir Peter Medawar, for example, who last September used the words "the deterioration of the environment produced by technology is a technological problem for which technology has found, is finding, and will continue to find solutions." Right, of course—but it can be hopeless just to be right. The real point is that we have got to get ourselves a technological system in which we don't despoil in the first place, and an economic system that doesn't depend on abandonment of responsibility for waste disposal at the one end, and the overuse of resources at the other. Pollution is only superficially a matter of technology. At root it is the product of social irresponsibility, of mass shoulder shrugging.

Second, I don't think we should see this as a temporary situation that we can quickly put right by minor controls—by putting curbs on a few makers of smells and poisoners of fish. It is our whole urban and industrial system that is responsible. We have crammed ourselves voluntarily into cities before we have learned how to build them or service them. We cling to outmoded forms of government that half disfranchise cities like Toronto and aggrandize Prince Edward Island. And behind all of this vast social upheaval, the rush into the urban prison, lie the contradictions of an industrial system that is based on the use of power so profligate that we are burning in about four hundred years the fossil fuels that took over four hundred million years to accumulate. The coal, natural gas and oil will be gone in less than two centuries, at best calculations, and it is imperative that we get away from their careless use, with all that implies—not only because their supply is limited, but because it is their by-products that most threaten our environment.

And now to the shoulds. What positive things do we do to survive on a planet that no longer has an unexplored frontier that we can exploit to rescue ourselves? I could, of course, dilate as a mere amateur on the fallacies of an expanding economy, on the myths of productivity (in which we count only the things produced, and not the consequences of producing them), on the need for a steady-state world economy. I could do so because I am an amateur commentator. If I were a professional economist, I should be more wary, because I should have to live with my remarks. Amateur or not, I'm going to suggest that half the battle, in providing for the future environment, is going to be to create a stable economic system in which growth is not the first objective. We cannot for ever base ourselves on growth, and we are not very good at visualizing steady-state societies. When we had them in the past, like the high farming of East Anglia, or the Greek city-state, we had them because mankind could then tolerate a level of social injustice and deprivation that we can't countenance. So here is the first of the shoulds—to breed a race of economists who will look beyond the assumptions of the growth economy, as Kenneth Boulding has begun to do, and tell us how to create a just stability, a conservative society without underprivilege.

My remaining shoulds are specifically Canadian. This country has had its own myths. One is to identify economic health with unbridled resource exploitation, damning the environmental consequences: we are rich, we say, because Canada is physically rich. But how, in that case, has Japan, devoid of such resources, achieved its phenomenal growth? What of the sudden renaissance of the U.K. economy, one of the keys to which has been the deliberate phasing-out of coal, her only important natural asset? In both cases the answer has been the capitalization of talent, of enterprise, of *nous*, not natural resources. Of course I am not suggesting that we retire our forest industries, our mines and our oil-wells. The world needs them. I *am* saying that we need not mesmerize ourselves into thinking that natural resources are the only basis on which we can have a prosperous economy—or into allowing the less efficient of these industries to wreck our landscape and our atmosphere in the name of national prosperity. Their health, and our health, are better served by stringent environmental controls, and I believe that industry will agree to this, if it hasn't already accepted the inevitable.

I should like to plead for voluntary action. Environmental planning, design, restoration and control, are too important to leave to government alone. Any good government needs the support, but also the informed criticism and pressure, of free institutions whose object is to venture where politicians as yet can't. We have few such bodies in Canada. In Washington, by contrast, there are several well-endowed private institutions whose sole objective is to achieve for the American people a better balance between man and his environment. Resources for the Future is one such body that we could well imitate. It started out with the Paley Commission on Resources, but significantly it has shifted its effort towards environmental quality, which it publicizes and on which it conducts some excellent research. We need such a body in Canada, independent of the state, with its own staff and resources, in close touch with both those that want to keep Canada livable, and those who at present threaten that livability.

I think, too, that environmental quality means more than smell-free air, pure water and freedom from DDT. It means also access to a green and lovely countryside, highways from which we can see it, rather than billboards, cities that are graceful rather than disgraceful, houses that don't break our hearts and our pocket-books, journeys to work that don't break our spirit. When we say quality of the environment we often mean quality of life—and these things are the material side of it.

To awaken ourselves to this situation is a job for the seventies. In the universities we have begun, reluctantly and haltingly as usual, but still successfully, to put environmental studies on the map, and significantly the students are more willing to tread this path than some professors are to pave it. We have succeeded in seeing this as a new kind of challenge, one that puts society and technology together in the same curriculum. Nationally we need to look hard at the questions of jurisdiction involved. The milky sky that we so often see from Toronto, for example, gets to be that way because of smoke emitted in part beyond the border in the United States. The smoke that Toronto emits affects a wide area around—including, at times, New York State. Environmental problems are no respecters of boundaries. It would be a tragedy if Canada's chronic inability to solve her constitutional problems were to imperil the tackling of these threats to our future well-being.

In conclusion, let me reiterate my point that this is a man-centered question. We live in a society that has achieved for itself a high level of material affluence. But it has done so without counting the cost of the harm done to the natural environment that supports us. It has also allowed itself to create, in its cities, a growing exasperation between neighbours, a growing frustration of what we seek to achieve in life. I hope and believe that in Canada, at least, where the political freedoms still survive, and can still be perceived through the smog, we can throttle these difficulties before they throttle us.

Contributors

Gary Dunford is a free-lance journalist and the creator of Captain Canada on the Bruno Gerussi show. He lives in rural Ontario and is the author of *When An Otter's Heart Breaks*.

Lynn White, Jr., is professor of history at the University of California, Los Angeles. He is the author of a number of books, the most recent of which is *Machina Ex Deo*.

Kenneth E. Boulding was born in England and received his B.A. and M.A. degrees at Oxford. He taught at universities in Scotland and in Canada before going to the University of Michigan in 1949. He is at present professor of economics at the University of Colorado. His many books include *Economic Analyses* (1941) and *The Meaning of the Twentieth Century* (1964).

Peter Schrag is editor-at-large of *Saturday Review*.

Philip H. Jones is professor of civil (environmental) engineering at the University of Toronto. He is also Associate Director of the Great Lakes Institute and Vice Chairman of the Environmental Sciences and Engineering Programme. **Tom Davey** is managing editor of *Canadian Consulting Engineer*, and the winner of several journalism awards.

David Spurgeon is science writer for the Toronto *Globe and Mail.* He holds a M.Sc. from Columbia University and in 1968 won the top award in the Excellence in Science Writing Program sponsored by the Cornell Aeronautical Laboratory. He is the editor of *Science Forum* and is well known for his reporting on scientific matters.

Ronald Stewart is with the Atmospheric Sciences Research Center, State University of New York, Albany. **H. H. Howard** is with the Department of Biology, Skidmore College, Saratoga.

Charles L. Wilbar, Jr., served as Secretary of Health for Pennsylvania from 1957 to 1967. At the time of his death in 1969 he was on the staff of West Virginia University.

Robert U. Ayres is Vice President of the International Research and Technology Corporation in Washington, D.C.

E. F. Schumacher was Economic Adviser and Director of Statistics to the British National Coal Board until his retirement in 1970.

A. J. de Villiers is in the Department of National Health and Welfare, Ottawa. He is Consultant-in-Charge, Biomedical Unit of the Environmental Health Division. He was a participant at the Banff Conference on Pollution.

Kenneth Mayall is head of the biology section, Ontario Department of Energy and Resources Management, Toronto.

C. R. Harris is head of the soil pesticide section of the federal Department of Agriculture.

H. F. Kraybill is assistant director for scientific co-ordination, Bureau of Foods and Pesticides, U. S. Department of Health, Education and Welfare.

Edward T. Hall is professor of anthropology at the College of Arts and Sciences and professor of organization theory at the School of Business, Northwestern University, Illinois.

Marvin Lipman is a member of the advisory group of the Central Mortgage and Housing Corporation, Ottawa.

Abraham Hoffer is a medical practitioner at present in private practice in Saskatoon, Canada.

Francis T. Christy, Jr., is with the Resources for the Future in Washington, D.C.

Homer Aschmann is professor of geography, University of California, Riverside Campus, California.

David Lowenthal is associated with the American Geographical Society, New York.

Douglas L. Brooks is special assistant to the Director of the National Science Foundation, Washington, D.C.

Harvey S. Perloff is Director of Regional and Urban Studies, Resources for the Future, Washington.

John H. Dales is in the Department of Political Economy, University of Toronto.

John R. Sheaffer, of the University of Chicago, has recently served as special assistant to Robert E. Jordan, general counsel to the Secretary of the U. S. Army advising on natural resource management problems.

Lowell S. Fink is a graduate of the Institute of Air and Space Law, McGill University, Montreal, and a member of the bar in Texas.

D. A. Chant is chairman of the Department of Zoology at the University of Toronto.

F. Kenneth Hare is in the Department of Geography, University of Toronto.